Chocolate Shoppe Mysteries™

Bittersweet Demise

Mary M. O'Donnell

Annie's®

AnniesFiction.com

Books in the Chocolate Shoppe Mysteries series

Library of Congress-in-Publication Data
Bittersweet Demise / by Mary M. O'Donnell
p. cm.
I. Title
                    2017934568

AnniesFiction.com
(800) 282-6643
Chocolate Shoppe Mysteries™
Series Creator: Shari Lohner
Series Editors: Janice Tate, Ken Tate
Cover Illustrator: Bonnie Leick

10 11 12 13 14 | Printed in China | 9 8 7 6 5 4 3 2

Prologue

Nineteen-year-old Denholm Whitfield wiped the perspiration from his face again, using his already-damp handkerchief, and swatted at the black flies and mosquitoes that seemed to swarm everywhere. He had slathered a mixture of camphor and citronella on his skin that was supposed to keep the pests away, along with a solution of tobacco soaked in alcohol that was said to ward off the ticks that teemed in the bush. Those strong odors mingled with the lush smell of the dense foliage and the rotting vegetation on the forest's floor. He was near the front of a line of men making their way through a dense Yucatán jungle, each member hacking away at the creeping vines and branches to widen what he had been told was a trail.

As a young boy, Denny had been captivated by articles in *National Geographic* magazine which were written by the famous archeologist Sylvanus Morley. He had imagined what it would be like to look for artifacts and inscriptions on ruins from a civilization that had been absorbed by the jungle long ago. What he hadn't imagined was that, in his first year of college, he would be selected by Morley himself to be part of an expedition.

Despite the conditions, his excitement was palpable. He felt as if he were living out the adventure novels he had read during his boyhood about the mysterious Maya and Aztec civilizations. This was truly his own adventure. Who knew what treasures he might find?

1

Jillian Green surveyed the heavy-laden tables that had been so artfully arranged in her neighbor's front yard. Martha Stewart herself couldn't have done it better. Each table was covered with a length of pastel print fabric, ends flapping in the gentle early October breeze, and the wide variety of standard yard-sale items, from kitchen paraphernalia to gently used clothing, was appealingly displayed. It was early afternoon, and several other patrons were there, picking up this or that, looking it over, and then putting it back down or tucking it in their arms to purchase at the end of their perusal. Some were obviously quietly engrossed in looking for the perfect deal, and others chatted amicably the whole time, not adverse to finding something to take home, but not really caring if they did or didn't.

Jillian and her childhood friend, Savannah Cantrell, fell into the latter group. They had come to the yard sale together, having renewed a friendship that had been dormant for twenty years while Jillian had been living in California. Jillian had reluctantly returned last year to Moss Hollow, Georgia, to work in her grandmother's business, The Chocolate Shoppe Bakery. Even though the two friends hadn't exactly parted on the best of terms all those years ago, and had lived different lives since, they had managed to fall back into the easy friendship they once had.

Jillian and Savannah stopped in front of a table that held a strange menagerie that didn't seem to fit in with the rest of the sale: a pith helmet, an ancient black-metal Royal typewriter, several framed black-and-white photographs of some eroded stone structures in a heavily forested landscape, a few issues of *National Geographic* from early in the last century, an old rucksack with brittle leather straps, a straight-sided terra-cotta vase with painted images in chalky shades of ochre and rust, a pair of round-frame wire spectacles, a stack of faded leather-bound books, and a framed arrowhead collection.

Just as Jillian and Savannah exchanged puzzled looks, the yard-sale proprietress and Jillian's newest neighbor approached them. She was Tara Padgett, a petite blonde with a pixie haircut and big brown eyes. Jillian and Savannah had met Tara and her husband, Paul, at Moss Hollow Fellowship Church just a few weeks before, shortly after the couple moved into the community. Tara had told Jillian that she was holding the yard sale mostly to help get rid of belongings from their former home that didn't go with their new decor. The new house, which was huge and modern-looking, had been built near Belle Haven, Jillian's ancestral home. Her grandmother, Bertie Harper, disdainfully called such houses "starter mansions."

"You must be wondering where these things came from," Tara said. "They belonged to my great-uncle, who died recently."

"My condolences," said Jillian.

"Thanks. He had a good, long life. He lived to be ninety-nine. But I hardly knew him. His memory failed in his later years, and, at least for me, he was never easy to communicate with at the best of times. He liked to talk about things that I didn't have an interest in or even understood really. My cousin, Troy, and I are his only heirs. Our grandfather was his brother, and my great-uncle had no children. He sold most of his possessions years ago when he moved into an assisted-living facility. These were among the few things he had kept in his room." She laughed. "Some might think he was odd, but Uncle Denny was an archaeologist and a professor at Harvard. Troy wanted his journals, so he took those, and I kept this necklace." Tara grasped the chain at her neck and held up a pendant that was green jade with flecks of gold and carved in the shape of a chubby turtle. "I thought it was kind of cute. But the rest of this wasn't really of any interest to either of us, and since I was planning to have this yard sale after our move, I thought I might as well include it. You never know what people will buy."

Jillian tucked a strand of her long, wavy red hair behind her ear, leaned forward, and picked up the terra-cotta vase. She carefully rolled it side to side in her hands to look at the images on it. A memory came to her—a day when she and her ex-fiancé, David Drake, had driven down to San Diego from Los Angeles for a brief getaway. One of the places they visited was the San Diego Museum of Man where they saw artwork similar in style. She smiled wistfully as she recalled how David had been especially marvelous that day—witty, funny, smart, romantic. That day she had thought he was the most wonderful man in the world.

"What is it?" asked Savannah, seeing her smile.

Jillian shook her head slightly before answering, as if to indicate it was nothing. "I . . . I was just remembering an exhibit I saw at a museum once. The style of the artwork on this vase is similar."

That was all she said. David was one thing that Jillian still had trouble discussing with Savannah—with anyone really. He was the reason she had left California so abruptly. He had been indicted for embezzlement, and though she was innocent of any wrongdoing, her relationship with him had ended her advertising career.

It wasn't that it was a secret, though she wished it could be. That was more than she could hope for in a small town like Moss Hollow where the gossip mill was a thing of wonder. Somehow, the reason she had come to live with her grandmother and her great-aunt Cornelia Montgomery, Bertie's twin sister, had become general knowledge around town.

Jillian felt her face flush as she remembered that it wasn't long after their San Diego outing that David had been indicted and her life had been turned upside down. Needless to say, none of the qualities she had so appreciated that day could trump his criminal actions. She still didn't understand how he could seem so wonderful and be dishonest at the same time. Were there signs that she had refused to see? His actions clearly showed he had no regard for her or for their future together. Anger flared up, but it lasted only a moment, which was an improvement. *At least I didn't marry him. Thank God for small favors.* She focused on the vase, remembering again that good day. Maybe it was okay to remember it with fondness, before . . .

"Are you seriously thinking of buying that?" asked Savannah.

Jillian quashed her thoughts and hoped Savannah didn't notice her heightened color. "I don't know. I might. The exhibition I saw was about the Maya civilization. There were huge monuments that had been cast from the originals in the Yucatán, but there were smaller things that were real artifacts, like bowls and figurines and vases that sort of looked like this one. This must be a reproduction." She looked at the price tag that had been dropped inside the vase. "Three dollars. I think I'll get it."

"Well, there's no accounting for taste, I guess," said Savannah, scrunching up her nose. Then she laughed. "Actually, I might get the glasses and the pith helmet. They'll work perfectly for our outfits for the costume ball."

"*Our* outfits?" asked Jillian with raised eyebrows.

"James's and mine." Now Savannah's color heightened. "He asked me to the ball, and I said yes." James Wilson had been Jillian's boyfriend in high school and had broken her heart back then, but that was all in the past.

Tara interrupted. "Excuse me—what's this about a costume ball?"

"It's not as grand as it sounds—it's just a dance in the high school gym that is held during Moss Holloween for teens and adults," Savannah replied. "It's sort of like a sock hop with costumes. They play old pop songs like 'Monster Mash' and 'Werewolves of London.' You know about Moss Holloween, don't you?"

"Well, I saw a sign in the window at Puckett's Hardware when I stopped in to get a few things for the house last week, but I didn't look at it too closely. I just noticed they had misspelled *Halloween*, but . . . I guess not?"

"Right," said Jillian. "It's Moss *Holloween*. It's a festival the town holds each year during the last full weekend of October. It's sponsored by the Fraternal Order of the Brown Thrashers, a local service organization. The proceeds from the dance go to the Nathan County Hospital's children's wing, so it does a lot of good, plus the festival helps local businesses since it brings more tourists to town. I'm surprised that Ike Puckett didn't fill you in on it since you were in his store. He's the president of the Brown Thrashers—what they call the 'Grand Thrasher' at the lodge. He's not shy when it comes to telling people about the festival, and you, being new in town, would have been the perfect target."

"I'm not sure that he was there. It was a very young man who helped me find what I needed, and a girl checked me out."

"Those were probably Ike's teenage kids, Sylvia and Gerald," said Jillian. "They both work in the store after school. If Ike was in the store, you would have known it. If there was a picture in the dictionary next to the word *extrovert* it would be Ike. I just wish he'd dial it back on the pranks. Just being around him makes me nervous this time of year. I'm always afraid he's going to pull one of his tricks on me."

Savannah picked up the conversation. "The few days before the festival have developed into kind of a 'prank week,' and nowadays, Ike is the chief prankster. I'm not sure when the tradition started—well before Jillian and I were born. And it's mostly harmless, if you don't mind washing soaped windows afterward or getting rid of toilet paper draped all over your yard." She looked at Jillian. "Remember when we were in high school and someone TP'd Mayor Adcock's place with those big mimosa trees in the front yard, and it rained that night? It took forever to clean up that mess. If the mayor hadn't been a Thrasher that probably would have been the end of prank week."

Jillian signaled that she remembered with a half smile and a nod, and Savannah continued. "Anyway, there's always something going on—a 'ghost' on a wire might drop out of a tree as you're walking down the street or someone might toss a giant black spider on the windshield of your car while you're sitting in a parking lot. You know it's fake, but if you're not expecting it, it can be pretty jarring. I know this from experience. Last year someone took a life-size scarecrow decoration off of Lucille Ryder's front porch. She reported it to the police right away. Lucille's not one to put up with any nonsense. Gooder . . . I mean, Deputy Jones found the scarecrow posed with its legs crossed on a bench in front of Cap's Place—that's a little hole-in-the-wall pub just off Main Street where some of the old men meet to play checkers and cards in the afternoons. The perpetrators had glued a cigarette butt to the mouth of the scarecrow and had tied an empty beer can to its hand with baling twine. Lucille was mortified."

Savannah smiled. "They put a picture of it on the front page of the *Moss Hollow Chronicle*—along with a lot of other pictures from the festival, of course, but that was no consolation to Lucille. She made sure to let everyone know that she wouldn't be caught dead at Cap's herself, even if it does have a sign in the window that reads 'Tables for Ladies.'"

"But there's a lot more going on during Moss Holloween than pranks and the Saturday-night dance," said Jillian, not wanting Tara to get the wrong idea. "The streets of the town square are closed off and turned into a marketplace with lots of local crafts and fall produce, and all the stores feature specials. There's a haunted house, which is always fun. It's spooky, but generally not too scary—the proceeds from that go to the hospital too."

Jillian paused before continuing. "The local theatrical society puts on a play every year on Thursday and Friday nights. They usually alternate between *Arsenic and Old Lace* and *The Legend of Moss Hollow*. The latter's sort of a rip-off of Washington Irving's *Sleepy Hollow* that some townsperson wrote years ago, changing the locale and the characters' names to things like Oglethorpe and Calvert to make it Southern. I'm pretty sure it's *Legend* this year. On Sunday, in the early evening, there's a children's costume parade down Main Street that ends at the park where the festival concludes with a community bonfire."

"I'm not sure if I should be sad or relieved that I'm going to miss it all," said Tara, "but there's always next year. Paul and I have booked a cruise for the last week of October. It's our fifth anniversary, and . . ." Tara paused for effect, "it's our last anniversary before we welcome a new member to the family. We're expecting our first baby next April!"

Jillian and Savannah offered their congratulations.

"Thanks. We're so happy." Tara didn't actually need to say that she was happy—it shone on her face. "I was actually going to ask a favor of you, Jillian. While we're gone, do you think you might be able to come by and water my plants, and just check on things in general? You shouldn't need to see about the plants more than once or twice, and if you'd just keep an eye out when you drive by the place on your way into town, we'd really appreciate it."

"I'd be glad to," said Jillian.

They made arrangements to meet at a later date so that Tara could give Jillian a key and the alarm code and give her instructions about the plants. It was nearly half an hour later that Jillian and

Savannah made their final purchases. It turned out that Savannah bought not only the spectacles and the helmet, but also the arrowhead collection, the *National Geographic* magazines, the books—which all turned out to be adventure novels by the likes of H. Rider Haggard, Lew Wallace, and Rudyard Kipling—for a dollar each, and the rucksack to carry them in. She said her eleven-year-old nephew, Darren, fancied himself a budding Indiana Jones, and she thought he'd be thrilled to have things that had belonged to a real archaeologist.

Jillian not only bought the vase, but also the antique typewriter and the framed photographs. She thought the typewriter might look just right in the library at Belle Haven. She would replace the photos in the frames with something more pleasing. Between the two of them, they cleared the table that had held the last few possessions of Denholm Whitfield.

After the yard sale, Jillian and Savannah drove over to the neighboring town of Painter's Ridge to try out a tearoom that had recently opened there and then did some leisurely window-shopping. It was almost dinnertime when Jillian arrived home. Though she was finally adjusting to the "early to bed, early to rise" lifestyle that the bakery required, she still felt somewhat tired after having risen very early to help get the morning's baking started at the shop. But having the afternoon off to spend with Savannah had been fun, and she'd needed a little break.

Her first task was to carry in the bulky typewriter, which she decided must weigh at least fifty pounds. It was either that, or she was getting weak and needed to start working out like she used to when she lived in California and had a membership at a gym. She chuckled when she thought about how quickly she had adjusted from her big-city lifestyle back to the small-town manner of living. She considered that it might be a good thing to convert one of the unused rooms on the third floor into a workout room of sorts. *Maybe when I finish getting the rest of Belle Haven in tip-top shape*, she thought. *If that ever happens.* Progress had been made, but there was still so much to do.

After a struggle to get the thing inside, she deposited the typewriter on one of the small tables in the two-story library of Belle Haven. The library recently had been used as a setting for a film, mainly because of its slightly creepy tone as it had been allowed to deteriorate since Bertie and Cornelia had had neither the funds nor the energy to keep it up. Jillian planned to use the money from the film company to bring the library back to its

15

former glory and hoped there would be enough to landscape the remainder of the back gardens that were still rather jungle-like. She also wanted to do something with the old tobacco barn at the far edge of the property. Bertie was determined not to tear it down, so Jillian had been considering other options.

For now, however, she stepped back a few paces from the table and decided two things as she rubbed her hands together to get the blood flowing into her fingers again. First, the typewriter was a good purchase as it added just the right touch of antique utility to the library. Second, she was never going to move it again. Whatever dust had been on the table where the typewriter now resided could just stay there as far as she was concerned.

Returning to her car, she retrieved the framed pictures and the vase, and then entered the home office she had fixed up in a room off the front foyer. "Fixed up" was perhaps not quite the phrase. Her computer sat on a desk facing two tall windows that looked toward the front of the property, and she had a swiveling wooden desk chair. Other than that, the space currently resembled a storage room more than an office. In the midst of some renovations to the over two-hundred-year-old Greek-revival mansion, they had moved some of the less-desirable furniture into the relatively small room.

She stacked the frames against the back of an old horsehair sofa that had once been in the living room and then removed the tissue paper that Tara had so thoughtfully provided from around her Mayan vase, as she thought of it. It was quite dusty, so she popped out to the downstairs powder room to give it a gentle wash.

Returning, she placed it on top of a short stack of cookbooks beside her computer, still not entirely sure why she had bought it. When she had looked at the vase earlier, her mind was so filled with memories of David that she really hadn't seen it clearly.

Now she sat down in the desk chair and studied it again, this time just for itself.

The vase stood only about eight inches tall and had a diameter of five to six inches. There were bands of a dark-rust color at the top and bottom containing strange inscriptions, and in between there was a scene that encircled the vase, sort of like a comic strip, only the details were not funny. On the side she was viewing, a fierce-looking man with an elaborate headdress sat on a platform while another man sat on the floor looking up to him with . . . was that fear? On the other side of the man on the platform was something that looked like a strange sort of tree with a central trunk that forked at the top. Large, oval pods were attached up both sides of the trunk. Rather disturbingly, one of the pods seemed to have the face of a man.

Jillian retrieved her phone and took several photographs of the vase, turning it so she had images from all sides. Then she opened her laptop and tapped in the words *Mayan vase tree* into a search engine, looking for images. She clicked on an image that was somewhat different from the one on her vase but that contained a similar-looking tree, also featuring the face of a man on one of the pods. The photograph's caption read, "After he was beheaded by the Lords of the Otherworld, Hun Hunahpu's head was hung in a cacao tree."

"Eww." Jillian looked at the vase again. She thought she might lose her affection for the piece. She shook her head and typed in the search bar: *cacao tree*. This time colorful images of the real plant filled her screen, and the word *chocolate* caught her eye. She clicked on until she came to a description: *Botanical name: Theobroma cacao, Greek "food of the gods" + native plant name. Evergreen that grows within a 20-degree range north and south of the equator; its fatty seeds are used in making cocoa, chocolate, and cocoa butter.*

She looked at the vase, seeing it in yet another light, and at the titles on the spines of the books she had checked out from the library a few days ago. She had gotten the books with a plan in mind for the bakery, which she hoped to implement during the Moss Holloween festival. Now a new idea started to form in her mind . . .

A sudden knock on the door made her jump. Aunt Cornelia cracked open the door. "Are you busy, Jillian? Dinner's almost ready."

A chubby cream-and-brown cat at Cornelia's feet pushed the door open completely and sauntered in.

"Raymond! That is rude. We were not invited into Jillian's little office," said Cornelia.

Jillian sighed and turned to face the door. "Aunt Cornelia, you're welcome to come in anytime, and the cat is Possum. I wish you'd stop calling him Raymond, especially on those occasions when there are other people around." It was difficult to explain to other people that Aunt Cornelia believed that the cat channeled the spirit of her dead husband.

Possum had shown up at the doorstep of Belle Haven before Jillian had returned to Moss Hollow. An underfed kitten with a bare tail—hence the name "Possum"—had grown and filled out to a fairly large cat who seemed to be under the impression that they all lived to serve him. He was especially attached to Cornelia. Or perhaps it was the other way around.

Cornelia walked in and sat on the sofa next to the framed photographs. "I realize that you and Bertie don't believe, even after all the times Raymond has given us valuable information, but I wish you weren't so close-minded dear." She paused and her forehead furrowed. "What on earth is that on your desk?"

Jillian swiveled around, picked up the vase, and turned back to hand it to Cornelia so she could look at it. "I bought it today at Tara Padgett's yard sale. It belonged to her great-uncle who was an archaeologist, and I just thought it was . . . interesting."

"Aren't the Padgetts the ones who moved into one of those new houses down the road, where they tore down the old Randolph place and built all those characterless homes on their land? I never thought I'd see the day this neighborhood would become a suburban wasteland."

"You know as well as I do that those old buildings—the house and the barns—were beyond repair. No one had lived on that place for fifty years or more. If they hadn't torn them down, they would have fallen down. The barn already was halfway there. And the new homes are lovely. I'll grant you that they don't have the character of Belle Haven, but people generally don't build houses like this anymore. A double-decker front porch with white columns from the ground floor to the roof and a stained glass central dome just aren't in most people's budgets nowadays."

"Nevertheless, I don't like seeing them disturb these old places. You don't know what spirits of the past might get all stirred up."

Even while she was speaking, Cornelia's normally serene face contorted into a grimace as she turned the vase in her hand and studied it. She shuddered and handed it back to Jillian as if it were the most loathsome thing in the world. "Please take my advice, Jillian. There is something not right about that . . . thing. The vibrations that it gives off are very disturbing. You need to get rid of it as soon as possible, or at least get it out of this house. I already feel that Virginia Belle is not pleased."

Jillian took a deep breath and let it go. Virginia Belle was the first wife of Captain Hoyt Belle, who had built Belle Haven. She was known as the Belle Haven "haint" in local circles of people who talked about such things. Cornelia had sworn that she had seen the ghost on more than one occasion. On the other hand, Bertie barely tolerated such talk. It was an old family tale that both Bertie and Jillian wished would pass into the background a bit more, especially now that they wanted to attract people to Belle Haven as a location for events like weddings, birthdays, and anniversaries. They would prefer not to attract the sort who came with strange apparatuses hoping to document the presence of a real ghost.

"Aunt Cornelia, it's just an old reproduction vase. I don't see how it could be any trouble just sitting here on my desk."

"Come on, you two, supper's ready," Bertie announced as she arrived at the door of the office. She looked impatiently at her sister. "I thought you were going to get Jillian and come right back. The food is going to get cold."

"Jillian and I were just talking about this vase. I can feel it in my bones that it's going to cause trouble."

Bertie took a quick glance at the vase. "Oh pish. It's just some old thing. Not to my taste, but she can do whatever she wants with it."

"I might keep it here, but then again, I might take it into the shop to use in a display. I think these images have something to do with chocolate." Jillian twisted the vase around to show her grandmother. "According to the Internet, this motif is supposed to represent a cacao tree."

Cornelia shuddered for no apparent reason.

Jillian managed to resist rolling her eyes and tried to ignore her aunt. She continued. "I've been reading up on how to make chocolate truffles in these books I got from the library." She set the vase on the desk and picked up the top book to show Bertie the cover, which featured a tempting variety of white-, milk- and dark-chocolate truffles. "My kitchen skills have improved so much, I'm sure I can make them. With Moss Holloween coming up, it would be a good time to have something special in the shop—we could package them in something appropriate for the festival and market them as a sophisticated Halloween treat for adults. This vase could be the focal point for a display in the front window.

You know, something appropriately creepy for the season, as it were. Maybe we could have decorations like they use for the Day of the Dead, the Mexican holiday, with paper cutouts, sugar skulls, and such. In parts of California they hold that festival too—*Dia de los Muertos* as it's said in Spanish."

Jillian could read from Bertie's face that she was really trying to refrain from saying something negative. Her down-to-earth grandmother was generally not in favor of doing anything in the bakery that was different than what she had done for the past few decades. She liked to say, "If it ain't broke, don't fix it." But since Bertie and Cornelia had just recently celebrated their eightieth birthdays, Jillian knew that Bertie was trying, hard as it was, to cede more authority to her granddaughter.

"Well, you make a few of these truffles, and we'll try them out and see how it goes from there. If you're going to have them ready for the festival you're going to have to get a move on though. But right now, it's suppertime, so let's go."

Jillian knew better than to try to press the point with her grandmother when supper was waiting. She put the book back on the desk.

As they made their way to the breakfast nook off the kitchen where they generally ate their meals, Bertie broached the subject that Jillian had known would come up sooner or later, and that she had been dreading.

"I understand that Savannah is going to the costume ball with James Wilson."

"How did you know that?" Jillian asked. "Savannah only just told me this afternoon."

"I heard it . . . somewhere," she said noncommittally. "I was wondering if anyone had asked you to the ball."

Jillian knew exactly where Bertie was going with this. It had been a steady drumbeat since she returned to town that she wasn't getting any younger, and there was this good-looking, single mortician, Hunter Greyson, in town who was age-appropriate and an ideal candidate for matrimony, at least that was the case in both Bertie and Cornelia's minds. While Jillian had been initially put off by his career choice, she had to admit that Hunter was handsome, a good conversationalist, and a lot of other things that she found appealing. He certainly didn't fit the stereotype of the cold, grim undertaker from gothic novels she'd read. Even so, she was in no hurry to enter into another serious relationship. They were becoming good friends, however. In fact, they'd been out on several casual dates. But she wasn't about to admit to Bertie that she half-expected Hunter to ask her to the dance.

"No, Bertie. No one has asked me to the ball."

"Well, maybe you should ask someone yourself—women do that sort of thing nowadays—maybe that nice Hunter Greyson. Since he moved to town from Atlanta and took over running Greyson & Sons Mortuary from his granddaddy, and with him being the county coroner now, he's probably so busy he hasn't even given it a thought. You know how men are. But if he did think of it, I'd bet you'd be first on his list to ask. So you might as well bring it up."

"Honestly, Bertie. I'm not going to say anything to him about the dance, and don't you dare say anything either. That means you too, Aunt Cornelia."

Cornelia raised her hands in a gesture of innocence. "I wouldn't think of it, dear."

It's time to change the subject, Jillian decided. As they sat down to eat, she asked if the Southern Sweetie Pies would be holding their weekly meeting on the Sunday afternoon during Moss Holloween. The Sweetie Pies was a local group of ladies who got together to swap recipes, taste-test members' baked creations, and socialize. It included Jillian, Bertie, Cornelia, Savannah, and Lenora Ryan—a longtime family friend and baker at The Chocolate Shoppe, along with several other ladies from Moss Hollow.

"I think we'll cancel that meeting," said Bertie. "We're probably going to need some time to decompress after Saturday. I talked to Mayor Blackwater yesterday, and he's expecting a bumper turnout for the festival. They put advertisements for Moss Holloween in several newspapers across the state this year, including the *Atlanta Journal*."

"So, are you going to change your mind, Aunt Cornelia, and come to the festival this year?" asked Jillian in a slightly teasing tone.

She already knew what the answer would be. As far back as Jillian could remember, and as far as she knew, whenever Cornelia had lived in Moss Hollow, she always stayed close to home during Moss Holloween.

"Harrumph!" Cornelia said. "You know better than that, Jillian. I find the whole idea of 'Moss Holloween' totally abhorrent. It makes a mockery of All Hallows' Eve with its crass commercialism and awful pranks."

"That 'crass commercialism' helps us pay our bills until the Christmas season starts," retorted Bertie, "and I know you didn't always feel that way about prank week."

To Jillian's surprise, Cornelia blushed.

Bertie either didn't notice or didn't care as she continued, "Just because Burton Puckett . . ."

"Bertie! Don't you dare!"

Jillian watched as some sort of nonverbal communication passed between the twin sisters. While they seemed poles apart personality-wise, the connection between them was strong, and words weren't always needed. "What is it?" she asked.

"Never you mind," said Cornelia in a voice that signaled she had no intention of talking about it. In fact, there was little conversation to be had with Cornelia throughout the rest of the evening. Jillian couldn't help but wonder how the very mention of Ike Puckett's father could put Cornelia in such a state.

3

Jillian stood outside The Chocolate Shoppe Bakery looking through its large front window, feeling that all was right with the world. Contrary to Cornelia's prediction, no disaster had come to pass since she had acquired the Mayan vase. She hadn't so much as broken a fingernail.

It was the Monday morning prior to Moss Holloween, and she'd just put the finishing touches on the window display of the bakery. Now she was reviewing her hard work and seeing how it would look to passersby from the sidewalk. The display included traditional elements from the Day of the Dead holiday. She had strung multicolored paper-cutout banners across the top of the window. In the display itself, there were sugar skulls in various pastel shades decorated with startling faces, bunches of Indian corn in colorful baskets, and yellow and rust-colored marigolds arranged in black vases. Just for fun, using a stencil and a shaving technique she had read about on the Internet, she had carved a skull shape on a small pumpkin and put a flickering battery-powered candle inside.

Among these many-colored elements there were stark-white laser-cut candy boxes filled with truffles that had been wrapped in different bright colors of foil, some of which she had artfully allowed to spill over onto the pale-lavender cloth that lined the bottom of the display. At home on her computer, she'd worked up a sign in a block font with swirling designs within that read, *Treat someone special to our new Holloween chocolate truffles.* With the Mayan vase as the focal point, she thought it made quite an impression.

As confident as she had tried to sound to Bertie when she proposed it, she had pleasantly surprised herself that she had succeeded in making the truffles. After a couple of hiccups in which the chocolate had alternately seized and burned, she had finally gotten the hang of it. She managed to make a creamy ganache and was able to produce tempered chocolate with a beautiful sheen. It was all a matter of temperature and timing, and making sure that no water from the double boiler made its way into the chocolate.

With some trial and error, and more than a little help from Lenora, Jillian worked up three styles of truffles to present to Bertie. She tried to stick with a Latin American flavor palate to go with the Day of the Dead theme, so she ended up with a dark-chocolate truffle flavored with cardamom and vanilla, a cinnamon-flavored milk-chocolate truffle with a hint of cayenne and dusted with cocoa powder, and a white-chocolate truffle enhanced with chopped, roasted cashews.

As it happened, Bertie was impressed with the results, not bothering to conceal her own surprise. In the time remaining before the festival, Jillian went into full production mode in the evenings after the shop closed since the truffles could be made ahead of time. Maggie, the latest "front girl," who normally worked the register during the day, helped with packaging. It all turned out to be a lot of work, but she was sure it would pay off in the long run. At least she hoped it would. If it didn't, she would never hear the end of it from Bertie.

Bertie's face appeared on the other side of the window as if Jillian had conjured her up just by thinking of her. "Get in here," her grandmother mouthed while pointing at the floor with her index finger.

In her musings, Jillian had tuned out the rest of the world and hadn't noticed that the bell above the bakery door had rung several times while she had been standing there. Maggie had called in sick that morning, so she was sure that she'd be stuck at the register until closing time. *We really need to hire another part-time person—this week might be as good a time as any.* But there was no one else to help out today, so she took a deep breath and went in to face the line of customers that had begun to form.

She had waited on several customers, and was about to say the automatic "How may I help you?" when she looked up from the register to see Hunter Greyson's smiling face. His silver-streaked dark hair was longer than usual, and he had the beginnings of a horseshoe mustache plus a chin strip. She could only guess that it must be for the costume ball.

"Good morning, Jillian. You're looking lovely this morning."

"Uh, thanks," said Jillian without conviction, self-consciously touching her hair. Even though it was pulled back in a loose ponytail, she was sure it was at its unruly best, with red curls escaping. She'd been in the hot bakery since five a.m. and reaching in to put together the window display probably hadn't helped her hairdo either. She tried to avoid looking down at her white apron, which she was pretty sure was streaked with flour, cocoa powder, and God knew what else.

"I tried to call you a couple of times last week, but I couldn't get an answer."

"I'm sorry. I have been working every day at the bakery, including the evenings, to get ready for Moss Holloween. Did you leave a message?"

"Um, no. I really wanted to talk to you directly."

"Well, here I am."

Hunter looked around. The bakery was full of customers, and there was one person behind him in line.

"Why don't I let you help Hugh, and then maybe we could step outside for a minute."

Before Jillian could answer, Bertie was at her elbow. "I've got this, Jillian. You two go ahead."

How did she manage to hear that Hunter was in the shop and get to the register from the kitchen so quickly? was all Jillian could think.

Jillian said nothing, but untied her apron and removed it. There was nothing she could do about her hair now, but she wasn't about to be asked to the costume ball out on the street wearing an apron.

Standing outside in front of the bakery's window, the two of them drew the attention of not only customers entering the shop, but Jillian was sure that every head in the place was turned to watch them. Hunter must have noticed the same thing.

"Maybe we should take a little stroll down the sidewalk."

Jillian smiled. "I think that would be a good idea."

As they took a few steps, Hunter looked down at his feet as if trying to gather courage for what he was about to say. Jillian found it rather endearing.

He cleared his throat. "Jillian, you and I have become good friends. You're wonderful company, and I had fully intended to ask you to the costume ball, but I had a call last week from an old friend who is going to be in town for Moss Holloween. She saw an ad in an Atlanta newspaper. When she called, I . . . I . . . Well, it looks like she and I will be going to the ball together. I know you probably expected an invitation from me, and I just wanted you to know that I would have loved to attend the dance with you above anyone else in Moss Hollow, but it's just not going to work out this year. I hope you understand."

Did he just say "above anyone else in Moss Hollow"? Jillian blinked. *But not above someone from Atlanta, obviously.* Even though a certain amount of consternation was building within her brain, her Southern manners took over.

"Of course, I understand. The truth is, with the extra work of the festival, I've been so tired every evening, I haven't even given the dance a thought. When we close the bakery on Saturday, I'm sure I'll be exhausted. I'll probably just go home to a hot bath and a good book."

Though she hid it, much to Jillian's dismay, Hunter looked relieved. "I'm so glad you understand. Some of the Sweetie Pies said you were expecting me to take you to the dance, so I was worried you might—"

"They said what?" She felt her skin heat up and knew she must now be red from the top of her head to the tips of her toes. She momentarily pictured herself as a flaming-red hot chili pepper and mentally railed against her parents for passing along to her their ultra-fair skin that broadcast every change in her blood pressure. Hunter couldn't help but see that she was embarrassed.

"I'm sure they didn't mean to—"

Jillian interrupted. "Thanks, Hunter, for letting me know that you would not be asking me to the ball. I really didn't expect anything from you. I hope you have a wonderful time." She turned and strode back toward the bakery, but instead of entering the front door, she swept past it to the side alley that ran between the bakery and Puckett's Hardware, and turned into it to walk to the back side of the building.

Behind the building, she went straight to her car in the small parking lot, intending to sit in it for a minute to regain her composure, or at least her normal skin color. She was so rattled that she didn't remember until she had her hand on the door handle that it was locked, and that her keys were in her purse in the bakery. She wasn't prepared to go in there yet.

So, instead, she sat down near her car on the concrete curb that ran across the front of the parking spots and covered her face with her hands for just a moment. Almost immediately she berated herself. "Okay, Jillian. You're embarrassed, but it's not the end of the world." The truth she had to admit to herself was that she *had* expected Hunter to ask her to the ball. "Deep breath," she said. "I guess pride really does go before a fall, as the Good Book says."

She had asked Bertie and Cornelia to stay out of it. She didn't think they would go against her wishes and speak to Hunter. Anyway, if it had been one of them, Hunter would have said "your grandmother" or "your aunt" but he didn't. Would Lenora or Savannah have said that to him? She couldn't imagine it. She began ticking off the names of the other Sweetie Pies one by one. Then it came to her. Which of them were among the busiest busybodies in Moss Hollow? It had to be those two old dears, Wanda Jean Maplewood and Maudie Honeycutt. Jillian groaned. And who had been in line behind Hunter in the bakery? Hugh Honeycutt, Maudie's husband. Of course. Somehow she had the feeling that this was not the end of their meddling.

It took her several more minutes to regain her composure, trying to decide if it was only the embarrassment that was upsetting her, or if it was the fact that Hunter had said that he'd rather go with her than anyone else "in Moss Hollow." *So, some former girlfriend*—"'Old friend' indeed!" she said out loud—*rings him up and says she's coming from Atlanta for a visit, and suddenly I'm chopped liver?*

Then, trying to be reasonable, she began talking to herself under her breath. "Hunter and I are just friends. Of course, he's probably dating other women in town or from wherever. Why wouldn't he? I could date other people too. I just haven't. Yet."

She tried to think of some single man in Moss Hollow, other than Hunter Greyson, who she would like to spend a pleasant evening with. She thought of Possum's veterinarian, Shane West—handsome, pleasant, but much too young. Then there was Hunter's assistant at the mortuary, Oliver Kent—nice, but kind of creepy in some indefinable way she just couldn't quite put her finger on. What about Deputy Gooder Jones? *Never in a million years . . .* "Enough of this."

She headed over to the bakery's van that Bertie drove and looked in its large side mirror to see if her coloring was still in the realm of an Amelia Hybrid tomato. Her hair had not improved, but she hadn't expected it to. She didn't think anyone would notice that she was, for lack of a better word, unsettled.

She was wrong. When she walked into the kitchen through the back door, Lenora was there, chopping dates to go in a batch of pumpkin-bread batter, her strong, brown hands expertly rocking the knife back and forth. Lenora stopped what she was doing and watched Jillian as she tried to quickly pull a clean apron off the top of a neatly folded stack. She managed to grab a stray tie from an apron below, causing several aprons to fall to the floor and generally making a mess.

"Are you all right, honey?" The gentleness in her voice almost made Jillian cave and tell her all.

"Yes. Sort of . . . I should go up front and take over for Bertie." She didn't want Lenora to have a chance to look at her too closely with those kind eyes that had known her since she was a child. Instead of folding the aprons as she should have, Jillian picked up the ones that had fallen on the floor and pushed them into a rough pile, making her escape before Lenora could ask something else.

Up front, after Bertie had finished with a customer, she scanned Jillian's face with narrowed eyes and asked nothing about Hunter before returning to the kitchen to help Lenora.

Fortunately, the morning continued to be busy, so Jillian was able to momentarily forget her woes, such as they were. There was a lull in customers about one o'clock when she noticed a man of about fifty years of age standing outside studying her window display. His light-brown hair was streaked with gray, and he sported a well-trimmed beard and mustache. He wore a tweedy gray sport coat over a light-blue button-up shirt along with a university-stripe tie, giving him a very professorial look. He was definitely overdressed for a tourist, if that's what he was. She supposed he could have been in town on business. Either way, Jillian was certain she would have noticed him in Moss Hollow before now if he was a resident. It felt rather gratifying to have such a distinguished-looking stranger appreciate her work.

He looked up momentarily and seemed to stare at her through the window, though she didn't think he really could see her at her spot behind the register. Nevertheless, she averted her eyes and ducked her head. She stole a quick look and saw that he had turned from the window and was headed toward the front door. For the second time that morning, she wished she looked a bit more presentable.

"May I help you, sir?"

"I was just admiring your very interesting window display and thought I might purchase a box of truffles." His accent wasn't quite German, and it wasn't quite French, but something akin to both. Clearly, he had not been raised in Georgia.

After Jillian described the flavors of truffles that were available, and he had made a substantial purchase, he seemed in no mood to hurry along.

"I just came to town today, intending to visit . . ." He paused very briefly but Jillian caught it. "Some friends who turned out not to be at home. Is there a hotel nearby where I might stay the night?"

"There's the Southern Peach Inn. There's a brochure in the rack by the door."

He turned his head to look but stayed where he was.

"I was surprised to see what all was going on in your town today. I couldn't find a place to park on the street, so I parked behind this building. I hope that's all right."

"Normally that's just for people who work in the shops, but it's not a problem. You won't get a ticket or anything. The town's gearing up for our fall festival, Moss Holloween, so everyone's extra busy getting early deliveries, and a lot of shops hire short-term people, so parking on the square is at a premium."

"Is that what you are?" he asked. "Short-term, that is."

"No. Actually, the bakery is a family business. My grandmother started it a long time ago, and I only recently returned to Moss Hollow from California to help her run it. It looks like I'm here for the long haul." She started to feel a little foolish sharing personal details with this stranger, so she went into her standard tourist talk. "Normally, Moss Hollow is just a sleepy little Southern town. There's a brochure in the rack about Moss Holloween too, if you're interested in staying for a few days. It officially starts on Thursday evening with a performance of a play at the high school auditorium. For a small town, they put on a really great show. It's not professional, of course, but they've been doing it for years, and it's fun to watch the locals perform."

He smiled at her, and she found herself returning it.

"I might just stay for a while then. It depends on when my friends return."

Jillian wondered why he didn't just call them. Didn't everyone carry a cell phone with them nowadays? She was somewhat puzzled that he still didn't make a move to leave the shop, but seemed to want to prolong the conversation.

"I made a clockwise loop around the town square to stretch

my legs after a long drive, and I saw your window display on my way back to my car. The vase in the center—may I ask where you got that?"

"I bought it at a neighbor's yard sale. It's a reproduction that used to belong to her great-uncle who was an archeologist. Do you know anything about that style of art?" asked Jillian. "I think it's Mayan. I did a little research online, and it seems to have something to do with chocolate, and maybe some guy named Hun-a-poo, or something like that."

"I might know something about it," the man said. "I'm a museum curator from . . ." There was that infinitesimal pause again. ". . . out of town. Would you mind if I took a look at it?"

"No, I don't mind at all," said Jillian. "It would be great if you could tell me more about it."

She stepped from behind the counter and led him to the display where she reached in, picked up the vase, and handed it to him. She was rather puzzled as she watched him. He handled it with great care and concentration as he turned it to study the images. At the same time, Jillian sensed in him some reluctance to touch it. She thought of Cornelia's reaction to the piece. There was some similarity there, but something different as well—another level of . . .

Instead of handing it back to her, he placed it back in the display himself.

"Well, what do you think?" she asked.

"It's a . . . an interesting piece. It is in the Mayan style, and you're right about the chocolate—that motif does represent a cacao tree. Perhaps we could talk about it more this evening. Are you free for dinner?"

Jillian was taken aback, but somewhat pleased at the same time.

Before she could answer, he offered his hand. "I'm Quinten, by the way, Quinten Straub."

She shook his hand. "And I'm Jillian Green."

"I'm pleased to meet you, Jillian Green." He accented it with a slight nod of his head. "Will you meet me for dinner? At some place of your choosing, of course."

Jillian considered. She'd been working a lot of overtime the past few weeks and deserved an evening out. "That would be very nice." She walked to the rack by the door and took out a brochure and handed it to Quinten. "Crazy Fish Bar & Grill is my favorite restaurant in Moss Hollow. The directions are on the back. Shall we meet about seven?"

4

The rest of the afternoon seemed to drag by. About four o'clock, the fluorescent lights in the case where the baked goods were displayed began to flicker. Knowing that was a sign that they would soon give out altogether, Jillian took an opportunity to go to the utility closet off the kitchen to get new bulbs to replace the old ones. There were none to be found.

Bertie had already gone home, and Lenora was upstairs in the apartment she had begun renting from Bertie after she sold her house, just before Jillian had returned to Moss Hollow. She hated to disturb her, but she'd have to ask Lenora to come downstairs and watch the shop while she ran across the alley to Puckett's Hardware to get some new lightbulbs. She decided that when she came back she was going to ask Lenora if she had a cousin who would be interested in a part-time job. If there was one thing that abounded in Moss Hollow, it was Lenora's cousins.

At the door of the hardware store, Jillian paused. Since it was the beginning of prank week, she'd be walking straight into the lion's den. She could only hope that Ike Puckett was otherwise occupied, and one of his employees would help her instead. She somewhat doubted that he would try to pull a prank in the store—that couldn't be good for business—but he was so full of impishness, that she couldn't entirely put it past him.

To step into Puckett's Hardware was like stepping back in time. A plaque next to the front double doors proclaimed that the store had been founded in 1914 by Gerald Puckett, whom Jillian knew was Ike's great-grandfather and Ike's son's namesake. The Puckett family had intentionally retained its original atmosphere so that even tourists enjoyed looking around the place. The store certainly hadn't changed much since she was a little girl. It had the same worn wooden floor, the same over-stocked shelves, and the same old brass cash register. They did have a credit-card machine now, a concession that had occurred sometime in the twenty-year period when she was living in California. Despite the store's appearance, she had to admit that they kept the stock up-to-date. She'd never come looking for something in the hardware range that she hadn't found.

A tradition that was said to have started when Ike's father, Burton, took over the running of the store from his father, was its annual Halloween section. It included everything from cute children's costumes to scary masks and black creepy-crawlies. This year's offerings included polyurethane body parts—eyeballs, ears, hairy feet you could wear like shoes, and gloves that looked like real hands covered with blood. To her, the stock seemed a little slanted toward the gory side. She preferred princess costumes and fairy wings. She enjoyed Halloween as much as anyone, but there were limits when it came to the really gruesome stuff. Even so, she couldn't help but reach out her index finger to touch the "blood" on one of the hands. It looked so real it was hard to believe it wasn't liquid. She was glad to confirm that it was just very shiny paint.

"Well, Miss Jillian Green. I don't often see you in here. What can I do for you today?"

The sudden loud voice behind her almost made her jump out of her shoes. She heard a familiar chuckle. With her hand on her heart to try to steady it, she turned to face Ike Puckett. He was about ten years older than Jillian. She remembered what he was like when he was on the high school football team and she was in early elementary school. Then he was a typical teenager—thin with a full head of hair. Now late middle age had caught up to him and he wasn't so thin, but his hair was.

"Hi, Ike. I need two fluorescent lightbulbs for the bakery display case. I wrote down the serial number." She offered him a small piece of paper, which he ignored.

"I know exactly what you need. I keep telling Bertie she needs to update that thing with some new LED lights, but she won't have it." He shouted, "Tommy! Grab a couple of four-foot F32 tubes from the back for Mrs. Harper's bakery case next door." He continued in a more normal voice level for him, "Are you going to the play this year?"

"I might try to see it on Thursday."

"Our Sylvia has one of the main roles, and I'm playing her daddy—on the stage and in real life. My daddy even has a small non-speaking part, but he steals the scenes he's in anyway. It's a real family affair this year."

"How is your father since he retired?"

"Oh, he's just fine. He mostly goes fishing and plays cards down at Cap's. I think he's enjoying taking it easy. He still comes into the store once or twice a week, to keep his hand in and check up on me, I guess." He paused to laugh. "You know he's about the same age as your grandma and aunt Cornelia—maybe a couple of years younger. I think he was kind of sweet on Cornelia back in the day, before he met my mama."

"Really?" In her mind, Jillian heard again Cornelia's strident words when Bertie simply mentioned Burton Puckett's name. She didn't think Cornelia could have been very sweet on him.

Jillian watched the last customer leave the bakery shortly after five and hurried to lock the door before another straggler could enter. She was now experienced in the process of closing up the bakery, making sure everything was in order for the next morning, but it still took a certain amount of time to close out the register and tidy up. When she had finished, she grabbed her purse and glanced up at the wall clock. She'd have to take a quick shower at Belle Haven in order to get ready in time to meet Quinten Straub at Crazy Fish at seven.

She exited the back door, double-checking that it was locked, and then began rummaging in her purse to find her car keys as she was walking toward her car in the dusky light of the early evening.

She found her keys and looked up toward her car. A dark-green car that was unfamiliar to her had parked next to hers so closely that it looked like there was barely enough room to walk through. She wondered if she might have to get into her car on the passenger side. Then she noticed it. Atop the concrete curb where she had sat earlier, she saw something that stopped her in her tracks and made her gasp. It was a hand covered with dark-red blood.

Her surprise didn't last long. She quickly remembered the fake hand she had touched in Puckett's Hardware. She knew it was bound to happen. She'd put herself on Ike's radar by going into the hardware store. The Thrashers were always looking for someone new to the area or, like her, someone who had been away from Moss Hollow long enough to be considered fresh game. She looked all around the parking area, certain that Ike and possibly some of the other Thrashers were hiding somewhere near, taking a picture of her reaction for the *Chronicle*.

"All right, Ike Puckett," she said loudly, "you got me. You can come out of hiding now and get rid of this thing."

There was no response, so she strode over to it with the intention of just leaving it there and going home. As she came closer she realized that this was no prank. The hand was attached to an outstretched arm of a person lying facedown between her car and the green one. She immediately recognized the gray tweedy jacket, now askew on its owner. It was Quinten Straub. The hair on his head was tinted red, soaked with blood. She thought he must have placed his hand on the back of his head before he fell forward. Her heart beating wildly and hands shaking, she crouched down, intending to take his pulse, but when she felt his wrist, his skin was ice cold and there was no movement. He must have been dead for quite a while.

About a minute after Jillian had called the police, she heard the back door of the hardware store slam shut. She looked around to see Ike striding toward his enormous dark-gray pickup truck that was parked directly behind the hardware building. Not noticing her at first, he looked strangely serious and perhaps a bit worried, but when he finally saw Jillian, his expression changed to the familiar jovial one.

"Hey, Jillian. Twice in one day. Must be my lucky day. You havin' car trouble?"

Jillian stepped toward Ike, placing herself between him and the place where the body of Quinten Straub lay. "No. I'm waiting—"

She stopped speaking when the sound of a siren began nearby and continued to intensify.

Ike cocked his head. "Wonder what that's about."

She didn't offer any information, and they both just stood there as the siren got louder and louder, becoming almost deafening when the police car turned, a bit too fast in Jillian's opinion, into the alley, and the sound rebounded off the sides of the buildings.

With blue lights flashing, the car stopped close to where Jillian and Ike stood. A surreal silence followed after the car and the siren were turned off.

Jillian had hoped that Sheriff Coy Henderson would be the one to respond to her call. He was gruff, but he was an experienced law officer who took control of any situation with professionalism. But it was not to be. Instead, Deputy Goodman Jones stepped out of the police car. Though he tried to discourage it, most people still called him "Gooder," a nickname he'd had since he was in school.

First he nodded toward Ike. "Hey, Ike." Shaking his head, he looked toward Jillian. "Hello, Miss Green. When my mother said it was you that called the dispatch—again—I almost didn't believe her. Did you know that there are lots of people who have lived their whole lives in this town and have never once called the police?" He huffed. "Where's the body?"

"Body?" Ike looked confused.

"He's over here by my car," said Jillian. "You got here fast."

"I was just a few streets over." As he walked toward her car he asked, with an accusatory tone, "Did you touch anything?"

"I only touched his wrist to see if there was a pulse."

He looked as if he didn't believe her.

"Do you know who he is?"

"I just met him in the shop today. He said his name was Quinten Straub and that he was in town to visit some friends."

"Did he say where he was from?"

Jillian tried to remember what he had said. She was starting to get annoyed with Gooder. It seemed to her that the first thing to do was to check the body and then to secure the scene. Then he could ask questions. She was sure that's what Sheriff Henderson would have done. "He said he was a museum curator, but he didn't say where he was from. He spoke with a foreign accent."

"You mean like a Yankee?"

Jillian couldn't help but roll her eyes. "No, like a person from another country—maybe somewhere in Europe."

He bent his head toward Ike. "You go over and stand with Ike."

She complied, but thought he could have at least been polite about it and said "please" like a good Southern gentleman.

She and Ike watched as Gooder did the same thing she had done, crouching down to try to locate a pulse. She looked over at Ike. He had gone deathly pale. For someone who seemed to enjoy the more gruesome side of Halloween, judging by the contents of his store's seasonal display, she was somewhat surprised by his reaction to death. Her surprise lessened when she remembered that someone had mentioned that Ike's mother had passed away a few years ago after an illness. But even that was not the same as being near someone who had died by an act of violence, and Jillian had no doubt that was the case with Quinten.

Jillian reached out and touched Ike's arm to get his attention. "Did Sylvia and Gerald work after school today?"

Ike's expression shifted. "No. Now I'm glad they both had other things to do. Sylvia is practicing her lines with some of the others that are in the play, and Gerald had a computer-club meeting after school." Tears actually welled up in his eyes, but he blinked them away.

"Are you okay, Ike?"

He shook his head and looked again toward Gooder. "Is there really somebody dead over there?" From where they stood, the only thing visible was Quinten Straub's lifeless, blood-covered hand.

"I'm afraid so."

As he shook his head in disbelief, another siren sounded and, soon, with red lights flashing, an ambulance entered the alley. Paramedics stepped out and Gooder waved them over to where the body was. After determining for themselves that he was dead, they covered the body with a sheet and were about to depart when Hunter Greyson showed up in the older-model black sedan that he used for official business for both the mortuary and as county coroner.

He only nodded his head toward Jillian and Ike, and went straight to the body.

Another police car showed up, and two more policemen got out. There was a hive of activity as people and vehicles came and went, including a hearse from the mortuary to take away the body. A few townspeople had gathered at the street end of the alley to try to see what was going on, but the police had blocked off the parking lot from all directions.

When Hunter was ready to leave, he approached Jillian and Ike. Asking them both, but looking more at Jillian, he said, "Are you all right?"

Jillian opened her mouth, but no sound came out. Maybe she was even more shook up by the discovery of Quinten than she realized.

"I'm okay, I guess," said Ike. "It was Jillian that found him."

Jillian found her voice. "I'm okay too. It was just a shock."

"Gooder said you knew the man."

"Not really. I only met him today."

"Well, call me if you need to talk or anything."

"I think I'll be all right, but thank you. I'm sure you're going to be busy with this now, and your other plans for the weekend." She could have kicked herself for adding that last part, but it was out of her mouth before she could stop it.

Her meaning was not lost on Hunter, but he answered evenly, "I'm here for you, Jillian, if you need me." With that he turned away and got in his car and left.

After Hunter was gone, Gooder approached Jillian and Ike and proceeded to ask standard questions, including their names, which he knew full well, along with dates of birth, addresses, and phone numbers.

When it appeared he had asked his last question, Ike asked, "Is it all right if I go now? I'm supposed to be at the auditorium by seven for rehearsal."

"Yes, you can go. We'll contact you later for a statement."

"I don't know anything except for what I already told you. I never even met the man and didn't know there was a dead person back here until you showed up."

"We may still need to ask a few questions. I'll let you know."

Ike stalked over to his truck and was soon on his way.

"Can I go too?"

Gooder looked around. The forensic team was packing up the tools of their trade and the evidence they had gathered. "Yeah, you can go as soon as they're finished. We ran the tags on the green car, and it is a rental registered in the victim's name. The keys were in his pocket, so we'll move it down to the police station this evening." He paused and looked at her with an accusing expression that she should have been used to after all the times she'd seen it, but it still perturbed her. "I don't know how you're involved in this yet, but I'll figure it out."

Jillian was near to being outraged. "Gooder Jones, the only way I'm involved in this is that I found him. I told you I never set eyes on him before today and that's the truth."

"Trouble just seems to follow you around like a puppy, don't it? Since you came back it's been one thing after another. Everyone knows you had some trouble out there in California too, and that's why you came back home. I'm willing to bet even Bertie and Cornelia don't know the whole story behind that. I reckon you know the routine by now and I shouldn't have to say this, but I will anyway. Don't leave town."

Thankfully, for Jillian, Tuesday passed without a hitch. On Wednesday, no new information had been released about the death of Quinten Straub as far as she knew. In spite of that, news that she had found the body must have spread quickly around town because both days at the shop were as busy as if Moss Holloween had already begun. Jillian wondered if customers were coming around to see firsthand if she would be arrested for the murder of the stranger.

Bertie and Lenora both told her not to mind them. She could endure the covert looks and whispered conversations as long as they bought the goods that the shop offered. She'd had to ask several people to leave who were just sitting at the café tables without so much as a cup of coffee.

She thought she was handling the situation well until Maudie and Wanda Jean wandered into the shop. With everything that had happened, her earlier embarrassment with Hunter seemed like it should be a more insignificant thing, but she still felt it keenly.

"Good morning, ladies," she said with forced cheerfulness. "What can I get for you today?"

After they placed an order and paid, Jillian said, "If you want to take a seat, I can bring your order to you." That was something that Jillian and Maggie often did for older customers so they wouldn't have to stand and wait.

"Okay," said Maudie, "and when you come over, we have some information to share with you." She looked around the bustling room before saying in a loud whisper, "It's about Hunter and that woman from Atlanta that he's keeping at his place."

Oh no. That's all that I need. She felt the familiar rise of color to her cheeks as Maudie and Wanda Jean shuffled away toward a table. As Maggie took over at the register, Jillian donned plastic gloves to put together the ladies' orders and tried to think how she could avoid staying at their table to hear possibly slanderous gossip about Hunter and his old girlfriend. Maudie and Wanda Jean often got the wrong end of the stick. She really didn't want to hear it.

There wasn't a line at the register by the time she carried over coffees and crullers to the two ladies, so that excuse was out, but she could claim she was needed in the kitchen, which was true even though both Bertie and Lenora were in there.

But as soon as she set down the tray, Wanda Jean grabbed Jillian's wrist and wouldn't let go until Jillian sat down in a chair they had ready and waiting.

"Sit down, honey. This might take a minute or two."

Wanda Jean doctored her coffee with a packet of sweetener and two packets of creamer as she spoke in what could only be described as a stage whisper—she was trying to be quiet, but anyone in the room who wanted to listen could hear her. "We were so hopeful that Hunter would ask you to the costume ball. We did our best to push him in that direction."

Well, there was that confirmed.

Maudie took over. "When Hugh came home the other day and told me he saw you two together on Monday, and that you stormed past the front of the shop after you talked with him, we knew it had to be bad news."

"I didn't really storm—"

"Then yesterday afternoon," Wanda Jean interrupted, "after I picked up Maudie to go to Bible study over at Annalise's house"— Annalise Reed was another one of the Sweetie Pies—"we drove by Hunter's place and saw him with a woman about your age and height, only maybe she was a bit taller, and she had blonde hair instead of red like yours. Anyway, he was unloading her suitcases from a car and carrying them into his house! I can tell you I almost ran off the road. Brazen as anything."

"That doesn't mean—"

"But that's not all," said Maudie. "When we told Annalise what we'd seen, she told us something we didn't know. That Hunter used to be engaged to this woman when he lived in Atlanta. Her name's Raeanne Foster, and she dumped him nigh on to fifteen years ago and married some rich fella instead. I don't know if Foster is her married name or her maiden name. At any rate, now they're getting a divorce and she's looking to—what's that phrase they use on TV all the time? Hook up? That's it—she's looking to hook up with Hunter now."

It was all Jillian could do to keep from covering her face with her hands in her embarrassment. It was doubtful that the two older ladies understood what that term actually meant. She tried to interject some logic to the conversation. "How would Annalise—"

Maudie was on a roll. "You might wonder how Annalise knows so much. Well, she had been talking to Hunter's great-aunt Gertrude at the nursing home, and she told her all about it. That Foster woman broke young Mr. Greyson's heart all those years ago, and he's just been pining for her ever since. So now she's back in his life, and he just doesn't seem to care what people think, having her there in his house like that for everyone to see. It's disgraceful."

"I'm sure it's perfectly inno—"

"And have you seen him lately, with that awful mustache and that thing on his chin? And his hair is hanging down over his ears. I've a good mind to tell Hugh that if I die today, to take my remains to Reynard's Mortuary over at Painter's Ridge."

Jillian couldn't take anymore. To get their attention she stood up. "Ladies, I surely appreciate your concern for me, but please don't jump to conclusions about Hunter or his friend or former fiancée or whatever she is." She had an inspiration that she hoped would hit home. "Remember the Proverb, 'A perverse man stirs up dissension, and a gossip separates close friends'?"

If there was one thing a Southern lady of a certain generation could do, it was to be able to quote select verses from the Psalms and Proverbs. Jillian was at the very tip on the tail end of that tradition, which seemed to be quickly disappearing, but she could hold her own. Both ladies suddenly looked contrite.

"We certainly didn't mean to gossip," said Wanda Jean. "We were just trying to help, so you'd know what the competition is and wouldn't get your heart broken again, after what you went through in California."

Jillian ignored the reference to her past and sat down again. "I know that you two only meant to do right by me, but please understand: I'm not interested in competing for Hunter Greyson's affections or anyone else's. At least not right now. And please give Hunter the benefit of the doubt. He's a good and honorable man. I may not know a lot about his past, but I've known him long enough to know that, and so have you if you think about it."

Maudie sniffed and pulled an embroidered linen handkerchief from her pocket and dabbed at the corner of one eye. "I didn't mean what I said about going to Painter's Ridge when I die. I get carried away sometimes."

Jillian smiled and patted her hand. "We all do—get carried away sometimes, I mean. I appreciate your concern, but please, just let me handle my love life, such as it is. If I find Mr. Right, I promise you'll be among the first to know."

That afternoon, the teenage daughter of one of Lenora's many first cousins arrived to begin working in the bakery after school. Celia Ryan had some experience working in her uncle's local carryout, Cheap, Cheap Chicken, and Lenora had suggested her as a good candidate, so Jillian was certain that she would quickly catch on to running the cash register. She had made sure that Celia would be available to work some hours on Saturday during Moss Holloween too. Maggie had agreed to train Celia, so Jillian had entertained a small hope that she would have a chance to get away earlier than usual, but with the extra shop traffic, and with even more expected in the next several days, there was just too much to do. The truffles were selling briskly, and she took the time to work up several more batches.

Maggie and Celia had closed up the shop and had been long gone when Jillian looked out the window of the bakery and saw that it had gotten dark outside. Since she had discovered Quinten's body, walking to her car in the back parking lot was a different experience. Both afternoons since, she had made excuses to walk out to the van when Bertie was ready to go home. She didn't think she fooled her grandmother, but Bertie didn't say a word about it. When Jillian was ready to go home yesterday, it had still been daylight, and she made sure she had her keys and her phone in her hand before she left the kitchen to step outside. She would do the same this evening, but the darkness added an extra amount of apprehension.

Whoever killed Quinten was still on the loose. He or she could have left town or might still be around. Was it someone local or a stranger from out of town like Quinten? It bothered her that she didn't know anything about the case. She certainly couldn't ask Gooder. She thought about Laura Lee Zane, a fellow Sweetie Pie who happened to be another sheriff's deputy. She might be able to get some information from her, but even if she did, what could she do about it with all her other responsibilities?

She left the shop without incident and, on the way home, decided she should stop in at the Padgett's house to water the plants and check on things in general. She'd been keeping an eye out when she drove by in the mornings and evenings as she had promised, but hadn't had a chance to actually go into the house since they had left for their cruise.

She pulled into the drive, turned off her car, and rummaged in her purse to find the house key and the little slip of paper where Tara had written the alarm code. Several lights were on in the house. Tara had explained that the lights were set on timers to turn them on and off at specified times so it would look like someone was at home. She was about to get out of her car when another car pulled in the drive behind hers. She looked in the rearview mirror, but the headlights from the other car made it impossible to see who was there. It couldn't be the Padgetts. They weren't due back until early the following week.

Normally she wouldn't have been concerned, but with the recent murder still fresh in her mind, her palms began to sweat, and her heart started to beat a little faster. She thought of the crowbar she kept in the trunk, which was useless to her now. She double-checked that her doors were all locked and grabbed her phone. The engine of the other car stopped but its lights remained on. She heard a car door open and slam shut. She was about to dial 911 when a blond-haired man began tapping at the window.

He smiled, revealing perfectly white and straight teeth. His face seemed very familiar. Jillian decided to take a chance. She lowered the window a few inches.

"May I help you with something?"

"No. Not at all. I was just stopping by to see my cousin Tara. I didn't mean to block you in. Are you coming or going? I can move my car if you're going. I'm Troy Hansford, by the way." He smiled again.

That was why he seemed familiar. There was no doubt in Jillian's mind that Tara and this man were related. They had the same color hair, the same big, brown eyes, the same smile. It was almost spooky. The two could have been brother and sister rather than first cousins. He was obviously the older of the two, closer to her own age, she thought. She also recalled that Tara had said her cousin's name was Troy the day of the yard sale.

Jillian lowered the window completely and offered her hand, "I'm Jillian Green, a neighbor."

He shook her hand. "Pleased to meet you, ma'am."

"I'm afraid Tara isn't home right now."

"Really? Do you know when she'll be back? I just drove over to Moss Hollow from Athens after work to see Tara about some family business. I guess I should have called before I left. This is the first time I've been here since they moved into their new house." He held up his phone and laughed. "I used the app on my phone to find this place or I probably would have gotten lost. It looks pretty nice, as far as I can tell in the dark." He paused and looked around. "Did she tell you they're going to have a baby soon? I'm so happy for her and Paul. They're a great couple."

That clinched it for Jillian. "They're going to be gone for a few days. They're on a cruise to celebrate their anniversary. I'm only here because I promised Tara I'd stop by a few times to check on things." She decided to withhold the fact that she had a key, just in case. She'd leave and come back in the morning before work to water the plants.

His face showed an expression of frustration. "Oh, man, of course—the cruise. I completely forgot about that. She told me about it a few weeks ago, but I've been so busy with my car dealership, it just slipped my mind. And please don't tell her I forgot their anniversary. I stood up with them when they got married so I ought to remember."

"My lips are sealed."

"Thanks." He looked around again. "Well, I guess I'd better go then. It was nice to meet you, Mrs. . . ."

"Green. Jillian Green. And it's Miss Green, actually." She felt a little foolish saying that.

He smiled more broadly. "*Au revoir*, then, Miss Green. I'm sure we'll meet again."

The moment Jillian opened the front door of the bakery at six a.m. on Thursday morning, she already could tell it was going to be an even busier day than the previous two. Besides the regular locals, whom she expected to be at the door, there were several unfamiliar faces, which she assumed belonged to out-of-towners.

Among the new faces was a small woman in a black suit and a crisp, white shirt. Her dark-blond hair was pulled back severely, and she wore a minimum amount of makeup. She had an air of confidence. While the other customers formed into a queue at the register, the woman walked around the shop looking at everything carefully including the pictures on the walls and the front window display.

Eventually, when the line had lessened to just two people, she stepped in behind the last person. When it was her turn to order, she didn't return Jillian's smile. Her tone was terse. "I'd like a large black coffee to go."

Jillian filled her order and took the woman's money. Jillian was about to walk away when the woman said, "Are you Jillian Green?"

Jillian sighed inwardly. Last evening she'd read about the murder in the newspaper and had gleaned a few more details. The article had stated that Quinten Straub was a Swiss national who had been employed by a museum in Washington, D.C., at the time of his death. It didn't say why he was in Moss Hollow, but because of the international connection, the FBI had taken over the investigation. It also mentioned that *Jillian Green, of Moss Hollow, Georgia, found the body behind The Chocolate Shoppe Bakery* . . .

Now she'd have to deal with every crackpot who had read about Quinten's death in the paper.

She answered reluctantly. "Yes I am."

The woman reached inside her jacket and pulled out a badge which she quickly flashed and then put back in her pocket. "I'm Field Agent Reese Calloway with the FBI. I need to speak with you about the murder of Quinten Straub."

Jillian felt like every ear in the place was trained to hear her response.

"Of course," she answered somewhat shakily. "I'm expecting our front girl to be here shortly. Could it wait until she gets here?"

"Yes, that would be fine." She looked sideways at the other customers in the shop without moving her head. "Is there a place more private where we could speak?"

Jillian shook her head. "Not really. This is about as private as it gets in The Chocolate Shoppe."

"Then we'll have to talk in my car. I'll wait for you."

With that, Agent Calloway found a table where she sat with her back against the wall to watch the front door and Jillian and everyone else in the room. The chatter among the customers had become rather subdued as Jillian and Agent Calloway were speaking and did not resume its normal tone. Jillian didn't doubt that tongues would be wagging about her encounter with the FBI as soon as she and Agent Calloway left the room, and that it would be all over town before the day was out.

Maggie arrived, so Jillian popped into the kitchen to remove her apron and to tell Bertie and Lenora where she was going. She didn't look at their faces to see their reactions or wait for them to ask questions, but hurried out before they could say anything.

Agent Calloway had parked just down the street, and they walked in silence in the darkness. Sunrise was still about an hour away.

In the car, Agent Calloway took out a small device that resembled a ballpoint pen, but it didn't have a clicker. "I'm going to record our conversation." It was a statement, not a request. She pressed a button and laid the device on the dashboard.

"I have read your statement to the police on the day of the murder of Quinten Straub. Is it correct that you found the body?"

"Yes, I did. But you should know, I haven't made an official statement. Gooder, that is, Deputy Jones, just asked a few questions and took my contact information."

"I understand. Did you know Mr. Straub previous to the day of his death?"

"No. I met him that same day when he came into the shop. It was about one o'clock. I had looked at the clock just before I saw him through the window standing outside."

"What was he doing outside?"

"He was looking at my window display. I had just finished it that morning, and I was pleased that someone noticed it. Then he came in and purchased some chocolate truffles."

"What did you talk about? Please tell me everything that you remember. Even small details could be important."

Jillian thought back and recounted their meeting, including their discussion about the Mayan vase and their plans to meet for dinner.

Agent Calloway's eyebrows raised at the mention of the dinner date. "So you were planning to meet this man, whom you say was a complete stranger, for dinner that evening?"

Jillian felt rather defensive. "Well, yes. He seemed perfectly nice and said he was a museum curator, and I thought if there was something more that he knew about the vase, I'd like to hear about it. We were to meet at a public restaurant where people know me. There was nothing untoward about it."

Agent Calloway just looked at her for a moment and then

her eyes narrowed. "Do you know why Mr. Straub came to Moss Hollow, Miss Green?"

"No I don't. As I told you, he just said that he was going to meet some friends."

"Did he mention any names? Please think hard."

"No, I'm sure he didn't."

"Did he say if he'd been any other place besides Moss Hollow that day?"

"No." Jillian thought back. "He did say he'd had a long drive. Did he drive down from Washington?" She quickly added, "I read in the newspaper that he worked there. He only told me that he was a museum curator, but not where the museum was located."

Agent Calloway paused before answering. "No, he didn't drive from D.C. He flew into Atlanta Airport Sunday evening and rented a car. He stayed overnight in Atlanta."

"Well that's just over an hour from here. I wouldn't exactly call that a long drive."

"Nor would I."

"So, are you saying that Moss Hollow was not his first stop? How many miles were on his rental?"

"That's not your concern, Miss Green."

Jillian figured it was useless to ask, but thought she'd try anyway. "What about the museum? Did someone there know why he was here?"

"I think we're done here," said Agent Calloway brusquely, completely ignoring her question. "I may be contacting you again." She reached in her jacket and pulled out a card. "If you think of anything else that might be pertinent to this case, give me a call. You can go for now, but don't leave town."

Don't leave town—there was that phrase again. As Jillian walked back toward the bakery, she wondered if she was a suspect. Gooder had made no bones about his opinion, but then, most of what Gooder said was bluster. Agent Calloway was a highly trained law officer. She probably didn't accept anyone on face value. Did she know about Jillian's association with David Drake, a known criminal? Probably. She began to wonder if she might have to prove her innocence.

Later in the day, after lunchtime, Jillian was placing a tray of pumpkin-pecan muffins in the bakery case when Savannah entered the shop. They'd talked on the phone a couple of times since she had discovered Quinten's body, but they hadn't seen each other face to face in over a week. Jillian was surprised to see Savannah dressed in a flannel shirt and jeans instead of her normal attire for the workday—a skirt, blouse, and jacket to keep up her professional image as an accountant.

"Hey, have you got a minute?" asked Savannah.

Maggie was at the register. "Sure. I need a little break. Would you like a coffee and a muffin? Those pumpkin ones I just put in the case are fresh out of the oven."

"Definitely," answered Savannah. "I haven't had lunch yet, and any Chocolate Shoppe muffin would hit the spot."

While Savannah paid Maggie, Jillian fetched a coffee and a muffin for herself as well as Savannah. They found a table and sat down.

Jillian wanted to talk about her early morning visitor from the FBI with Savannah, but The Chocolate Shoppe was not the place for it, so she began the conversation proactively. "So what have you been up to today?"

"James and I were over at Yarn Charm to help set up the haunted house."

Yarn Charm was Moss Hollow's local yarn shop and was located in an old three-story Victorian mansion, complete with a square tower, and painted in a dark shade of green with its very elaborate gingerbread trim painted in even darker shades of green and purple. It was the perfect locale for a haunted house. Its owner, Gladys Glenshaw, dressed up as the witch from *The Wizard of Oz*, green skin and all, each year, to sell tickets at the door during Moss Holloween.

"That sounds like fun. How's it shaping up this year?"

Savannah chewed and swallowed a bite of muffin. "Really well. I think it's going to be extra scary. You know Greysons always donates a coffin for us to use. The past several years, Ike Puckett has dressed up like a zombie to lie in it and scare people as they walk by, but this year, since he's in the play, they needed someone else to do it, so Oliver Kent volunteered."

"Oliver Kent? Hunter's assistant at the funeral home?"

"Yeah, I couldn't believe it either, but he is so great. He stopped by in costume just before I left, and he scared the bejeebers out of me even though I knew it was him."

"What did he do?"

"It wasn't so much what he did as how he looks. He's made up to look like a vampire from an old black-and-white silent movie from the twenties . . . *Nos* . . . Nose-something, I think. Oliver had a still photo from the movie to show us how he'd copied the costume and makeup, and he said the name of it, but I can't remember exactly what it's called right now."

"Wouldn't it be *Dracula*?"

"No. It's something different." She looked puzzled and shook her head as if that would somehow shake loose the word she was searching for, but gave up quickly. "Anyway, when you see him you're almost certain that if a ray of sunshine were to hit him he would go up in a puff of smoke. That's how real he looks. Well, not real—it's a vampire. But you know what I mean."

"I'll take your word for it. Oliver looks creepy. Maybe when I go through the haunted house and see him, it'll ring a bell and I'll know which movie you're talking about, or maybe not. I've not watched that many silent movies, but when I have, I usually choose something funny like a Charlie Chaplin or Buster Keaton film."

"That's my preference as well, but don't miss the haunted house this year. Everything is scary fun, including, as usual, Gladys in her witch getup. But it's a good thing there's a different path through the house for families with little children. I think Oliver would be too much for them. He was almost too much for me, especially when he sort of rolls back his eyes and . . ." Savannah didn't finish the sentence but demonstrated with her head leaned back, staring at Jillian down her nose, doing her best to imitate Oliver's pose. Jillian just gave her a puzzled look.

"Well, I can't do it like Oliver can, but when you see him, you'll get it. Besides, it's for a good cause since all the proceeds go to the children's hospital wing. Speaking of which, are you going to the play tonight or tomorrow? James and I will be there tonight."

"Really? You two are getting to be quite an item."

Savannah looked serious, remembering very well Jillian's feelings twenty years ago when James had married someone else. Now that he was a widower, his and Savannah's friendship appeared to be blossoming into something more. "You don't mind do you?"

"No, of course not. That ship sailed a long time ago. I only wish you well. James deserves some happiness after, well, you know." They both knew what she was talking about, and she saw no need to dredge it up. "Anyway, to answer your question, I bought two tickets for tonight, but I don't know if I'll use them. Bertie already said she didn't want to go, and I couldn't drag Aunt Cornelia there if I tried."

"Would you like to go with us?"

Jillian didn't even have to consider that. "No thanks."

"So, Cornelia is still down on Moss Holloween?"

"Yes. I actually asked her about it a few weeks ago, just to be sure, and she hadn't changed her attitude. It was funny though, Bertie said something about her not always feeling that way about Moss Holloween, and she, Bertie that is, started to say something concerning Burton Puckett, but Cornelia just stopped her cold."

"Really? What could Bertie have said about Ike's dad?"

"I've no idea. It's the first I've ever heard anything about it. But when I was over at the hardware store, Ike said he thought his dad used to be sweet on Cornelia."

"You asked him about it?"

"No, it just came up in conversation when I asked how Burton was doing since he retired."

"Well, that is a mystery. We may have to delve into it sometime. Maybe after Moss Holloween is over this year." Savannah lowered her voice and leaned in toward Jillian. "Speaking of mysteries, do you know anything new about that dead guy you found?"

Jillian looked around the room to see if anyone was listening. She concluded there probably was. Though she had wanted to avoid this conversation for now, in an even lower volume she said to Savannah, "A lady FBI agent was in here this morning."

Savannah's eyes grew larger. "You're kidding."

"I'm not."

"What did she want?"

"We went out to her car and she asked me a bunch of questions. I just told her everything that I knew. She recorded it." She looked around. "I'll call and tell you more later."

"Wow. Are you okay?"

"Yeah, I am, for the time being. There's too much going on in my life right now to get too bent out of shape. I was up at four this morning so I could stop by the Padgett's house and water their plants before I came to work. Which reminds me. Guess who I met last evening."

"Who?"

"Tara's cousin Troy. Remember she mentioned him when she was telling us about her great-uncle? I have to say, her cousin is rather handsome and charming. And he was not wearing a wedding ring—not that it matters really."

"No, of course not. Not really. That would only matter if you were interested." Savannah smiled. "What does he look like?"

The bell over the front door rang and Troy Hansford walked into The Chocolate Shoppe Bakery.

"Turn around and see for yourself."

Troy saw Jillian just as Savannah turned around. Jillian could see that he was as surprised to see her as she was him, and even better, that he was pleasantly surprised. His expression changed to a brilliant smile as he walked over to their table.

"Hello, Miss Green. It's wonderful to run into you again." There was a slight emphasis on "Miss."

"Please call me Jillian. This is my friend, Savannah Cantrell. Savannah, this is Troy Hansford, Tara Padgett's cousin from . . . I'm sorry, I forget."

"Athens, Georgia. I'm at your service, ma'am."

"It's very nice to meet you," said Savannah, shaking his proffered hand. Then she stood up and picked up her coffee cup, plate, and napkin as she said, "I wish I could stay, but I have an appointment this afternoon. Please take my chair."

Jillian was not fooled. She doubted there was an appointment, or at least one that was so pressing that Savannah needed to leave immediately.

Troy offered his thanks and sat down. Noticing Jillian's apron, he said, "So, you work here?"

"Yes. It's my grandmother's bakery actually. I came home to help out about a year ago."

"Where were you before that?"

"I lived in LA. I worked for an ad agency."

Troy whistled low. "Must have been quite the culture shock coming here."

"There has been some adjustment, but it hasn't taken long. I grew up here, until I went away to college." Jillian decided it was time to move the conversation away from her life. "I'm surprised to see you're still in town. I thought you'd head back home."

"Well, I was going to, but I was exhausted, so I decided to stay at a motel overnight. I stopped at the Peach Inn, or whatever it's called, and they told me every place in town was booked, but they called over to Painter's Ridge and found a room for me in a decent place. They also gave me a brochure about your little festival here, so I decided to hang around and see what it's all about."

"Can you be away from your business that long?"

"Yeah. I own a classic-foreign-car dealership in Athens, but I have good people working for me. I'll probably be on the phone a lot, but that comes with the territory."

"Well, I'm glad to see you again." Jillian began to stand. "I should get back to work. Can I get something for—"

Before she could finish her sentence and stand completely, Troy reached out to take both her hands so she would sit back down. His hands remained on hers. "Don't go yet. Since I'm going to be in town for a couple of days, I'd love it if you'd let me take you out to dinner this evening."

Jillian was flattered. It was hard not to be. But this was the second invitation to dinner she'd had from a virtual stranger in the last week, and the first time hadn't turned out so well. She was about to say no thanks, when she looked up and saw that Hunter had entered the shop and was standing in line. There were a couple of older ladies ahead of him placing their orders, and behind him was a man of about fifty. He had coal-black hair with some strands of pure white, and he was short in stature but powerfully built. His features were indicative of a South or Central American, and he had a tanned complexion, both naturally and as if he spent a lot of time in the sun. Dressed in a button-up shirt with sleeves rolled up and slacks, his clothing was somewhat rumpled as if he'd slept in it, and beneath his deep-brown eyes were dark circles. Both men were observing her and Troy, but it was Hunter who won her attention. She made a snap decision.

"I'd love to have dinner with you. And, if you're interested, I have two tickets for Moss Holloween's play this evening."

She was rewarded with another stunning smile. At that moment, his phone rang. He looked at the screen and then said apologetically, "Forgive me, but I have to take this."

"I understand. We'll talk later."

Jillian got up and walked behind the counter. Maggie was filling the ladies' order, and they had wandered over to sit at a table, so Jillian had no choice but to take over the register to wait on Hunter. She was still feeling rather awkward with him.

"Hi, Jillian. I haven't seen you since the parking lot . . ." He let the words trail off. "Are you all right?"

"Yes, I'm fine. Thanks for asking."

While she took his order and then his money, she wondered if he might know anything else about Quinten's murder. "I read that the FBI has taken over the case." She decided to withhold that she'd spoken with Agent Calloway.

"Yes. They showed up pretty quickly to take the body and all the evidence that was gathered to their lab in Atlanta. They'll do the autopsy there, or they may have already done it. The FBI doesn't tend to keep me in the loop."

Maggie came back from delivering the ladies' order and offered to fill Hunter's, so Jillian had no excuse but to remain at the register. Instead of stepping aside to let the dark-haired man order, Hunter stood there. "I'm sorry about the other day," he said softly.

She thought about acting like she didn't know what he was talking about, but decided not to play coy. "I'm sorry too.

I overreacted." She remembered what Maudie and Wanda Jean had said, and thought a moment about mentioning his visitor from Atlanta, but thought the better of it. She was glad she didn't.

"The old friend I told you about is here now. She's going through a rough time—a divorce. You probably heard that she's staying at my place." Jillian didn't exactly nod, but her expression signaled that she knew. "I'm sleeping at the mortuary while she's here." He laughed. "It's not the most comfortable place to be—especially this time of year. I figure some of the Thrashers will get together to play some sort of prank on me. The expectation of it is almost worse than the real thing. Last year someone wrapped my car in plastic wrap. Maybe that lets me off the hook this year."

"One can always hope." She smiled, wondering why he hadn't identified this "old friend" as his ex-fiancée. Maybe Maudie and Wanda Jean had gotten that wrong. It wasn't like he had any reason to tell her that anyway. It was interesting that he wanted to let her know he was staying at the mortuary. He probably wanted to make sure that word got around town so that people like Maudie and Wanda Jean wouldn't take their business to Painter's Ridge. If that was the case, he'd have to tell someone else. She wasn't about to spread news of his current living arrangements, even if it did come from the horse's mouth.

Hunter looked around at Troy who was still talking on the phone, but had gotten up and was heading for the door. "Who's your friend?"

"He's Tara Padgett's cousin, Troy. You remember Paul and Tara from church—they moved here recently."

Hunter nodded in affirmation.

"I just met Troy yesterday."

Hunter's eyebrows raised. "He seemed like he was being rather familiar for someone you just met."

"Well, it's not really your business." She said it with more of an edge than she intended. She could see that Hunter was taken aback.

"No it isn't. You're right."

Now she felt bad. He looked as if she'd hurt his feelings. At that moment, Maggie handed him his order, and with no more chitchat, he left.

Jillian might have gone after him to say—she wasn't sure what. It was a moot point since she had hesitated to make the move. She could have asked Maggie to take over the register, but she didn't, and as she debated, he was through the door and gone.

The dark-haired man stepped up to place his order, speaking in a clipped British accent. She was somewhat surprised, expecting, if anything, to hear a Spanish accent. While Maggie was filling his order, she asked in a friendly manner if he was in town for the festival.

"No I'm not." His expression was grim and he seemed disinclined to elaborate.

Jillian wasn't sure what to say, so she just smiled. "Well, I hope you have a chance to enjoy some of the festival. They'll close off the square this evening so that the vendors can start setting up."

He nodded, but didn't respond otherwise. There was an awkward silence between them until Maggie gave him his order and he left the shop.

She watched as he stopped at the front window. She couldn't tell if he was staring at the display or at someone sitting at one of the tables just past it. His expression remained grim, but was joined by something else. She wasn't sure if it was angst or surprise or what, but it set her nerves on edge. He glanced up and down the street before looking back through the window, this time in the direction of the register where Jillian stood. As before, when Quinten Straub had done the same thing, she didn't think he could see her, but she wasn't sure. She turned quickly and went into the kitchen.

Troy showed up a while later, apologizing for the length of his phone call, and they made arrangements for the evening. Jillian offered to meet him at the restaurant, but Troy insisted that he would pick her up at Belle Haven. She started to give him directions, but he said he would use his phone app to find his way there. The play was to begin at eight, so Jillian called to make reservations at Crazy Fish Bar & Grill for six thirty.

In the late afternoon, Jillian was busily working, making sure the kitchen was clean and ready for the following day. Before she returned to Moss Hollow she hadn't been much of a baker—if by "much of" one meant not at all. It took her a long time to understand how crucial each of the elements was for consistent results—the quality of the ingredients, the precision of the measurements, the importance of timing and attention. And when she began, she had not appreciated that running a bakery demanded a tight production schedule. Customers had expectations that had to be met or they would not return. Even a small-town bakery had to be run in a professional manner.

Lenora had taken off a little early, having decided to stay at her sister's house across town Thursday through Saturday night because of the street noise from the festival. She complained that the previous year her sleep had been disturbed more than once, and she wasn't about to endure that again. Since Lenora had moved into the upstairs apartment, it had been convenient for Jillian to be able to pop upstairs to ask her this or that, or to ask her to watch the shop if she had to pop out for a minute. Lenora didn't seem to mind, but Jillian knew it wasn't fair to continue to do that. That's why she had wanted to hire Celia.

Maggie and Celia were closing that evening, making it possible for Jillian to leave early enough to get ready for her date. They would make sure the bakery was cleaned and ready for opening the next morning. Then they would lock the front door from inside and exit through the back door.

Things went smoothly at work, so by six o'clock, Jillian was at Belle Haven sitting at her computer, showered and ready to go, watching through the windows for Troy's arrival. She looked down at her attire and hoped she hadn't overdone her wardrobe for the evening. Since he had only seen her in her work clothes, with her hair pulled back and minimal makeup, she had chosen to dress up more than she would have if she was just going to the play with Bertie or by herself. She wore a mottled dark-gold dress, the bodice fitted to the waist, with a pleated skirt that flared slightly and ended just at the middle of her knees. Her thick red hair hung loose and wavy over her shoulders, her peaches-and-cream complexion accented with simple gold dangly earrings and a gold, chunky chain necklace. She'd taken extra care with her makeup, outlining her bright-green eyes with a soft-brown pencil and smoky eye shadow to enhance them, but not so much that she looked like a raccoon.

Neither Bertie nor Cornelia had said much when she told them she was going out with Troy Hansford. She hadn't mentioned the dinner date she'd arranged with Quinten. There'd seemed no point in doing that as it would only make them worry about her. Neither of the twins had mentioned Hunter since Monday. She didn't doubt that they had heard about Raeanne Foster through the Sweetie Pie grapevine. Even so, she was under the impression that they didn't approve of her going out with Troy. She would have thought any warm-blooded male would have fit the bill.

But maybe they were right. Besides his resemblance to

Tara, she didn't have any substantial proof that he was who he said he was. Since she was at her computer, she decided to check it out, typing *Hansford car dealership Athens Georgia* into the search bar. She was relieved when she saw a page for Hansford's Classic Foreign Cars. The home page displayed a large showroom with a wide variety of cars. The cutline under the photograph listed Ferrari, Porsche, Mercedes-Benz, and other "preowned" models for sale.

She glanced up from the screen to see that Troy had arrived. In the darkness at the Padgett's house the night before, she hadn't been able to see his car, but now she had the full view of it. She didn't know enough about specific car models to be able to name it at a glance, but this one was a shiny black sports car that looked antique and expensive, something like what James Bond might drive. She was suitably impressed, though she supposed with a car dealership he had his choice of cars to drive.

As he got out of the car and stood up, she was glad that she had taken some extra effort. For someone who had appeared to have come to Moss Hollow on a whim, Troy was well-dressed, wearing a dark-tan, muted-plaid sport coat over a striped shirt with a tie and black trousers.

She allowed him to ring the bell before she got up from her desk to answer the front door. She didn't want him to know that she had been watching for him, even though she had been. However, she forgot to consider that she might not be the only one who was watching for him. When she opened the door to the office, Cornelia was already at the front door, her hand on the doorknob and Possum at her heels. Bertie stood, her eyes trained on the front door and drying her hands on a dish towel, at the opening of the foyer that led to the dining room through which one could reach the kitchen.

Jillian didn't have any experience with the two of them

waiting to meet her date. In high school she had only dated James Wilson, who was born and raised in Moss Hollow. Since she had returned home, she had only been out with Hunter, whom they both knew before she did. She wondered what Troy was in for. There was no stopping them now. She quickly and quietly closed the door to the office and leaned her head against the door to listen.

She could only hear muted voices through the solid wooden door, a fact that usually she considered a good thing but now made her wish her ancestors had skimped a bit more on materials when they built the place.

The voices faded away. She waited a minute and then cracked open the door to listen. She opened the door a bit more to look out and saw that the foyer was empty. She stepped out and followed the sounds of voices toward the living room. At a short distance from the doorway, she stopped to watch. She needn't have worried about Troy. He seemed to be holding his own, having maneuvered Cornelia and Bertie to sit on the sofa while he stood before them in front of the fireplace. He seemed to be doing particularly well with Cornelia whose reservations appeared to have melted away before his charm. Bertie, on the other hand, was not quite as favorable, asking one question after another about where he grew up and about his family, which he answered with good-humored frankness.

Before Bertie could go too far, Jillian made a noise to attract their attention and walked into the room. Troy looked her way, taking in her appearance from head to toe with an approving smile. He walked to greet her, taking her hands and quickly kissing her on her cheek before stepping back. "You certainly are beautiful this evening, Miss Jillian Green."

She laughed. "And you clean up very handsomely yourself, Mr. Troy Hansford."

"Thank you, ma'am. I always aim to be prepared. Some people bring along a backpack as their 'go bag,' carrying things like a hunting knife, a fire starter, a compass, and trail mix. I always bring along a garment bag with a jacket, shirt, tie, and trousers. You never know when you might need to look your best."

He looked around at Cornelia and Bertie. "I was just getting acquainted with your aunt and grandmother." He looked around the room, which had been one of the first rooms in the old mansion to be refurbished after Jillian's return. "This is an amazing home you have here. It's hard to believe that any of these antebellum mansions still exist. And it looks like you've taken good care of it."

"We've been working on it," said Jillian. "It's been in the family for over two hundred years, and it takes a lot of upkeep."

"I can imagine."

"Well, shall we go?" asked Jillian. She hoped they could get away without Cornelia or Bertie offering some sort of advice that would be more appropriate for a teenage girl than a grown woman. She should have known better.

"I expect you to be home early this evening," said Bertie. "We've got a big day tomorrow, and we'll have to get an extra-early start in the morning."

Troy answered before Jillian could. "I'll have her home right after the play's over, ma'am."

"See that you do, young man."

After they had gone outside and Troy was opening the car door for Jillian, she said, "I'm sorry about what Bertie said. Sometimes my grandmother forgets that I'm a grown woman."

He laughed as she sat down, and just before he closed the door, said, "Don't worry about it. Your grandmother can't scare me off. If there's one thing I know, it's how to handle people. You learn that in the sales line of work."

Jillian was sure he meant it innocently enough, but something about the way he said it unsettled her. She barely knew him. Was Moss Holloween really so interesting to someone like him that he would want to hang around town for it? Was he really surprised to see her when he walked into The Chocolate Shoppe?

Business at the Crazy Fish Bar & Grille was bustling when they arrived. The parking lot was nearly full, and through the large picture windows, Jillian could see patrons sharing meals, talking, and laughing. If this was any indication, Moss Hollow was in high spirits this evening.

Located on the edge of town, it wasn't an elegant restaurant, but it had a lot of character with an unusual paint scheme of periwinkle-blue siding with green trim, and rainbow-painted wooden fish shapes "floating" across the exterior. The interior was rustic with exposed beams, hanging lamps that resembled brass maritime oil lanterns, and booths built with shiplap. The most important thing was that the seafood was fantastic.

Jillian was glad she had had the forethought to make reservations, but even so, there was a short wait. As the hostess was leading them to their table, she saw Savannah and James at a booth, but they were in an intense conversation that she didn't want to interrupt just to say hi.

After the usual procedure of ordering drinks and then food, Troy began telling Jillian about himself and asking general questions about her life. It was the pleasant conversation of two people getting to know one another. Jillian found herself relaxing and putting aside her earlier misgivings. *It's just a date, not a lifetime commitment. Enjoy yourself, Jillian.* So she did.

It wasn't long before the conversation got around to his cousin, Tara. It was Troy who brought her up. "How did you first meet Tara? Did you stop by with a loaf of fresh bread from your bakery?"

"No—I should have done that though. We've had several new neighbors of late with that new development coming in, and I'm afraid I've not been very good about going out of my way to meet them all. Paul and Tara started attending the same church I go to, and that's where I met them."

"Well, that's a good thing. You should know that they aren't just attending to meet people in a new town. Paul and Tara have always been churchgoers. She grew up with that."

"What about you?"

"Not so much. Our mothers were sisters, and they were close, but our dads were worlds apart." He seemed anxious to move away from the subject. "But enough about that. Did you go to Tara's yard sale? I don't know if she told you, but our great-uncle, who was an archaeologist, died recently and left behind some unusual items. Tara said she was going to put the few things that remained that neither of us wanted into the sale."

"Yes, I was there, and I actually purchased a few of your uncle's old possessions. I got the typewriter, which is now in the library at Belle Haven, the framed photographs—I'm going to reuse the frames with some different photos or artwork when I get a chance—and that reproduction Mayan vase."

"Really? I mean, I can see the typewriter—that's actually pretty cool looking, and as I recall, it still works—and reusing the frames is a good idea, but that old vase creeps me out. Why did you want that?"

"It's hard to explain. At first, it brought back a good memory to me . . . that's not really important now, but once I had it home, I did some research and found out that one of the motifs is a chocolate tree. Well, not a chocolate tree, but the kind of tree that chocolate comes from. I put it in the bakery's front window for my Halloween display—didn't you see it?"

"No. I guess I didn't look very closely. I'm not much of a

window-shopper." He paused, seeming to be trying to recall the display. "Nope. I can't remember it at all. Sorry. I'll have a good look before I come in for coffee and another one of those pumpkin muffins of yours tomorrow."

"So, you're sticking around?"

He laughed. "I think I'll have to see Moss Holloween to the bitter end now. That way, I can report to Paul and Tara what they missed, not to mention being able to enjoy the delights that Moss Hollow has to offer." He looked at her meaningfully.

Jillian was glad she didn't have to say anything after that as the waitress arrived with their meals. The flow of their conversation was interrupted for a time as they ate and compared the dishes they had ordered. Jillian had just given Troy a taste of her salmon-cashew stir-fry when she looked over his shoulder. There she saw Hunter and a woman she assumed to be Raeanne Foster were being seated by the hostess. She wasn't sure if it was by design or accident that Hunter's place at the table gave him a direct line of sight toward Jillian, but if he had noticed that she was even there, he didn't show it.

Raeanne's back was to her, but she could tell that she was quite tall. She had long blond hair that reached the middle of her back. They appeared to be having a pleasant conversation, punctuated by the sound of Raeanne's laughter, which Jillian could hear even over the sound of the general din in the restaurant. She continued to watch a moment as Raeanne reached across the table to lay her hand atop Hunter's. It didn't seem to Jillian that she was having a particularly "hard time" as Hunter had said. In fact, she seemed to be having the time of her life.

Troy said something to her, but when Jillian didn't answer, he turned around to see what was distracting her. "Am I interrupting something?" he asked.

Jillian had the grace to blush. "I'm so sorry. I . . . um . . . that's . . ." She couldn't find the words to say.

"Someone you've dated?" he asked.

"Well, that's pretty shrewd of you. Yes. I've had a few dates with Hunter Greyson, but we're not exclusive or anything. We're just friends."

There was another peal of laughter from Raeanne. Jillian took a glance. It didn't appear to her that whatever Raeanne had found so funny was affecting Hunter in the same way, his mouth set in a sort of wry grin. With raised eyebrows she looked back at Troy who was somewhat bemused.

Jillian was repentant. "I'm so sorry. I promise to give you all my attention from here on out."

"And I will hold you to that." He glanced at his watch. "What time did you say the play starts?"

"Eight." She glanced at her own watch. "Oh! I didn't realize it was getting so late." She looked around and saw that Savannah and James had already left the restaurant. "We'd better finish up and head over to the auditorium. Do you mind if we skip dessert?"

"Not at all."

After they'd finished their meals, and Troy had paid the check, leaving a generous tip, they headed outside. The sun had set since they had been in the restaurant, so the parking lot was now illuminated by the tall lampposts that ringed the area. There was sufficient light, but a fog had begun to gather, making the atmosphere seem spooky and mysterious.

When they were almost to Troy's car, the dark-haired man she'd seen at the bakery earlier got out of his vehicle, a dark-color Jeep that looked like it had been through a hailstorm. She couldn't explain it, but she felt a coldness as he passed by her on his way toward the restaurant without seeming to see her at all. She glanced back at Troy, who was a few steps behind her, and thought she saw a look pass between the two men. If someone would have asked her, she would have said it was a look of pure hatred.

Troy and Jillian got to the auditorium and found their seats with plenty of time to spare. There was a pleasant hum around the room and a certain amount of excitement. The houselights were still up. Some people were already in their seats, but there were still many milling around, talking to neighbors and friends. Jillian saw James and Savannah speaking with Mayor Blackwater. In the program, Jillian read that he was slated to say a few words before the play began, both as a welcome to visitors and as an official opening to the festival.

Jillian stole a look at Troy, who seemed to be taking it all in, but his face was passive and she hadn't known him long enough to read it. He had been very quiet since they had left the restaurant. She wasn't sure if he was annoyed about her distraction with Hunter and Raeanne, or if it was their brief encounter with the dark-haired man that was filling his thoughts. What was it that she saw pass between the two men in the parking lot? Or was it just her imagination? She wondered if she should mention the man, but decided that now was not the time. She scanned her memory for a safe subject.

"As I recall, Tara said you decided to keep your uncle's journals. Have you had a chance to read them yet?"

"Yes, I have." He paused. "Well, that's not quite true. I've started reading them. There are several. He led a really fascinating life as an archeologist in the field and as a professor at Harvard. It's too bad that he lost his memory in his later years. He was an extremely erudite man, and I have vague childhood memories of him being very robust, you know, a man's man. But we didn't have much contact when I was older, and well, the last ten years of his life were spent in the memory unit of an assisted-living facility. I think he was happy enough, and he was well cared for. The things he kept must have been like anchors to a past that was slipping away."

"That is so sad when that happens. Dementia is a terrible disease. Did he never marry and have a family?"

"I think he might have been married at some point, but maybe it didn't last. I don't really know for sure. If there were children, I never heard of them or met them, and since Tara and I were the only ones named in his will, I have to assume there were none. I guess we're a strange family. He and my grandfather were years apart, and I don't think they were all that close, but still, there must have been some sort of bond. My mother and Tara's used to tell stories about Uncle Denny, so they had to have been around him sometimes. When I was a kid, I guess I wasn't interested enough to ask questions, and now, when I'd like to know more, it's too late."

"But you have the journals now. Maybe those will fill in some of the blanks."

"Yes. Maybe. I hope so. But from what I've read so far, the journals seem to be mostly about his adventures in the field. Maybe his later ones will have something, but it doesn't seem he wrote much about personal things—at least not about family."

As he had talked about his family, he sometimes looked almost melancholy, but he seemed to cast that off and his face brightened. "I'm actually thinking of writing a book based on the journals—maybe a biography, or I could use them as a basis to write a series of books of fiction. I haven't decided yet. I've been reading the oldest journal, with entries that date from the late

1930s. Uncle Denny was just nineteen when he went on his first expedition to Central America."

"Sounds like an exciting prospect for a young man."

"Doesn't it?" said Troy. "He first met the famous archeologist Sylvanus Morley at a lecture, and later, Morley offered him the chance to be part of a team that was headed for the Yucatán."

"I'm afraid I don't know much about archaeology. I've never heard that name before," said Jillian.

"Apparently, he was well-known in his day. From what I've read so far, Uncle Denny thought Morley was the best at what he did, and he hoped to pattern his career on his. Even when he wrote about the conditions he was subjected to in the bush, his excitement at being there just sort of leaps off the page. According to the journal, the team that he was with was looking for an as-yet-undiscovered Classic Maya site. The leaders of the group had found reference to the place in a copy of a text that was said to predate the Popol Vuh, and they had investigated to the point that they thought they knew the general area where it should be."

"Three questions: Did they find it? The site, I mean. And if they did, was there treasure? And what's a Popol Vuh?"

"Well, if they did find it, I haven't gotten that far in my uncle's journal yet, so I'll have to let you know. About the treasure, since Uncle Denny wasn't exactly a rich man, I'd have to guess no. But, as they say, one man's trash is another man's treasure. I think these were all academic types, so they were probably more interested in hieroglyphs than gold and jewels.

"To answer your third question, as I understand it, the Popol Vuh is sort of a Mayan bible that includes a creation story and a hero myth. To tell you the truth, this is all new to me. I hadn't heard of Morley either, or the Popol Vuh, but I looked them up on the Internet. What did we do before the Internet?"

Jillian laughed. "Well, as I recall, we looked in dictionaries and encyclopedias and made trips to the library."

"I remember those days too, but that was long ago." Troy chuckled. "Since I started my own business, I haven't had much leisure time to spend reading and studying. I've traveled a lot, but it's almost always been associated with work. Now that I've started reading Uncle Denny's journals and thinking about his life, it makes me realize I need to make time for other things. This is the first time in ages I've taken off a few days just for myself." He reached over and took her hand. "And I'm having a wonderful time. Thanks for that, Jillian."

"I'm having a wonderful time too. Thanks for asking me out." An idea occurred to her. "How do you feel about dressing up for Halloween?"

He smiled. "I think the last time I did that I was maybe eleven or twelve, so I think I felt pretty good about it then. Why do you ask?"

"Well, on Saturday evening, there is a costume ball at the high school gym, and I was wondering if you'd care to go with me." She felt pretty bold, asking him out. Bertie would be proud—or would she? She had wanted Jillian to ask Hunter to the ball, but maybe she wouldn't consider this a good thing.

"Now there's something I never thought to hear—'costume ball' and 'high school gym' in the same sentence."

"It's really just a sock hop with costumes. It's for charity, and it's really a lot of fun."

"I'd love to go, but I'm afraid I don't carry a costume with me in my garment 'go bag.'"

"You forget I live in a virtual museum. If we don't have something you can use as a costume at Belle Haven, then my name isn't Jillian Green."

He smiled. "Then it's a date. I would be pleased to escort you to the ball, Miss Green."

The lights flickered. The few people left standing took their seats, and Mayor Blackwater began his prepared remarks. Moss Holloween had officially begun.

The play had its scary moments, but mostly, it was funny, often skewing into comedic melodrama. The Puckett family shone. Jillian thought Sylvia had a real talent for the stage, and Ike was pretty much playing himself, sometimes actually winking at the audience. The real charmer was Burton Puckett. Jillian had never spent much time around him, but his antics on stage gave her a good sense of his personality. He never said a word, but he stole every scene that he was in.

It was just the sort of entertainment that Jillian needed. The events of the past several days faded away, and she laughed more than she had in a long time. Troy laughed with her and she began to feel as if she had known him much longer than she really had.

With an intermission at the halfway point, it was after ten before the play was over. Stepping through the outer doors into the night, Jillian saw the fog had intensified since they were in the auditorium, and a halo of mist hung over the cars in the parking lot. Just before they reached Troy's car, she yawned. She tried to stifle it, but couldn't, so she covered her mouth with her hand which drew Troy's attention.

He was sympathetic. "What time were you up this morning?"

"Oh, about four a.m."

"Ouch. Is that the regular start of your day?"

"Thankfully, no. Not quite. I . . ." She hesitated to tell him why she was up so early. But then, she really had no doubts now that he was Tara's cousin. It wouldn't hurt for him to know that she had a key to the Padgett's house. "I stopped by Paul and Tara's to water the plants. I promised I would while they were gone."

He looked puzzled. "Why didn't you just do that when you were there . . ." He seemed to have a realization. "Ah. You didn't want me to know you had a key."

"Sorry, but I wasn't completely sure you were who you said you were then, and I thought it was better to err on the side of caution."

"And you were quite right to do so. So, does this mean you trust me now?"

She laughed and her tone was mock-serious. "Let's not get carried away, Mr. Hansford, if that's your real name. If Tara Padgett is really your cousin, can you tell me her birthdate?"

He answered in a similar tone of voice. "She was born October 27, 1985, a Sunday, at ten fifteen in the evening. There was a light drizzle outside, and the St. Louis Cardinals had beaten the Kansas City Royals that day to win the World Series. Does that satisfy my lady?"

"I have no idea. Is it true?"

"Which one—the birthdate or the World Series?"

"Both."

"I'm afraid I'm not sure about Tara's birthday—I'm pretty sure it's in the fall. I seem to remember a princess-themed birthday party or two that I was subjected to that occurred a couple of months after the start of school. As far as the World Series goes, I lied. It was the Royals over the Cardinals."

"Then the answer is definitely no. Anyone who lies about the World Series will never have my trust."

"Curses. Foiled again."

She laughed and yawned at the same time.

"Let's get you home. Your grandmother will probably be waiting at the door."

"My grandmother had better be in bed fast asleep."

As Troy steered the car out of the parking lot, Jillian's mind went to the bakery as it often did now that she was an integral part of it. Had Maggie and Celia double-checked that both the front and back doors were locked? She imagined an open door and a team of Thrashers busily soaping all the interior windows including the bakery case. Surely they wouldn't break and enter—but if the door was open, would it be breaking and entering? And Lenora wasn't there to hear if any shenanigans were going on. She sighed loudly.

"What is it?" asked Troy.

"I hate to ask, but would you mind if we stop at the bakery for a minute? I'm certain that Maggie and Celia remembered to lock the doors, but part of me thinks it would be a good idea to check. I won't be able to sleep until I'm sure."

"Not a problem. What's the best way from here? Or shall I check my phone?"

"No need for that, just make a left at the next street and then another left, and we'll be headed in the right direction."

After a few more twists and turns—Jillian had forgotten that the town square was already closed off—they were able to get to the parking lot behind the bakery. She was thankful for the tall utility lights. In the place where he lost his life, the memory of Quinten Straub's murder came back to her. She supposed it always would. It didn't seem possible that it was only three days ago. She wondered if the FBI knew a lot more than Agent Calloway had indicated. Or was that just a sham to see what Jillian knew?

Whatever the case, there was a more visible police presence in Moss Hollow than normal. She'd seen more patrol cars on the streets, even out toward Belle Haven which was technically outside the city limits. Even so, that was probably as much to do with the increased volume of people in the town as it was worries about a killer on the loose. His death hadn't seemed to have curbed people's social activities. If anything Moss Hollow was busier than she'd ever seen it. She wouldn't be surprised if the locals thought that since he was a stranger, it was nothing to do with them. Whoever killed him must have come and gone. It couldn't possibly be one of their own.

Troy followed her to the back door. She already had her keys in hand. First she rattled the doorknob. It was locked. She unlocked it and stepped inside, switching on the lights. She'd forgotten how bright they were and was temporarily blinded.

With her hand shading her eyes, she said to Troy, "Come on inside. If you'll just give me a moment, I'm going to check the front, and I'll be right back." He stepped inside and closed the door behind him, squinting as he did so.

Learning her lesson from the kitchen, she switched on the lights in the bakery case only. Her eyes quickly adjusted to the lower light level. The case lights provided just enough illumination so that she could walk around the sitting area without running into something. She checked the front door. It was locked. After she had determined to her satisfaction that all was well, she walked to the front window to look through it into the street.

The street looked eerie in the darkness and the fog. The atmosphere was more like a Jack the Ripper movie than the charming little town that she knew. She thought the street would be deserted by now, but there were a few people remaining, still working on booths in the town square. There were occasional loud voices punctuated by the sound of a hammer. She could see why Lenora wanted to sleep somewhere else during the festival.

Tomorrow the various booths would be filled with a variety of handcrafted items from local craftspeople and produce from local farmers. They would be at their booths as early tomorrow morning as she intended to be at the bakery. It was going to be a busy, busy day. She hoped she would have a chance to at least walk through the town square to see what was being offered this year.

At the thought of the new day, she yawned and had started to turn from the window when something moved in the shadows across the street. For a moment she thought nothing of it, as if it might be a cat or a dog. She was about to lean forward over the window display to try to confirm what it was, when a man stepped out of the shadows and began to cross the street. She was certain it was the same dark-haired man she'd seen twice already that day.

She hurriedly stepped back from the window, knocking over a chair in the process and nearly falling herself. She wasn't sure if the man saw her or if the sound of the chair falling could be heard in the street, but he changed direction and was quickly out of her line of sight.

Troy came through the kitchen door. "Jillian, are you all right?"

"Yes. I'm okay. I just knocked over a chair."

"Should I turn on the lights? Where's the switch?"

"No, it's okay. I'm ready to go." She set the chair upright and then stepped back up to the front window so that she could look down the street in the direction the man had headed, but there was no sign of him.

After she had turned out the light in the bakery case and they were both in the kitchen, she said, "Troy, there was a man in here today during the same time you were, and then we saw him in the parking lot as we were coming out of the restaurant. He was dark complected with black hair. At first I thought he might be from Central or South America, but when he placed an order, his accent was definitely British. Do you know him? It's just that I thought I saw a look pass between the two of you."

Troy looked perplexed. "No. I'm pretty sure I haven't seen anyone I know since I came to Moss Hollow. And I don't remember seeing someone of that description here at the bakery. I vaguely remember someone like that in the parking lot, but I wasn't paying much attention, I'm afraid. Why do you ask?"

"I think I just saw him outside through the front window. He looked like he was walking straight toward the bakery—that's when I stepped back and knocked over the chair—and then he veered off in a different direction."

Troy put his arm around her shoulders in a manner that was very brotherly. "Do you think your suspicions might have more to do with the stress you're under than anything else?"

Jillian was about to object, but before she could answer, he continued. "You haven't mentioned it, but I read that you found a dead body behind the bakery." Jillian opened her mouth to say something, but he continued on. "Look, I'm not doubting that you saw someone out there just now—it might even be the same man you saw earlier today—but could it be that your experience of finding that body has you ascribing motivations to him that aren't really there? I presume there are a lot of strangers in town. He could even be one of the vendors, setting up for tomorrow."

Jillian looked down and took a deep breath. What he said made perfect sense. Then why were her instincts still telling her that something was very wrong?

The drive home took longer than usual because of the fog, but as they came near their destination, Belle Haven stood out like the glowing beacon of a lighthouse. Either Bertie or Cornelia had turned on all the front porch lights on the first and second floors, and the bright lights of the foyer shown through the glass of the arched transom above the front door and the long narrow windows that flanked each side.

It was an unusual thing for either woman to have done, having grown up through the tail end of the Great Depression and World War II. Those ingrained habits of thrift remained. Jillian had been told by Bertie more than once not to leave lights on when she left a room, especially as they were trying to save every penny to keep Belle Haven afloat. It was only because of a concerted effort and several special events that had been held at Belle Haven of late that they had been able to restore some of its lost glory. Riding up the long, curved driveway, even in the fog or maybe partly because of it, the old mansion looked particularly impressive.

Troy's laughter intruded on her thoughts. She looked at him quizzically.

"I think your grandmother wants to make sure you find your way home. Or maybe that you're not alone in the dark with me."

"I think it might be both reasons."

He parked the car at the front and got out of the car in order to walk around to open her door. He took her hand as she got up and continued to hold it as they walked toward the front door of the house.

Jillian had been thinking on the way home that the drive to Painter's Ridge would not be a pleasant or particularly safe one for Troy, considering the conditions, and that she should offer to let him stay at Belle Haven for the night. After all, there were plenty of extra bedrooms. She didn't think Bertie or Cornelia could say much considering some of the people they'd recently invited to stay at Belle Haven.

"Please don't take this the wrong way, but since the fog is so bad, we have several extra bedrooms, and you are welcome to stay here instead of driving to Painter's Ridge."

"Thanks, but I think I'll just head back to the motel. I'll drive carefully, I promise."

Jillian wasn't sure why, but she actually felt some relief that he wasn't staying.

When they reached the door, she turned to face him and thanked him for a lovely evening.

He replied, "Thank you for inviting me to the play. I enjoyed it." Still holding her hand, he gave her a friendly peck on the cheek. "Get a good night's sleep, Jillian. And don't worry about me. I'm an expert at looking after myself."

He grinned and his white teeth caught the light and seemed to sparkle. Bertie would have called it a Cheshire Cat grin. Jillian imagined the rest of him disappearing bit by bit until, as in *Alice in Wonderland*, only the grin remained. Without the blond hair, the big brown eyes, and the classic Roman nose, the grin on its own could be interpreted as either mischievous or rather sinister.

After she had unlocked the door and was inside, she turned to watch him go. He hopped down the steps as if he was in a hurry. Once he was inside his car, she closed and locked the door. She turned off all the lights before she began making the trek up the elegant curved staircase to her bedroom on the second floor. There was no sign of Bertie or Cornelia. *At least they didn't stay up waiting for me.*

It was eleven thirty by the time Jillian slid into bed. She changed the time on her alarm clock. She was not going to get up at four a.m. tomorrow. Four thirty would be early enough. She would have laughed at that, but she felt too exhausted. *That's what I get for trying to have a social life.*

I't seemed like she had just closed her eyes when the alarm sounded. She fought the impulse to roll over and go back to sleep. After a few groans and stretches, she made herself get up and then put on her bathrobe and slippers before heading downstairs for a much-needed cup of coffee.

She passed Cornelia's closed bedroom door on her way to the staircase, an indication that she was still abed, which was normal. Cornelia had moved back to Moss Hollow five years ago, after her husband passed away, but she didn't work at the bakery. She did her part by doing what she could at Belle Haven, mostly working in the surrounding gardens.

Bertie's bedroom was downstairs, and she kept the door to her "master suite" closed all the time, so it was harder to tell if she was up or not. However, the smell of coffee wafting from the kitchen was a sure sign that Bertie had already risen to meet the day.

Jillian walked in, expecting to see her grandmother, but she wasn't there. Jillian poured herself some coffee and went to sit at the table in the breakfast nook. There she found a note on the table from Bertie: *Headed to the bakery. Get there as soon as you can. Busy day ahead.*

"As if I didn't know that," she said out loud. "Well, I'm having my coffee first and maybe something to eat." She took a sip of coffee and closed her eyes, waiting for it to do its magic. She wasn't feeling it and decided a high-protein breakfast was called for. She got up and put a couple of strips of bacon in a skillet on the stove, planning to fry an egg to go with them. She would worry about her arteries next week after Moss Holloween was over.

It wasn't long before Possum showed up and began winding his way between and around her feet. Bacon was his kryptonite in that it was his weakness. It never failed to bring the cat out of whichever of his many hiding places he happened to be. He usually slept in Cornelia's room, which probably meant he had woken her up to open the door for him as soon as the smell of bacon drifted through the crack under the door and into his nostrils. Jillian walked to the kitchen door and listened, but didn't hear any indication that her aunt had remained up after letting the cat out.

She had just finished eating and was going to head upstairs to get ready for work when the landline phone in the kitchen rang. The caller ID showed that it was a call from the bakery. Jillian picked up the receiver and without even a hello, said, "Honestly, Bertie, I'll be there in a little bit. I've just finished eating breakfast and was heading upstairs to get dressed."

Bertie's voice was tense. "Well, get here as fast as you can and bring your aunt Cornelia too. Someone broke into the shop last night and trashed the place. Hurry, and maybe we can get it in good-enough shape for customers before opening time." With that, she hung up the phone and left Jillian with the handset at her ear, temporarily frozen in place.

A moment later when Jillian went into action, she practically ran to the stairs and then bounded up them two at a time. She knocked on Cornelia's bedroom door with urgency. When Cornelia almost immediately said, "Come in," Jillian opened the door to find the lights were on and her aunt sitting at her vanity table brushing her hair. After she explained the situation at the bakery—the little she knew—it didn't take long for the two of them to get ready to go into town.

In the back parking lot at the bakery there was a police car parked next to the bakery's van. It was hard to fathom that the police had been called to the bakery twice in one week. She hoped God didn't mind frivolous prayers and prayed that it wasn't Gooder Jones who had answered the call. Seeing him once in a week was more than enough.

When Jillian walked into the bakery's kitchen, she expected to see a disaster, but it looked like it normally did. Lenora was busy getting the day's bake started. She looked up from her task. Seeming to read Jillian's mind, she skipped her normal "Good morning, honey" and simply said, "It's the front." She tilted her head toward the door that separated the rooms. "Bertie's in there with Laura Lee. She called the police right after she called you. My oh my, what a mess."

As Jillian went through the door, followed closely by Cornelia, she braced herself for the worst. She scanned the room. Chairs and tables were knocked over, napkins, and torn-open sugar and creamer packets strewn across the floor, along with all the fall/Halloween decorations that they had placed around the room. Artwork had been pulled off the walls and destroyed along with the frames that had surrounded them. The glass rectangles from the frames had been shattered, and there was glass everywhere. Bertie was watching Laura Lee as she took photographs of the room from every angle.

"How long will this take?" Bertie asked. She glanced at Jillian and Cornelia without verbally acknowledging them. "We have to get this mess cleaned up."

Even in her deputy's uniform, Laura Lee didn't behave all that differently than she did when she was dressed for church or on Sunday afternoons for Sweetie Pie meetings. She was solemn to be sure, but it was sympathetic, not impersonal. Her friendly and energetic personality shone past her attire. She wasn't one to be puffed up by her badge of office like a particular man Jillian could name.

"I'm almost done," answered Laura Lee. She took a few more photos before stopping. "Ideally, we should leave this as it is and do a complete investigation—brush for prints and so on."

"Laura Lee Zane, you know as well as I do that you'll find the fingerprints of everyone in Moss Hollow, including your own, in this place. We simply can't afford not to open today."

Jillian heard the slight rise in her grandmother's tone of voice that in someone else she would have interpreted as panic. At least she hoped it wasn't panic. It only reinforced her feeling that she needed to do everything she could to bolster their income by making Belle Haven a moneymaker instead of a drain on their finances. She hated to see her grandmother stressed out. Bertie was tough, and most women her age couldn't work as hard as she did, but there were limits, even for her, and something like this could push her past them.

Laura Lee took a deep breath and looked around the room and then back at Bertie. "I'll go out to the car and call Sheriff Henderson and see what he says. Please don't touch anything until I come back."

After Laura Lee went through the kitchen door to head out to the police car, Jillian took the opportunity to grab her smartphone out of her pocket and begin taking her own photos so she would have them to show to the insurance adjuster.

The exterior glass of the bakery case seemed to be undamaged, but the interior lightbulbs had been shattered, raining thin white glass over everything inside. Fortunately, the bakery case contents consisted only of empty trays since leftover baked goods were not left there overnight. She'd have to run over to Puckett's as soon as they opened to get new bulbs.

Seeing that the paper banners over the window display had been torn down and crumpled, she walked over to photograph the damage. The sugar skulls and carved pumpkin were smashed. The flowers and leaves on all the marigolds had been ripped off, and the vases they had been arranged in were shattered so that water had splashed everywhere. The candy boxes and the sign she had made were ripped to shreds, and, worst of all, the Mayan vase was broken into shards.

She turned to look at Bertie and Cornelia. "Who would do something like this?" She didn't really expect an answer. "I stopped here last night after the play, and everything was fine. I made sure both doors were locked when I left."

Bertie looked perplexed, shaking her head. "The back door was locked when I got here this morning. When I saw this, I thought maybe it was the front one they came through, but it was locked too."

"Was any money stolen?"

Bertie shook her head. "No, nothing in the kitchen seems to have been disturbed. It doesn't look like the safe was tampered with, and all the money is still in there."

"It's just vandalism, that's what it is," said Cornelia. "I've told you time and time again that Moss Holloween is just an excuse for bad behavior. It was only a matter of time before someone took prank week too far."

Bertie scoffed at her sister. "There hasn't been something like this in a hundred years of Moss Holloween pranks. You know that as well as I do. I don't think this has anything to do with the festival."

"What then?" asked Jillian. "And why only trash the front of the shop?"

Cornelia's eyes grew large. "It's that awful thing you bought at that yard sale—that vase thing. I knew it would bring trouble with it. I felt it as soon as I touched it. Thank God it wasn't at Belle Haven, or this could have happened there."

Jillian closed her eyes and rubbed her temples with the tips of her fingers. "Aunt Cornelia, it has nothing to do with that vase."

"How can you say that after all that has happened? Someone murdered within walking distance of this place and now this?"

Jillian shook her head. "That vase sat on my desk at Belle Haven for a few weeks before I put it in the display here, and nothing happened. Please, Aunt Cornelia, we have to think about this logically. You might be on the right track about one thing. Could this have something to do with the murder of Quinten Straub? Maybe someone thinks we know something more about it and this is a warning of some sort not to say anything."

The discussion was interrupted when the door to the kitchen opened and Laura Lee walked in. "Okay, Bertie. The sheriff says you can do what you need to, but he'd like me to put the larger broken stuff like the frames and artwork in boxes. We might get lucky and pull a print off of them."

Jillian asked, "How do you think they got in?"

"I don't know, but a professional burglar could have opened either door easily. Locked doors only keep out honest people. You may have to think about getting an alarm system. Bertie, you said only you and Lenora and Jillian have keys. Are any of them missing?"

"I opened the shop this morning," answered Bertie as she reached in her pocket and held up the key.

All eyes turned on Jillian. "I put my key back in my purse after I left last night, but I'll double-check and ask Lenora about hers." She went into the kitchen and found her key ring with all the shop and house keys attached to it in her purse. Lenora confirmed that she had her key as well.

After Jillian reported back, Laura Lee asked, "Are you *sure* that nothing is missing from the bakery, Bertie?"

"Not that I can tell. Certainly nothing of any value."

Laura Lee shook her head. "Doesn't make sense, does it? What kind of burglar breaks in, trashes only half the place, takes nothing, and then locks the door on his way out? There has to be another explanation. If you do discover that something is missing, no matter what it is, please call the station."

"Do you think this has something to do with Quinten Straub's murder?" Jillian asked.

"I don't know. Could be. I guess we'll have to let the FBI know about it and maybe they'll want to investigate too. The chief wants me to dust the doors and the safe for prints. Maybe they tried to get into the safe and just couldn't get it opened so they trashed the place as sort of a payback."

Seeing Jillian's skeptical expression, she continued, "I know. It doesn't sound feasible to me either. Anyway, after I'm done with the doors and the safe, I'll take care of picking up the frames and the artwork to take along to the station. And while I was in the car, I called Annalise. I know she's an early riser; maybe not usually quite this early, but I knew she wouldn't mind, and she didn't. She's going to call a couple of the other Sweetie Pies to see if they can come and help clean up."

Jillian would have hugged her if they hadn't been on opposite sides of the bakery case. But she could voice her appreciation. "Thanks, Laura Lee. I can't tell you how glad I am that it was you who answered Bertie's call."

Laura Lee laughed knowingly. She'd been witness to enough conversations between Jillian and Gooder to know exactly what Jillian meant. She only grinned and put on a voice meant to mimic a character in an old TV police drama. "Glad to be of service, ma'am."

With that they set to work. First Jillian retrieved some of the flattened boxes from the back to reassemble and re-tape for Laura Lee to use to gather the evidence. Then she helped Bertie remove the trays from the case and carry them into the kitchen to be run through the dishwasher. After making sure the power to the case was off, she removed the ends of the bulbs that remained in the sockets. She vacuumed out all the tiny pieces of glass and then washed all the interior surfaces.

Bertie stayed in the kitchen to help Lenora with the baked goods. There was no point in cleaning up if nothing was ready to sell. Cornelia was clearing out the front window display, picking up larger pieces and putting them in a small box. Laura Lee had told her not to bother to save anything from there since it was mostly sugar and pumpkin and flowers, and everything was soaked with water anyway.

During all this activity Annalise and Savannah showed up. They had parked in the back, but walked around to the front door to knock. Jillian let them in and they pitched in immediately, righting the chairs and tables, and sweeping up the debris.

When Jillian finished cleaning the bakery case, she decided to look out the door to see if Ike Puckett's truck might be parked out back yet. It was a longshot since the hardware store didn't normally open until eight, and with the play, it seemed unlikely that Ike would come in early. When she saw the truck was there, she almost shouted, "Yahoo!" With a word to Bertie, she walked over to the building and pounded on the back door. It was just a few seconds before Ike opened the door. He looked like she had felt earlier that morning, before coffee and before the adrenaline began pumping into her system after Bertie's call.

Ike spoke with some concern. "Hey, Jillian. What's going on over there today? I saw Laura Lee in her police car when I got here. Is everything all right?"

"Not exactly. Someone broke into the bakery last night and trashed the front area. That's why I'm here. I need new bulbs for the bakery case."

"Sure." He stepped back. "Come on in and I'll get them for you."

She stepped through the door into the stockroom. She'd never been in that part of the store before. Near the door was Ike's desk, a bulky thing that was cluttered with invoices and receipts. There were freestanding shelves and shelves around the walls of the room, all jam-packed with merchandise.

As Jillian followed him down an aisle, he said, "You say someone trashed the bakery? I hope it's not too bad. Is there anything I can do to help?"

"It's bad enough," said Jillian, "and thanks for the offer, but I think we've got it handled. Annalise and Savannah have come to help, and Aunt Cornelia came in with me this morning after Bertie called to let us know what had happened. Lenora and Bertie are on top of the baking, so if we can't open at exactly six, it won't be long after that."

She paused, deciding to ask a question that had to be asked. "Ike, do you know if any of the Thrashers might be behind this?"

He stopped and turned to look at her. His face registered shock. "Of course not! None of us would ever do anything malicious. We might do things that are inconvenient, but it's a cardinal rule that no one ever does anything that will actually damage property or hurt someone. No, Jillian, it wasn't any of the Thrashers. I can assure you of that."

Jillian sighed with relief. "I'm sorry, Ike, but I had to ask. I didn't really think it was one of you." She was anxious to change the subject. "Why are you here so early today? Not that I'm complaining, mind you, but I thought you'd be sleeping in after last night's performance."

He turned again and started walking down the aisle as he

said, "I'd like to be sleeping, but I need to catch up with some paperwork. You saw my desk. Being in the play has been a lot of fun, but it has cut into some of my regular duties. You know how it is when you run your own business."

"Yes I do. By the way, I was at the play last night and really enjoyed it. You and Sylvia and your dad were all just great."

"Thanks." He smiled broadly. "Sylvia has decided she wants to be a theater major when she goes off to college next year." The smile lessened. "Not sure how I feel about that. I kind of hoped she'd take business courses, you know, so she could help take over the store when I'm gone. Neither of my kids seems much interested in taking over this place."

"Maybe that will change. Give them time. Look at me. It wasn't my plan to work at the bakery, but here I am. And it's taken some time, but I'm glad to be here."

"You're right. I'm not planning to retire for a good long time yet. A lot can change in twenty years."

Jillian thought it was interesting that he mentioned the same number of years that she'd been away from Moss Hollow and answered, "It sure can."

Ike stopped in front of a partitioned space where there were several boxes of different heights standing on end. He put his hand on the end of one of the boxes. "How many of these do you need?"

Jillian closed her eyes tightly to try to visualize the bakery case to count the number of bulbs. "I think . . . six."

"You think?" He hefted up the box. "Tell you what. How 'bout I just carry this box over to the bakery, and I'll install the bulbs? That'll save time all 'round."

"That would be wonderful, Ike. Thank you."

"Glad to do it."

Ike followed her back down the aisle and she held the door for him as he stepped outside. The last time she'd been in the parking lot with Ike was the day she found Quinten Straub's body. It couldn't hurt to ask if he'd seen anything unusual since then. She would've liked to have eased into it, but there was no time.

"I was wondering, Ike, if an agent from the FBI has been around to see you."

"Yeah, she was over here just yesterday. She was at the door as soon as we opened. Agent Calloway, I think her name was. Did you talk to her too?"

"Yes. She was at the bakery's front door when we opened yesterday. Did she say anything new about the murder?"

"Not that I can think of. Nothing that I hadn't read in the paper."

She paused a moment. "There was a man, an out-of-towner, in the bakery yesterday, maybe you saw him in the hardware store? He had coal-black hair with maybe Central or South American features, and spoke with a British accent."

They had just reached the bakery's back door. "Yeah, I think I saw somebody who looked like that—but I didn't talk to him. Tommy was the one who helped him."

"So he bought something?"

"Yeah. I'm not sure what though. Might have been some tools. Do you want me to ask Tommy?"

"Yes, would you please?"

"Do you think it might have something to do with the break-in?"

"I don't know, Ike. It might."

She wasn't entirely sure that it had been the same man from the bakery and the restaurant whom she had seen through the window last night, but she couldn't shake the feeling that whoever he was, he was somehow tied to what had happened in the bakery and maybe to the murder of Quinten Straub.

11

When Jillian stepped through the back door of Belle Haven that evening, she felt like running a hot, lavender-scented bubble bath in the huge upstairs claw-foot tub, then climbing in and staying there for at least an hour. But she couldn't. She'd have just enough time to take a quick shower and get dressed before Troy arrived.

Earlier in the day, he had stopped in the bakery for coffee and a muffin, and in the busy atmosphere they had spoken just long enough to arrange for him to come to Belle Haven for dinner that evening and look for a costume for tomorrow evening's costume ball. She was regretting having invited him for dinner, but they both needed costumes and it would have seemed impolite not to ask him to share the evening meal. What was done was done.

Cornelia had hitched a ride home with Annalise that morning, so even though her day had had a busy start, the majority of it had been spent within the peaceful confines of Belle Haven. When Jillian called to let her know there would be a guest for dinner, she sounded delighted that Troy would be there. She even said she would set the dining room table and make it all "very fancy." Jillian told her that they would be keeping it casual since the plan was to look for costumes, but she wasn't sure that it sank in.

Bertie was still at the shop when Jillian told her about the invitation, and while she didn't voice any displeasure, she wasn't enthusiastic either. *But that's just Bertie*, thought Jillian, though she imagined how it would be if Hunter was the guest instead of Troy. She was pretty sure the reaction would have been different.

Since they would be foraging through old clothing in search of costumes before dinner, Jillian kept her wardrobe for that evening casual with a pair of jeans and a green-and-navy tartan-plaid cotton top with a crisscross front. Starting at the nape of her neck, she quickly and loosely plaited her hair, bringing the end forward so it hung over her left shoulder.

Feeling like she had her second wind, she was just coming down the stairs when the doorbell rang, and this time, she didn't hesitate to answer it, shouting "I've got it!" so that Cornelia and Bertie would leave it to her.

She had warned Troy that the uninhabited third floor of Belle Haven, where there were trunks full of old clothing among many other disused things, could be pretty dusty, so he was dressed similarly to herself, in jeans and a perfectly pressed cotton khaki button-up shirt.

"Don't tell me," she said after the appropriate greetings, "you always bring jeans and a khaki shirt in your garment go bag in case you need to scrounge around in an attic for something."

"Exactly."

"Shall we head up and see what we can find for costumes? Cornelia tells me dinner will be ready about seven, and that should give us enough time to find something."

Just before they began walking up the wide staircase, Troy looked up. In the roof over the curved staircase he observed the round, stained-glass dome that towered above. "That is spectacular."

Jillian smiled. "I agree. You should see it when the sun is overhead. It bathes this whole area in a beautiful golden light. It was one of Captain Belle's better ideas. He was the ancestor who had this place built."

"So, your relatives have been here a long time. Does that

mean you're thinking of going to the dance as an antebellum Southern belle?"

"Most definitely not. Mark my words, there will be at least a half-dozen women-slash-girls in hoop dresses at the dance, if not more. It's the go-to costume around here. I'd like to try to find something a bit different."

"I'm all for that. You say this dance is like a sock hop? Do they play sock hop–appropriate music?"

Jillian laughed. "Yes. Mostly pop songs from the sixties, with a select few from other decades thrown in. You haven't lived until you've seen a grandma in a hoop skirt doing the twist."

"I'll look forward to that."

They had reached the narrower set of stairs that wound its way to the third floor. Jillian noticed that the steps had gotten quite dusty. As they started to climb the steps, she said, "Sorry about the dust. I have been up here within the last couple of months, but keeping this area clean is low on my priority list."

"Must be hard to keep a place this size clean."

"It is. We have a lady come in once a week to do the heavy stuff, but she can only do so much in a few hours, so this part of the house doesn't get a lot of attention."

They had reached the top of the stairs and Jillian headed toward one of the closed doors. She opened it and turned on the lights to reveal a mishmash of objects, including a long rod full of hanging clothes, all of which were either encased in garment bags or covered with plastic dry-cleaner bags. Above the rod, there was a long shelf holding multiple hat boxes. There were several steamer trunks as well, from a variety of eras it seemed, and she walked to one and opened it. "Not sure where we should begin. You can pick a trunk or start with the hanging clothes. I'm not sure exactly what we're looking for, but I guess we'll know when we find it."

"If you don't mind, I think I'll start with the hat boxes. That should be very interesting."

While Jillian knelt down beside the trunk and started pulling out articles of clothing, he reached up to take down a tall hat box. He opened it and pulled out a shiny black top hat. He placed it on his head. It fit perfectly. "What do you think?"

Jillian turned and smiled. "I think it's definitely you." There was a niggle at the back of her brain that said, *You've known this man for two days. How do you know if it's "definitely" him?* but she ignored it.

"Is there a mirror?" He looked around the room. "Wait, I see it over there." He stepped over two old rolled-up rugs to get to a tall mirror in an elaborate gilded frame that was propped against the wall. He raised his forearm in a motion to begin to remove the dust on the glass with the sleeve of his shirt, but when Jillian saw what he was about to do, she shouted, "Wait!" She got up from her knees and grabbed an old apron she had put aside from the trunk. She tossed it to him. "Use this."

After he had dusted the mirror, he admired himself for a few seconds. Turning to Jillian, he said, "I'm having a thought. How do you feel about steampunk?"

Jillian had heard of several steampunk nightclubs in LA where people went attired in the style, but she'd never been to one. She thought about the images she'd seen on the Internet of people dressed up in steampunk costumes, a cross between nineteenth-century fashion and sci-fi, often with mechanical touches—gears and goggles and pocket watches. "I think I like that idea. Mind you, I'm *not* going to wear a bustier."

He grinned. "Rats. That's what I was hoping for, but I'll try to overcome my disappointment."

They rummaged for about forty-five minutes, laying aside the occasional item of clothing and commenting on it. By the time Jillian looked at her watch and decided it was time to wash up for dinner, they had accumulated an impressive collection of possibilities.

Jillian had found several lacy petticoats, a floor-length black taffeta skirt with a ruffle around the bottom, a white linen blouse with a stand-up collar and lacy cravat and cuffs, a pair of black crocheted gloves, a black-veiled hat, and a black beaded clutch with a mirror on the inside of the flap.

Troy had found a white shirt with a white bow tie, a double-breasted brocade waistcoat, and a long, black frock coat with burgundy satin lapels. None of the pants he found appeared to be long enough when he held them up next to him, but he decided he could just wear the black trousers he'd brought with him.

Jillian ran her fingers through a box full of old costume jewelry and found a number of what she considered gaudy brooches that she thought would be perfect for her purposes, plus an attractive but broken pocket watch that would look great attached to Troy's waistcoat.

Putting on the top hat again, Troy said, "I'm getting quite excited about this soirée of yours, Jillian. This is going to be fun."

Jillian left Troy alone in the living room while she went to help carry food from the kitchen to the dining room. Carrying a platter of sliced baked ham with sufficient portions to serve twelve people, she paused in the doorway to admire her aunt Cornelia's handiwork.

The dining room table was covered with a deep-rust linen tablecloth with a subtle leaf pattern. A physalis Chinese lampion plant, with its little "lanterns" that look like pumpkins, in a glazed blue-and-white flowerpot, served as the centerpiece. It was flanked by thick turned-wood candleholders topped with lighted mottled-orange pillar candles. The table was set with one of the several china services that had been passed down through the years at Belle Haven. This one was white with an outer ring of blue swirls punctuated with bouquets of white flowers, tiny blue berries, and small red apples. The overall effect of the table was very pleasing to the eye.

After a few more trips between the kitchen and dining room to carry in bowls of creamy scalloped potatoes and cider-glazed mixed vegetables, and a plate of corn bread, plus various accompaniments, Cornelia declared that dinner was ready.

Jillian went to the living room to retrieve Troy, but he wasn't there. The door to the library was open, and she found him standing at the Royal typewriter that she had bought at Tara's yard sale, running his index finger along the keys. He seemed to be deep in thought.

"I see you found more of our secret hoard of dust," said Jillian.

He didn't appear to be surprised by her voice, but looked up and around at the books in the shelves along the walls. "This is a wonderful room. It's a fitting place for my uncle's old typewriter. He mentioned it in one of his journals. He bought it secondhand from a fellow who used it to transcribe Morley's field notes."

"It would be interesting to know the history behind it. Maybe later you can tell me more about it. But right now, dinner's ready, and believe me, we don't want Bertie coming after us."

He paused a moment, seeming reluctant to leave, but followed her to the dining room where Cornelia and Bertie were already seated at the table. After taking their seats, Troy said, "Thanks for inviting me for dinner. The table looks lovely. I don't often get a home-cooked meal."

"It's our pleasure to have you," beamed Cornelia.

"Let's eat," was Bertie's sole intonation. She picked up the ham platter, took a slice, and passed it to Troy. Jillian thought her grandmother looked tired—more tired than usual after a day's work. Of course the thought of the destruction in the shop would be plaguing her. Jillian had been so busy during the day she hadn't thought about it much, except when the occasional local customer had asked what had happened. She wasn't sure if it was because they noticed the bare walls and empty display, or if it was simply that word had spread that quickly. It was probably some combination of both.

As Cornelia passed the vegetables to Jillian, Jillian noticed a redness on her fingers. "Aunt Cornelia, what happened to your hands? Did you burn them?"

Cornelia held out her hands, palms up to show them to Jillian. Her palms and fingers were stained with blotches of a faded brick-red color. "No, they aren't burned. It was something in that display of yours. I noticed it after I had cleared out some of the pieces. I tried to wash it off, but, as you can see, it stained my skin."

"That's odd," said Jillian. "There was nothing in there that should have done that. Are you sure it was from something in the display?"

"Positive. I was going to save the cloth you had placed in the bottom of the display, but after I had removed the larger pieces I could see that it had the same thing on it. I knew that if it wouldn't come off my hands it wasn't going to come out of that cloth either, so I just gathered it up and put it in the dumpster with the rest of it." She looked at her hands before putting them in her lap. "I suppose it will wear off eventually. I can always wear gloves out in public until then."

"I'm sorry, Aunt Cornelia." Jillian paused to think. Could it have been the paper or the sugar skulls? She had touched the paper herself. She unconsciously looked at her own hands. There was no hint of a stain, and besides, the papers had been many different colors, not just one. The sugar skulls were colored, but they were smashed almost to a powder. Cornelia wouldn't have been able to pick up pieces of them. She wracked her brain but couldn't imagine what could have stained her aunt's hands in such a way.

Troy spoke up. "Excuse me, what are you talking about?"

"Oh, I'm sorry, Troy," said Jillian. "You wouldn't have heard, but maybe you noticed that we were missing a window display at the bakery. Remember? I told you last evening that that's where I had placed your uncle's vase as part of the decor. Someone broke in last night and wrecked the bakery. I'm afraid your uncle's vase was smashed."

Troy looked shocked. "Wow. I can't believe it. I'm sure I saw you lock the door last night. How did they get in?"

"I did lock it, and it was locked when Bertie got there this morning. Someone must have picked the lock."

He shook his head. "I guess even small towns aren't safe from crime anymore. Do your police have any leads on who might have done it?"

"None that I know of. Maybe the FBI will have better luck."

"The FBI? What have they got to do with a small-town break-in?"

"I shouldn't have said that. I don't really know that they will look into it. It's just that Laura Lee—she's a local police officer—said that she might call them to let them know in case it has something to do with Quinten Straub's murder."

"How could that be? I thought you said you didn't know the man."

"I didn't, but maybe the murderer thinks we know something."

"Do you know something?"

Jillian gave a bitter laugh. "No. Nothing that I didn't tell the police. I only talked to the man for a few minutes."

Bertie clapped her hands together once to get their attention. "Enough about this! We should have better dinner conversation topics than murder and mayhem. Mr. Hansford, help yourself to some corn bread. Cornelia, get those potatoes started around, and Jillian, pass me those vegetables. It's all going to be cold." She looked pointedly at Troy. "Make sure you save some room for desert. You don't want to miss Cornelia's almond-lemon pound cake served with warm cranberry-apple compote."

"Yes, ma'am," he answered rather meekly as he picked up a piece of corn bread. Then he looked across the table at Jillian and winked.

12

After dinner, Troy told Jillian he would pick her up at a quarter to eight the next evening since the dance was to start at eight. Holding three hangers together for the coat, waistcoat, and shirt over his shoulder, and a used shopping bag for the rest of his scavenger finds, he bid her a good night.

Jillian, Cornelia, and Bertie worked together to clean up, so they finished quickly even though they didn't put the antique china in the dishwasher. They were all feeling pretty tired, especially after eating a full meal plus a slice of Cornelia's rich pound cake.

Before Bertie went to bed, Jillian had insisted that she should sleep in tomorrow and let her and Lenora handle the opening. That didn't get any argument then, but tomorrow morning might be a different story. She'd have to wait and see if her grandmother would take her advice.

As it turned out, Jillian was up first the next morning, which was Saturday, and had the coffee ready before she saw any sign of Bertie. When she headed out the door, Bertie was still in her nightclothes, but said she would be in about eight.

The drive to town gave Jillian a little time to think about the bakery. She wished there was something she could do to redecorate, particularly since Saturday was bound to be the busiest day of the festival. Tourists would think The Chocolate Shoppe wasn't trying very hard to get their business. But she just couldn't see where she would have the time to do anything about it.

When she arrived, she found that Lenora was already in the kitchen.

"Good morning, honey. How'd you sleep last night?"

"Very well, actually. You?"

"I always sleep soundly, though, I have to say, I will be glad to be back home tomorrow night. Coralee's guest room is comfy enough, but it's just not the same thing as sleeping in my own good bed."

"So, one more night away at your sister's?"

"Yes. They'll be taking down the booths and cleaning up the town square late tonight, so it won't be quiet around here."

Jillian grabbed an apron and proceeded to put it on. "Are you going to the costume ball tonight?"

"Oh my, no. But Celia's going. She's got a date with a nice young man from Painter's Ridge. He's the son of some close family friends and he's a freshman at Morehouse—studying engineering."

Jillian smiled. "That's wonderful. She seems like a really sweet girl, and I'm so glad you recommended her. She's picked up on how we do things around here very quickly. I don't know how we would have managed this week without her."

Just then the staff door to the customer area opened and Celia walked in. "Good morning, Miss Green."

"Good morning, Celia. I didn't realize you were already here."

"Cousin Lenora picked me up this morning so we could surprise you."

Jillian looked back and forth between the two, but they both just smiled. "Okay, I'll bite. What surprise is that?"

Celia opened the door and waved for Jillian to follow her. When Jillian saw what Celia had done, tears unexpectedly welled up in her eyes. She had redecorated the café, adding a touch of autumn to the room. The front window display area was lined with a fall-design fabric and decorated with a variety of small pumpkins, gourds, and Indian corn spilling out from a cornucopia-shaped basket. There was even a Mr. and Mrs. Scarecrow with burlap faces, and straw hands and feet sticking out of fringed plaid-fabric clothing.

"Don't you like it?" Celia asked, seeing Jillian blinking away her tears. "Cousin Lenora bought the corn and the pumpkins and the gourds yesterday at a booth on the town square, and she already had the basket. And last night, she and Coralee made the table decorations. And I made the scarecrows myself."

"Oh, Celia, I love it all. I can't believe all the work you've done. I had given up on being able to redecorate, and here you've done it. Thank you so much!" She gave her a big hug, and when she went back to the kitchen she thanked Lenora in the same manner.

That act of kindness set the tone for most of Jillian's day. She was thankful that the day was progressing as planned. Maggie and Celia worked the front register, where the stream of customers seemed unending, and Lenora, Bertie, and Jillian were in the back trying to keep up with the demand.

At three in the afternoon, the truffles had sold out and Jillian was debating whether to make another batch that late in the day. Yesterday she'd quickly made a hand-drawn sign for the top of the bakery case to draw attention to them, and both days she had cut up several small samples of the truffles so that customers could try them. That had done the trick. The shop would close at five, so she decided it wasn't worth making more at that point, but she felt a certain amount of pride knowing that Bertie would have to admit that the truffles were a success. She started to think about the possibilities for Christmastime and Easter . . .

"Miss Green?" It was Celia at the kitchen door.

"Yes?"

"There's a man out here who says he needs to speak with you. He says it's important."

"Do you know him?"

Celia looked behind her, and then back at Jillian to whisper, "No, but he's got a British accent."

Jillian felt the hairs on the back of her neck stand up. "Does he have coal-black hair?"

Celia nodded.

Jillian looked at Bertie and Lenora. Lenora would be leaving soon; in fact, it was already past her quitting time. Jillian had hoped that Bertie could go home soon too. It was an inconvenient time for this, but at the same time she was dying to know who the man was and wondered why he wanted to talk to her. She looked at Celia. "Tell him I'll be out in just a moment."

Bertie looked up from what she was doing. "Don't be long."

"I won't be."

She went into the front area where every table was full. There was still a line at the register, but at least it wasn't trailing out the front door at the moment as it had been earlier. The black-haired man was standing on the other side of the bakery case waiting for her. She had to excuse herself several times as she came out from behind the counter and navigated through the queue of people to where he was standing.

He looked better today—less tired, less rumpled, and his demeanor was more pleasant, if still serious. Was it him that she had seen through the front window on Thursday night? She still wasn't sure, which was why she hadn't mentioned it to Laura Lee. He held out his hand. "Madam. My name is Dr. Hoon Middleton."

She couldn't help the slight rise of her eyebrows. She hadn't expected the "Dr." part. She shook his hand. "I'm Jillian Green. How may I help you?"

"Is there somewhere less crowded we could speak?"

"Sir, I'm sorry but this is just not a good time. As you can see, we're extremely busy, and I can't get away right now."

He looked annoyed. "Ms. Green. This is very important." He lowered his voice. "It has to do with the Mayan vase you had in the window. May I ask where it is now?"

Jillian's face registered her surprise. Part of her still wondered if he was the one responsible for the destruction in the bakery. Could this be a ploy to deflect suspicion? Maybe he had seen her through the window that night and thought she had told the police she had seen him. Then she thought of what Cornelia had said. Maybe she had been right all along. Maybe the vase was the cause of all this trouble, though, perhaps, not in the mystical way that Cornelia thought. "I'm sorry, but the vase was destroyed in a break-in yesterday."

Now he looked shocked and somewhat saddened. "No. It can't be. Are you sure? I've come all this way, and after . . ."

He didn't finish the sentence, and Jillian was at a loss to understand what was going through his head. "Look, I don't know what this is about, but if it's something to do with that vase, I don't think I can help you. If you know something about the other things that have been going on around here, you should contact the police."

"Believe me, Miss Green, I have been in touch with the authorities. Even if this is true, and the vase is destroyed, I would still like to speak with you. Would you be free later this evening or tomorrow?"

Now Jillian was annoyed. "Of course it's true. Why would I lie about that?"

"Please, Ms. Green, I didn't mean to say that you would lie. Only that you may not understand the situation. Will you meet with me?"

Jillian's first inclination was to flat out say "no," but her curiosity got the better of her. "I can't this evening, but tomorrow afternoon . . ." She paused to try to think of a place that was both public and private so they could talk. "Meet me tomorrow afternoon at two at the library; it's a couple of blocks down the street from here. I'll request one of the study rooms so we can talk." The glass-enclosed room was about the safest place she could think of.

"Thank you, Ms. Green. I will see you tomorrow." He paused as if he was reluctant to say something, but then decided to go ahead. "Please be careful. There are forces at play here that you don't understand."

With that he turned and left the bakery and Jillian standing with her mouth open. She wasn't sure if what she'd just heard was a warning or a threat.

It was a quarter after five before they managed to close the bakery for the day. Jillian was glad that the working part of the weekend was finished for them. The Chocolate Shoppe Bakery was never open on Sundays, even during Moss Holloween, giving them all a much-needed break.

She had been distracted since Dr. Middleton had paid her a call and felt like she needed to talk to someone. Sitting in her car in the back parking lot, she first made sure her doors were locked and then took out her phone and punched in Savannah's phone number.

"Hello?" Savannah calmly answered, even though there was a mixture of sounds in the background, including strange music, wailing, squeals, laughter, and an occasional scream. The wailing was especially loud.

"Savannah? Are you all right? Where on earth are you?"

"Is that you, Jillian?" She didn't wait for a reply. "I'm sorry I can't hear you very well with all this noise. I'm working at the haunted house this afternoon and Amber French—you know, she's a waitress at Crazy Fish—is really into her character. She's a damsel-in-distress ghost—you know, pale face, lots of gauzy material waving around." Savannah paused, and almost shouted, "Amber, give it a rest for a minute!" Things were a little quieter. "Okay. Talk quick. I think the next group is about to come up."

Jillian felt a little disappointed. "Never mind. I wanted to talk, but you're busy."

"My shift ends at six. Have you been through the haunted house yet?"

"No, I haven't had a chance."

"Well, the bakery's closed now, isn't it? Why don't you come on over? You can go through the house and then we can have a chat after I'm done here."

Amber started wailing again. "That's the next group coming up—gotta go. See you in a few." The line went silent.

Jillian chuckled. "I guess I'm going to the haunted house."

There was no point in trying to drive there. It would be faster to walk with all the traffic and pedestrians, and it was doubtful she would find any parking space near Yarn Charm anyway. She did a little window-shopping as she made her way past the booths in the town square, but didn't have time to stop and browse as she would have liked.

She soon reached the three-story Victorian that served its owner, Gladys Glenshaw, as both home and place of business. Near the front door on the porch was a table, and at that table sat Gladys, in full witch regalia, selling tickets to the haunted house. A line of people had formed, trailing across the porch and down the wide front steps all the way to the gate of the elaborate wrought-iron fence that surrounded the property.

Jillian stepped up to the end of the line, hoping it wouldn't take too long. She glanced at her watch and thought that if she didn't make it inside soon enough, she'd just wait for Savannah on the porch instead of going through. She could still buy a ticket to support the charity.

The line moved faster than she expected, and in just a bit less than ten minutes she was in front of the table ready to buy her own ticket. She looked back to see that the line was just as long as when she had arrived. It was a popular destination for the festival.

"Hello, Jillian. On your own today?" Gladys said pleasantly, in contrast to the costume she was wearing. She had on a black dress that covered her from just under her chin down to her feet and a tall, pointy witch's hat. The only skin that was visible was that of her face and hands, and they were bright green. Her fingernails were painted deep red. Jillian wondered how she got her skin to look that color and how hard it was to remove.

"Yes, I just need a ticket for one."

Gladys took her money and handed her a ticket. "Just go inside and follow the sign up the staircase."

The front door was open, and Jillian had her hand on the handle of the screen door to pull it open.

"Oh, wait, dear," said Gladys.

"Yes?"

"Please tell your aunt Cornelia I just got a new shipment of that bamboo yarn I was telling her about at garden club."

"I will. Thanks, Gladys." Jillian smiled. If this was any indication of the scariness that awaited her in the haunted house, she thought she just might survive it.

In the foyer, ghostly music played. Strands of fake cobwebs were strung across the gingerbread trim that accented the arched doorways. In one corner there was a black cauldron with white mist from dry ice pouring over the side and covering the floor. The door to the yarn shop was closed, and opposite to that, a red-velvet rope closed off the wide entrance to the living room. A sign in the shape of an arrow, with *Ghosts & Ghouls Ahead!* printed in gothic letters, pointed toward the staircase straight ahead.

Jillian looked up the wide set of stairs. They were dimly lit from above, but at the side on each step there was an electric candle to help light the way. Two teenage girls had just reached the top. Behind them was a family consisting of a mother, father, and four rambunctious boys, ranging, she guessed, from about five years old to thirteen or fourteen.

As she progressed up the steps, she heard Amber's ghostly wailing intensify. The teenage girls had gone on, and the family paused on the landing. She heard Savannah's voice say, "I'm sorry, but only thirteen and over can go up to the third floor." Then Jillian heard one of the boys say, "But Daaad, it's not fair."

"Sorry, son, but not this year. It won't be long before you're old enough. You go with your mother and brothers. Jack, are you sure you want to go upstairs?"

The boy must have nodded in the affirmative because Jillian saw the two of them head down a narrow hallway, presumably to take another set of stairs up to the third floor. When she reached Savannah, who was sitting on a high stool holding a small flashlight, she heard the screams of the teenage girls and a pounding of feet overhead.

Savannah seemed unconcerned. "This is the third time those two have been through since I've been here. Oliver Kent as 'Nosferatu' is a big hit."

"Ah, that was the name of the movie you couldn't remember. You said it was 'Nose-something.'"

"Right. I asked him and committed it to memory so I could tell you. So, are you going for the full treatment or the milder version?"

Jillian looked upward. "How bad can it be? I'll give it a go."

Savannah laughed. "You'll see." She pointed the flashlight down the hallway. "Just take the stairs back there and follow the path that's laid out upstairs. At the end, take the stairs in the tower to come down. You can either continue on the tour through this floor or go on down to the first floor and out through the kitchen door."

"Well, whatever I do, I'll meet you just outside the gate when you're finished here."

Savannah shined the flashlight on her watch. "Won't be long now. I'll see you out there."

With that, Jillian made her way to the staircase. It was much narrower than the main staircase, with just enough room for one person to pass at a time. At the top was a closed door with a sign: *Please close door behind you.* She opened the door, stepped through, and closed it as requested.

It was much darker and quieter than below—at least now that the teenage girls had departed. She wasn't even sure if the dad and his son were still up here. There must have been a sound-effects CD of some sort playing because she heard in succession the soft hooting of an owl and the flutter of wings, the brief howl of a wolf, a shuffling sound as if something was slithering across the floor, and then the creak of an opening door, or perhaps an opening coffin. The path was marked on the floor with fluorescent-tape lines and arrows to point the way to go.

Jillian took a deep breath and started along the path. There seemed to be movement in the darkness around her, but she couldn't make out anything specific. Something brushed across the top of her hair, and she reached up but nothing was there. She noisily drew in a breath and quickened her step when it felt like a hand was on her shoulder from behind.

She turned a corner and saw a figure ahead, but was only surprised for a moment until she realized she was looking at herself in a mirror. Suddenly the image in the mirror changed to a creepy-looking ghoul who gestured threateningly and cackled loudly. Just as unexpectedly, the mirror then appeared to shatter with a loud *crack* which made her jump and her heart beat faster.

The path turned again and she had the feeling she was not alone. She had her eyes cast downward, looking slightly ahead on the path because she thought she saw something move across it, when a cold hand touched her arm. She almost screamed.

She looked beside her to see the vampire, Nosferatu, rising up out of his coffin. That is, she saw Oliver Kent, wearing a skull cap to cover his hair, pointy ears, and a prosthetic mouthpiece with elongated rotten-looking teeth that distended his lips. His vacant eyes and eyebrows had been exaggerated with a heavy application of black makeup pencil, and his skin glowed white in the semidarkness.

"Oliver—is that really you?"

The vacant look disappeared, and he reached up and took out the teeth with some difficulty as each one of his fingers ended with a long, curved, and pointed fake fingernail. "Miss Green, you're supposed to scream and run away." He sounded disappointed. "There's a tacit quid pro quo here when you buy a ticket. We attempt to frighten you, and you are willing to be frightened."

"I'm sorry, Oliver. I guess I'm just not a screamer, but I was really close. Honest. You do look positively creepy."

That seemed to satisfy him. "Thank you."

The door she had entered in must have opened because a brief shaft of light created shadows in the room.

"Shhh! Hurry along!" He put the ugly teeth back in, laid down, and crossed his hands over his chest, ready for his next victims.

Jillian made her way to the tower and found the stairs going downward. When she reached the second floor, she decided in for a penny, in for a pound, and followed the tour route, finding it very child-friendly with a lighter atmosphere and only vaguely scary vignettes. It was much noisier, too, with music and Amber's wailing, and she heard squeals and laughter more often than screams.

When she had completed seeing all that the haunted house had to offer, she found her way out the kitchen door in the back of the house and around to the front gate. She waited only a minute or two before Savannah showed up, sooner than anticipated.

"My replacement got here early, so I'm ready to go. I had intended to walk home, but since you're here, maybe you can give me a lift."

"Of course. I left my car at the bakery. It'll give us a chance to talk."

As they began walking, Savannah asked what Jillian thought of the haunted house.

"I thought it was excellent. And Oliver was as creepy as you said. If you hadn't told me it was him, I probably would have been more scared. In fact, he scolded me for not being frightened enough."

Savannah laughed. "He's a strange man. Likeable, but strange."

"How did they do that thing with the mirror? I think that *crack* when the glass shattered got my heart beating faster than anything else."

"I don't know exactly, but what you saw was just a projection. There wasn't a real person behind it. And, of course, the mirror wasn't broken, it just fools you into thinking that it is."

Jillian laughed. "Broken but not broken."

For some reason, it wasn't the image of the shattered mirror that flashed through her mind, but the image of the Mayan vase lying in pieces across the fabric in the bottom of the window display.

By the time they reached the parking lot behind the bakery, Jillian had told Savannah about Dr. Middleton and that she had agreed to meet with him at the library the next day. She repeated his rather dire warning, if that's what it was. Still standing outside Jillian's car, Savannah urged her not to keep the appointment, or at least not alone.

"Didn't you say that FBI person gave you a card? Why don't you call her?"

"And say what? 'A man wants to meet me at the library to talk about an old vase that may or may not be broken'?"

Savannah's forehead furrowed. "What do you mean, 'may or may not be broken'?"

Jillian took a deep breath. "Well, first, last evening, I noticed Aunt Cornelia's hands were stained brick-red at dinner, and she said it was from something in the display. But there was nothing that I put in that display that would have caused that. Then, when you said the shattered mirror was just a trick to fool you into thinking it was broken when it really wasn't, it made me wonder—maybe the Mayan vase wasn't broken at all."

"I'm not following. How could it not be broken? Everything in that window display was destroyed. We all saw it."

"I'm saying that we saw what we expected to see. As you say, everything in the display was torn or smashed or broken; therefore, those shards of terra-cotta had to be the Mayan vase. But what if they weren't? What if someone stole the vase, replacing it with bits of something else?—maybe a flowerpot painted to look like the real vase. But when the water from the flower arrangements splashed on everything, the paint got wet and stained Aunt Cornelia's hands."

"Maybe it was the real vase that got wet, and the paint on it stained Cornelia's hands."

"No—I washed it shortly after I brought it home to Belle Haven because it was so dusty. Nothing came off on my hands then or afterward when I handled it."

Jillian looked around the parking lot, her eyes landing on the dumpster next to the building. Savannah followed her gaze.

"No, Jillian. No. I am not dumpster diving." She looked at her watch. "James is picking me up for the costume ball, and I have to get ready."

"So do I. But it won't take that long, and you don't have to get in. You won't even have to get your hands dirty. You just have to help me get in and stand watch."

Savannah's expression showed her distaste for the scheme. "You know it's going to be disgusting in there. There's food that's been in there for days, and who knows what else."

"I know. But most of the trash will be in bags. You do realize they'll probably come around to empty all the dumpsters tonight after they're done taking down the booths in the town square, and then the evidence will be long gone."

Savannah relented. "Oh, I hate myself. All right. Let's get this over with."

The two of them opened the lid on the dumpster. It was nearly full.

"We're going to have to take out this top layer so we can get down to Friday morning's trash."

Savannah rolled her eyes before grabbing a bag. "So much for not getting my hands dirty."

Working together they quickly pulled trash out of the dumpster until they couldn't reach anymore. Then Savannah laced her fingers together to let Jillian put her foot in to give her a lift to get over the side. She landed with a crunch.

"What was that?" asked Savannah.

"I'm not sure. It might have been eggshells. Or it could have been glass."

"Be careful. Remember all that glass we swept up? This was a bad idea."

"Don't fuss. It'll be all right."

Savannah muttered a reply under her breath that Jillian couldn't understand, so she carried on. She handed a few more bags of trash to Savannah until she saw a corner of the lavender-colored fabric that had lined the window display. Under it was the small box in which Cornelia had placed the pieces she had picked up from the display. Jillian crouched down to move a few things aside and opened the box to look inside to make sure it was the right one. Having confirmed that it was, she was about to lift the box and fabric to hand them to Savannah when she heard a door slam. It was just a few seconds later she heard Ike Puckett's voice.

"Savannah Cantrell, what in Sam Hill are you doin' over there?"

"I . . . ah . . ."

Jillian pictured Savannah standing knee-deep in trash bags, trying to come up with a convincing excuse. There was no other option. She stood up. "Hi, Ike."

"Jillian! What are you doin' in there?"

"I . . . ah . . . lost an earring. That's right. I lost an earring, and Savannah is helping."

"Okay, then." He paused a moment before asking, "Do you need my help?" He didn't sound enthused at the thought.

"No thank you, Ike." She looked down and spotted a short length of black wire. "In fact, I think I've found it." She crouched down and picked up the wire between her index finger and thumb, and held it aloft. "See, here it is! Isn't that great, Savannah?"

Savannah's expression was deadpan. "Fabulous."

Ike's mouth twitched. "Well, I'll leave you two ladies to it then. Will I see you at the ball this evening?"

"Absolutely, wouldn't miss it for the world!"

They watched as he got in his truck and pulled away.

"Oh, good grief, this is going to be all over town isn't it?" said Jillian.

"Yep."

"Well there's nothing we can do about that now. Besides, I've found it." She tossed the piece of wire over her shoulder and crouched down again to pick up the box and the fabric. She handed them to Savannah before pulling herself out of the dumpster, landing on the pavement with a thud. They put all the other trash back in the dumpster and closed the lid before they examined their finds.

Jillian opened the box and picked up one of the larger shards of terra-cotta. She rubbed her thumb over the surface, looked at her thumb, and then held it up for Savannah to see. It was covered with a reddish powdery substance. "The real vase wasn't like this. I think this whole thing was staged just to cover up the theft of the vase."

"Why would someone want to steal it anyway?"

"That I don't know. Maybe Dr. Middleton knows the answer to that question. Maybe Quinten Straub knew why and that's why he was killed."

Jillian put the box and the fabric in the trunk of her car. After she dropped off Savannah at her little yellow house, she headed toward Belle Haven, prodding her white Prius just past the speed limit. As she passed by the Padgett's house, she spared it a glance. The pre-timed lights were on as she expected and everything looked as it should. She promised herself she would stop by there after church tomorrow and go inside to see if the plants needed water and if everything else was all right. There were still a couple of days left before the Padgetts would return from their cruise.

At home, she drove through the *porte cochere* and parked in back, and then entered the house through the door into the kitchen. It appeared that Bertie and Cornelia had already eaten and cleaned up, but they had left a pot of vegetable-beef soup simmering on the stove for her. She was hungry and the smell of the soup made her even hungrier, but she had already determined that a good hot shower was called for before she even thought about touching any food. She glanced in the living room where Bertie sat reading the evening newspaper and Cornelia appeared to be crocheting a doily with ecru thread. She greeted them with an, "I'm home," but breezed on by and headed up the staircase.

A short time later, dressed in her bathrobe and with a towel wrapped around her wet hair, she came back downstairs and ate a bowl of soup. After she had rinsed her dishes and put them in the dishwasher, she stopped at the entryway to the living room.

Bertie looked up from the book she was now reading. "Are you going to be ready in time?"

Jillian glanced up at the clock on the mantelpiece. "It's going to be close. If I'm not back down before Troy gets here, I assume you will let him in."

Bertie scoffed. "Of course. Just don't get too attached to him, Jillian."

"What is that supposed to mean?"

"I'm just saying, he's not from around here, and it's unlikely that he'll be around that much after this weekend."

"First of all, I have no plans to get 'attached' to anyone right now. And secondly, if I do I can make that determination myself."

"Well, that didn't turn out all that well last time, did it?"

"Bertie!" It was Cornelia who spoke up. "Jillian, you go and get ready. I want to talk to your grandmother."

Jillian wasn't about to argue with her aunt or her grandmother. For one thing, she didn't have time for it. For another, though what Bertie had said hurt her feelings, she wasn't wrong. It hadn't turned out so well last time. But she hoped she had learned something from it. She turned and walked away before anything else was said, not wanting to hear the two most important people in her life exchanging, perhaps, strong words about her.

A while later, Jillian was upstairs in her bedroom standing in front of a long, freestanding mirror. Adding a final touch to her outfit, she bent down and bunched up the hems of the petticoat and black taffeta skirt together just at her knees, revealing her white opaque stockings and mid-calf, tie-up boots. She pinned the bunched-up fabric in place on each side using two of the gaudy brooches she had found upstairs the night before.

She stood up to reevaluate her look once more. She had applied heavy eye makeup and a dark-red lipstick with blue-pink undertones on her lips. After she dried her hair, she divided it into three sections, loosely braiding each section. Then she wound the plaits around the back of her head, tucking in the ends and pinning them in place. She wore a matching set of an antique silver necklace and earrings that had black onyx pendants.

She readjusted the black-veiled hat she wore, and just as she pulled the veil down over her eyes, there was a knock on the door. "Come in."

Bertie opened the door, came in, and sat on the edge of the bed. "Troy's here. He's talking with Cornelia in the living room."

"Okay. Thank you." Jillian picked up the black crocheted gloves and proceeded to put them on.

"Jillian, I'm sorry for what I said. Cornelia pointed out that you are a grown woman, and it's not really my business. And what happened before, with David Drake, that wasn't your fault. You couldn't have known."

Jillian pulled up the veil from her eyes and sat down next to her grandmother. "Thanks, Bertie. I know you only want what's best for me. I've always known that. As far as David goes, I feel like I should have known that something wasn't right, but what's past is past. For now, I'm content with how things are, being here at Belle Haven with you and Aunt Cornelia. You don't have to worry. I'm not going to run off with a car salesman from Athens." She put her arm around Bertie's shoulders and gave her a kiss on her soft cheek which left a dark-red imprint.

"It wouldn't hurt to remember what a fine man Hunter Greyson is."

Jillian couldn't help but smile. Bertie was nothing if not tenacious, and even though it really got to her sometimes, she wouldn't have her grandmother any other way. "I haven't forgotten that. Though, it may be that there is someone else who has captured his heart."

"Oh, pish. You mean that Raeanne Foster? I've seen her. That scrawny blonde doesn't hold a candle to you."

"I think you might be a little bit prejudiced. I've seen her too. She's quite pretty, and the term these days is 'fashionably thin.'" It was time to change the subject. Jillian stood up and twirled around. "What do you think of my costume?"

Bertie cocked her head, looking over Jillian's outfit from the hat to the shoes. "It's certainly . . . interesting. Is all of that from upstairs?"

"Everything except for the stockings and the boots." She clicked the chunky heels. "I bought these boots when I lived in

California, but I haven't worn them very often. I thought I might as well get some use out of them."

"You know you can't wear shoes like those on the gym floor. Coach Hardesty and the school board will be keeping an eye out."

"I know. That's why I'm wearing these too." Jillian reached down to pull up the top edge of a multicolored-stripe sock from the inside of one boot. "With all the black and white I'm wearing, I decided a little color was called for."

She stood up and looked in the mirror once more. Satisfied, she picked up the beaded clutch she had found upstairs from the dresser and dropped the tube of red lipstick inside to join the handkerchief and comb she had already placed there. The taffeta skirt had a hidden pocket on the inside of the waistband, so she carried her cash there. She would leave her phone home tonight. She snapped the purse shut. "Well, I guess I'm ready."

She offered her hand to her grandmother, which she took, using it to help pull herself up from the bedside. "I hope you have a good time tonight, sweetheart."

"I'm sure I will. Playing dress-up and dancing to the oldies—how could that not make for an exciting evening?"

The Moss Holloween costume ball was in full swing when Troy and Jillian arrived. The parking lot was nearing capacity, and it took them several minutes to find an empty space. They followed the flow of people heading from their cars to the front doors of the building, all dressed in a wide variety of costumes from homemade to expensively rented. Jillian had already spotted one woman wearing a hoop skirt, but she didn't think it was anyone she knew.

She and Troy made a striking couple, if Jillian did say so herself. In his top hat and black frock coat he was an imposing figure, and it seemed to her that he knew he was. But that was okay with her. She had no illusions about Troy or her friendship with him, and friendship was all that it was, in spite of Bertie's warning. She planned to just enjoy herself for the evening, with no thoughts of Quinten Straub, FBI Agent Reese Calloway, the vandalism in the bakery, Dr. Hoon Middleton, or the Mayan vase.

As they neared the entrance, she could already hear music playing as the doors opened and closed. At the door, over Jillian's objection that she had invited him, Troy insisted on paying for both their tickets. The ticket taker stamped the back of each of their left hands with an image that had the words *Happy Holloween!* encircling a smiling jack-o'-lantern.

They entered the foyer where they passed a concession stand, currently manned by fellow Sweetie Pie Annalise Reed and her husband, Byron, vice president of the Moss Hollow Savings & Loan. They were dressed like George and Martha Washington complete with white wigs. Byron was near the correct height for

George, and Annalise had the correct amount of "padding" for the pleasantly plump Martha. It was a good choice. Annalise looked up from her task, and she and Jillian made eye contact, but the Reeds were both busy with customers, so Jillian just waved as they passed by. Seeing Annalise reminded her that she should send a card of thanks to her, Savannah, and Laura Lee for helping to clean up the bakery.

Jillian and Troy entered the dimly lit gym which was decorated with crepe-paper streamers and several spinning mirror balls suspended from the rafters, plus a variety of autumn/Halloween props. A dais had been constructed on one end of the gym for the DJ, who was dressed like Beetlejuice in a black-and-white striped suit with his eyes ringed in black and his hair sticking up all over his head. Jillian wasn't sure if it was a wig or his own hair. Around the outer edge of the gym there were tables and chairs where people could take the occasional break. The floor was filled with costumed people dancing to "Love Potion Number 9," doing every sort of dance from the jerk to the Watusi.

Jillian first learned the dance names from the sixties and how to do them when she was small and danced with her mother to all her old records. Those were good memories. Now she rarely ever saw or heard from her parents, who had decided, when she was a senior in high school, to sell their little house in Moss Hollow and to buy a Silver Bullet RV in which to travel across the country. She had been left in the care of her grandmother, who was a widow by then, and after she went to college in California, she hadn't returned to Moss Hollow for the next twenty years—not until circumstances had forced her to.

She hadn't been thrilled about coming back to Moss Hollow then. Now, she was thankful that she was home, and that she was doing something to help her grandmother. Though, as she thought about it, it had probably been even more of a help to herself. Life was funny. When she'd left California she thought her life was ruined. Now she was starting to get the hang of running the bakery, she was living in the loving embrace of family, and she had good friends. She was happy. She couldn't ask for more. Well, maybe she could think of a few other things, but all in good time and not tonight.

Jillian led Troy up into the bleachers to find some empty seats to leave their shoes. Troy looked around as they passed by pairs of shoes already discarded by people on the dance floor. "Do we seriously have to take off our shoes?"

"Absolutely. You can't do the mashed potato properly unless you do."

"Excuse me? We're going to be mashing potatoes?"

"It's a dance, silly. It seems I'm going to have a lot to teach you. Just take off your shoes. Besides, you don't want to get in trouble with the basketball coach by scuffing up his floor. He's six foot five."

He laughed as he sat down to untie his shoes. "Good thing I didn't wear a pair of socks with a hole in the toe."

Having removed their shoes, they headed down to the dance floor. They had just reached the bottom of the steps, when the DJ put on "Monster Mash" and a general *whoop!* went up from the crowd. Jillian scanned the sea of dancers and saw a pith helmet wobbling up and down close to the middle, so she grabbed Troy's hand and led him through the press of people toward the helmet.

As she expected, it was James Wilson, Savannah's date for the evening. When she had first returned to Moss Hollow, Jillian was shocked at how much he had aged. Now, as he danced, she could see in his face that he had recovered from both the shock of the death of his wife and the treatment he had endured from her for all those years. He'd always been rather shy, but he seemed to be happy now.

Besides the pith helmet, he wore a grayish-white linen uniform-type jacket and matching breeches that stopped just below his knees where the ends were buttoned around knee-high socks. On his belt he had a holster with the handle of a neon-pink water pistol sticking out of the top.

Jillian wondered who James was dancing with now. She didn't think it could be Savannah, who had mahogany-colored shoulder-length hair. It was someone with a shaggy mane of hair under a scruffy-looking soft hat with the wide brim turned upward, and dressed in a too-large striped shirt with no collar and gray canvas pants. There was a toy cowboy rifle that Jillian had seen for sale at Puckett's Hardware strapped across the person's back. When James saw Jillian, he waved and said something to his dance partner. The person turned around and Jillian was shocked to see it was Savannah, wearing a fake mustache no less.

After introducing Troy to her friends, practically shouting to be heard over the music, Jillian had to ask, "So who are you guys supposed to be?"

Savannah answered, also shouting, "Isn't it obvious? We're Stanley and Livingstone." It got suddenly quieter as the song ended.

James turned to face Savannah, offering his hand to her and speaking in a sort of sing-song accent, ending the last syllable of the last word on a higher note, "Dr. Livingstone, I presume?"

Savannah took his hand and answered in a not-too-bad, if slightly exaggerated, Scottish accent. "Yes, and I am thankful that I am here to welcome you, sir." Obviously they had been working on this routine.

Jillian laughed, "You two are too much. What sort of accent is that supposed to be, James?"

James responded in a mock-offended tone: "It's Welsh, of course."

Jillian looked skeptical. "Of course. What was I thinking? Why isn't one of you wearing the glasses you bought at the yard sale?"

"They turned out to have belonged to someone with really bad eyesight," said Savannah. "We couldn't use them."

Jillian could sense that Troy was getting impatient with the conversation. The next song began—The Monkees singing "I'm a Believer." She said, "I guess we should dance."

So they did. Jillian was pleased to see that while Troy might not know the official names of dances from the sixties, he easily picked up all her moves.

A few songs later, after Savannah and James had taken a break from dancing, Jillian's eyes landed on Hunter Greyson and Raeanne Foster on the dance floor. Raeanne was dressed as an antebellum Southern belle, wearing a red gown with the dreaded hoop skirt and a wide V-neck that revealed her well-tanned shoulders. Jillian had to admit she was lovely, but with a certain amount of hardness around the eyes and mouth. She berated herself only slightly for the unkind thought, adding, *It's true though.*

Hunter looked very handsome and distinguished in the garb of a Southern gentleman, wearing a white wool suit and vest with a black Western-style bow tie around the stand-up collar of his white shirt. His facial hair had grown in nicely, and his currently longish hair was swept backward. On someone else his clothing might have brought to mind Colonel Sanders, but on Hunter the overall impression was that of virility. With some reluctance, Jillian pulled her eyes back to Troy, who was watching her with that look of bemusement she had seen on his face in the restaurant when he had caught her watching Hunter and Raeanne there.

He said, "Let me guess. That person that you have previously dated is here."

She felt herself blush, but she didn't think he could tell since everyone's color was heightened in the hot and crowded atmosphere of the gym. When she didn't answer right away, Troy put his right arm around her waist and took her right hand in his left. They spun around together so that he was facing in the direction of Hunter and Raeanne.

Still holding her close, he said, "Is it the fellow in the white suit?" There was no point in denying it. "Yes."

"And that blonde, I suppose, is his date?" There was no point in answering. She simply nodded.

"Hmm. She looks familiar. I think I might know her."

"Really?"

"Why don't you introduce us, and we'll find out?"

"Really?" She seemed to be at a loss for different words to say.

"Yes, really." He let her waist go to twirl her around, still holding onto her hand.

The DJ was in between songs when they reached Hunter and Raeanne, who looked like they were about to head for the edge of the floor to take a break. That is, until Hunter saw Jillian approaching. The look that passed between them was not lost on Raeanne, and her eyes narrowed until she looked toward Troy. Then her eyes opened wide. She was the first to speak.

"Why Mr. Troy Hansford, fancy meetin' you here, in this little backwater town, of all places."

Since Jillian had never heard her speak, she wasn't sure if she really talked that way or if she was trying to sound like Scarlett O'Hara in character with her costume.

Troy took Raeanne's gloved hand and leaned down to kiss it. "It's Mrs. Foster, isn't it? It's lovely to see you again. I just got a 1954 silver Mercedes-Benz GT Roadster into the showroom that your husband might be interested in."

Raeanne tilted her head in a manner which suggested she was blushing, but Jillian didn't see it. She half-expected Raeanne to open the fan hanging from her wrist and flutter it in front of her face. "Please call me Raeanne, and I'm afraid my husband and I are currently separated."

"I am so sorry to hear that," said Troy, in a manner that suggested he was not sorry at all.

Hunter cleared his throat to interrupt the exchange and held out his hand to Troy. "I'm Hunter Greyson."

Troy took his hand, saying, "Troy Hansford."

They held the handshake for a moment longer than necessary. Jillian observed their grim expressions and their tightening grips. When they let go, Jillian had the impression that Troy would have liked to have rubbed his hand to get the blood flowing again, but instead covertly flexed his fingers.

Jillian broke the momentary silence, offering her hand to Raeanne. "Jillian Green. I'm pleased to meet you."

Instead of a real handshake, Raeanne only took the tips of Jillian's fingers in her own. "Raeanne Foster. Pleased to meet you as well." Jillian could tell there wasn't any genuine feeling behind those words.

Hunter said, "Well, we were just headed for the concession stand to get something to drink—"

He was interrupted when the DJ put on the song, "Smoke Gets in Your Eyes." Raeanne swooned. "Oh, I love that song."

"Then, may I have the honor of this dance?" asked Troy.

She had the grace to look at Hunter. "Would you mind, darling?"

"Of course not."

Troy didn't ask Jillian if she minded, but swept up Raeanne in an embrace to waltz her toward an empty area of the dance floor, leaving Jillian standing with her mouth open.

There were a few moments of awkwardness while Jillian and Hunter watched their dates dance with each other. Jillian had to admit they looked good together. What were the odds that two people who knew each other because one's husband had apparently bought classic cars from the other one would both turn up in Moss Hollow at the same time?

Hunter broke into her thoughts by asking, "Did you want to dance, Jillian?"

"Not really. But something to drink sounds good."

Hunter sighed in relief. "That's great. Do you mind if we step outside for a moment to cool off too? I'm regretting this wool suit now, but it was the only one from the family-manse attic that fit me."

"Well, you look great in it, and cooling off for a few minutes would suit me fine."

They both went to the bleachers to put on their shoes. After she finished tying up her boots, Jillian grabbed her clutch and then followed Hunter to the foyer. There, he purchased two colas at the concession stand where Annalise gave them an approving smile. Jillian could almost feel her gaze following them as they went through the outer doors to stand in the night air. She was sure that Bertie, and probably the rest of the Sweetie Pies, would get a full report.

It was a little chilly outside, but not unpleasant. There were a few others outside, cooling off or just getting away from the noise for a while. The sky was clear, but there was too much ambient light to see many stars. Only the Hunter's Moon shone brightly in the sky. It seemed almost blinding as Jillian looked at it.

"The full moon is beautiful, isn't it?" Hunter asked softly.

"Yes. I think autumn is my favorite season. Once, about this time of the year, my parents took me up to the mountains in north Georgia to see the change in the color of the leaves, and we found a place where we could watch the Hunter's Moon come up over the horizon. It was so huge and a beautiful golden color. That was a great trip."

She felt a little catch in her heart at the thought of that time with her parents. It seemed she had too few of those sort of memories. A few tears unexpectedly moistened her eyes, and she turned away so that Hunter wouldn't see her blink them away, pretending to look at another part of the sky.

She heard Ike Puckett's voice from behind her. "What are you two doing out here together? I thought I saw you come with different folks."

She turned to see Ike and his wife, Jean, dressed as Popeye and Olive Oyl. Jean was generally a quiet woman who smiled often. Of course, when Ike was around there wasn't much need for her to say anything, but she was chatty enough when she came into the bakery on her own.

Hunter replied, "Hello, Ike, Jean. We did come with different dates, but we were thirsty, and our dates still wanted to dance, so we changed partners for a bit."

Ike slapped him on the back. "It's a good trade if you ask me."

Jillian wished she could sink into the concrete.

Hunter was diplomatic. "I'm always glad to spend time with Jillian, and Raeanne is an old friend."

"Yeah, I heard . . ."

Jillian rushed to interrupt Ike before he could go any further. "So, how did the play go on Friday night?"

"Oh, it was great. I think we did even better than Thursday night when you were there with that blond fella. Didn't you think it was good last night, Hunter?"

"Yes I did. I didn't see it on Thursday, so I can't compare, but I enjoyed it thoroughly. Sylvia was wonderful, and your dad made me laugh every time he was on stage. I can see where you and Sylvia get your talent and your sense of humor, Ike. As they say, the apple doesn't fall far from the tree."

Ike grinned. "Yeah, my old man had a blast doing the play this year. He doesn't drive at night anymore, but he wanted to come to the ball tonight for a little while, so we brought him along. He's inside at one of the tables on the east side of the gym, or at least he was. I know he'd like it if you have a chance to say a few words with him. I'll probably run him home before it gets too late." Ike looked at his watch and then at Jean. "Well, Miss Olive Oyl, we'd better get inside." He looked back at Jillian and Hunter. "We're supposed to take over for the Reeds at the concession stand. We just came out to cool off for a while."

"We'd better get back inside too," said Hunter. "Our dates will be wondering where we've gotten to."

Inside, Jillian excused herself to go to the ladies room while Hunter proceeded to the gym. The restroom was packed. She tucked her gloves in her clutch while she waited her turn. Before she left, she washed her hands, glancing in the mirror. In spite of some strenuous dancing, her hat was still in place. Her lipstick needed refreshing, but with the number of women jostling for time at the sinks and the mirrors, she was afraid she'd end up with a smile like the Joker from *Batman*. A mistake with dark-red lipstick would be unforgiving.

In the opposite direction from the gym, just past the restroom area, the hallway made a right angle. She stepped around the corner and leaned against the wall. She took the tube of lipstick from the clutch and used the mirror on the flap to redo her lip color. When she finished, she put her gloves back on before snapping the clutch shut.

For some reason, she wasn't feeling any rush to return to the dance. She looked down the darkened hallway through the green metal folding gate that had been extended to block off the classrooms beyond. This was the same building where she had attended high school. There were good and not-so-good memories associated with that phase of her life, but then that could be said of all the years that followed. Even though she was satisfied with her current situation, she had been through some disturbing events since she'd returned to Moss Hollow.

Her mind drifted to Quinten Straub and then the Mayan vase. What was the connection? And what did this man, who said he was a doctor, want to tell her? She wondered if Dr. Middleton was still in town that evening. With all the people in costumes, he could be at the dance and she wouldn't even know it. Most people didn't wear masks, but there were quite a few who did. She raked her mind over the various costumes she'd seen, and how, like Oliver Kent, there were several who were almost impossible to identify as people she knew or didn't know. What if that man was at the dance, spying on her . . .

Oh, stop it. You're getting paranoid . . .

Jillian's thoughts were interrupted when she thought she heard voices down the hallway. There was silence for a minute, and then she heard a woman's laughter. She could have sworn it sounded like Raeanne, but she couldn't be sure. She looked more closely at the folding gate. She hadn't noticed before, but it was slightly open. It was normally locked during after-school functions like the dance or basketball games. She took a step toward it, but realized it was going to be impossible to walk quietly across the tiled floor with boots on. She debated a moment whether she should just walk away, or if she should take off her boots and investigate. The boots came off, and she tucked the clutch into one of them.

She slowly slid the gate open a little more, just enough to be able to step sideways through to the other side. The gate did emit a creak or two as she moved it, but it must have gone unnoticed by those down the hall as she still could hear the occasional voice.

Then her conscience started bothering her. Was it any of her business if there were people in the classrooms? Then she thought, *I'm a taxpayer. What if someone is vandalizing the school the same way someone vandalized the bakery?* She needed to find out.

All the classroom doors were closed, and presumably, should have been locked. Each door had a large rectangular window in the top half, so it was possible to look inside without opening the door. All the lights were turned out, but, at least on the east side of the building, the full moon shone through the windows so brightly it was possible to see quite a lot.

She padded slowly down the hallway toward the sporadic sound of the voices. It had been quiet for a while, and she was nearing the end of the hallway. She thought for a moment she must have imagined the voices, when she heard the laughter again, a bit louder and behind her. *Rats! I passed them.* She turned around and listened again. This time she zeroed in on the correct door when she heard a man's voice. It was coming from a classroom on the east side.

She reached the door and crouched down in front of it, slowly raising herself up just enough so she could look through the bottom of the door's window. She clamped her lips shut to keep from gasping. Standing by the outer windows, outlined by the moonlight, there was a couple kissing. It was Troy and Raeanne.

After a moment of shock when she almost lost her balance, Jillian left as quietly as she could and was back down the hallway and through the gate in no time. Without bothering to put the gate back as it had been, she picked up her shoes and clutch, hurried past the restrooms, through the foyer, and into the gym.

She stopped when she realized she didn't know exactly what she was going to do. Should she tell Hunter? She didn't think she could. Had there been a romance—she hated to use the word "affair"—between Troy and Raeanne before tonight? She realized how little she really knew about him. Should she call Bertie and ask her to come and get her? She looked at her watch. It was already close to ten o'clock. Bertie and Cornelia were both likely already in bed.

She looked across the gym and saw Hunter near the dais talking with Mayor Blackwater, who was dressed like the lord mayor of London in a red cape with a giant medallion hanging from a chain around his neck. James and Savannah were dancing to a slow song—not a good time to disturb them. Maybe if she could just sit for a few minutes, some answers would come to her. She saw an empty place at a table next to Burton Puckett, who was wearing the same costume he had worn for the play.

She walked over to him. "Excuse me, Mr. Puckett, are you saving this seat?"

"Yes I am."

"Oh," she said. She started to walk away.

"I'm saving it for you." He grinned and pulled out the chair for her.

She said, "Thanks," and sat down, putting her boots and clutch under the table. "I don't know if you remember me, but I'm Jillian Green."

"Of course I remember you. You're Bertie's granddaughter. How are Bertie and Cornelia? I see Bertie once in a while at the bakery, but it's been a long time since I've seen Cornelia. Not that she would talk to me much, anyway." He looked rather sad about that.

"They're both fine. Neither one was interested in coming to the costume ball tonight."

"No, I don't imagine Bertie is one for dressing up much. She never was. But Cornelia, she used to love to dress up for Moss Holloween."

"Really? She'll hardly even leave the house during Moss Holloween now."

Mr. Puckett's face registered something—was it regret? Jillian wondered if he would tell her what had happened between him and her aunt. Obviously, whatever it was had occurred a long time ago. It must have been pretty bad for Cornelia to carry a grudge for so long.

Jillian's curiosity got the better of her. She had to ask. "Mr. Puckett,—"

"Please, call me Burton."

"Thank you, I will. Burton, I know something happened that made Aunt Cornelia dislike Moss Holloween, and I know it has something to do with you, but I don't know what it is. Would you tell me?"

"Have neither Bertie or Cornelia said anything?"

"Not before this year. I teased Aunt Cornelia about coming to the festival since she never has in my memory, and it was Bertie who brought up your name. And when she did, I thought Aunt Cornelia would have a conniption fit. She actually forbade Bertie to say anything more."

"Then maybe I shouldn't either."

"Look, how long ago did this happen—fifty, sixty years? I love my aunt Cornelia, and I know that if I was holding a grudge for any length of time, she'd have a few words to say to me about it. Don't you think it's time this was settled?"

"I've thought that for a very long time, but as I've said, she'll barely speak to me. And I can't blame her really. I suppose I crossed the line."

Jillian looked at the sweet old man and was now imagining a number of awful things that he might have done in his youth. How terrible was it?

He seemed to come to a decision and sighed deeply before beginning. "Well, it was about sixty-two years ago now. I was a couple of years behind Cornelia and Bertie in high school. I guess you could say I had a bit of a crush on Cornelia. So, I hatched a plan to get her to notice me.

"See, their older cousin, Genevieve, had come to stay with them when their parents went to Athens to see the Georgia Bulldogs play the Alabama Crimson Tide. The Belle twins were seventeen or eighteen then, and could've stayed on their own, I suppose, but I guess their parents wanted someone more mature to look after things at Belle Haven.

"So, without saying exactly what I planned to do, I told Genevieve that I was sweet on Cornelia and wanted to surprise her. She wasn't from Moss Hollow, so she didn't know about prank week. I guess she thought it was kinda sweet, so she let me and a few of my friends into Belle Haven while the twins were at choir practice or something of that nature. We went upstairs and rigged up a thing so it looked like the Belle Haven haint was walking down the stairs from the third floor."

Jillian's mouth dropped open. "You didn't."

"I'm afraid we did. And it was pretty darned good too. We'd

dressed up Tom Wilkes like the ghost 'cause he was kinda small anyway, and then used a projection machine to . . ." He paused. "Well, that's neither here nor there. The thing is, when Cornelia and Bertie saw it, it was Cornelia that believed it, and she ran downstairs to use the telephone to call every one of her friends and tell them she'd seen the haint and how it was real and all that. Bertie was on her heels and tried to stop her, but Cornelia would have none of it.

"We kept quiet for a long while, just listening at the top of the stairs, but Tom, he started laughing, and then the rest of us couldn't help but join in. That's when they heard us. When Cornelia got back up the stairs and saw us standing there, she was madder than a wet hen. She called us 'horrible little boys,' and I think that's about the last thing she ever said to me besides the minimum that politeness dictates. I think it was one of the other guys who told her it was my idea, so they were off the hook. Except maybe Tom, I don't think she ever talked to him again either. But then, he's been gone for quite a while now."

"I'm sorry about your friend," said Jillian. "When did he pass away?"

"Oh, he's not dead. He moved to Texas. I still get a Christmas card from him every year."

"Oh." She wasn't sure if Burton was serious or not. "So that's it? You pranked Cornelia and Bertie, but Aunt Cornelia has stayed mad about that all these years? That doesn't sound like her."

"You don't understand. After she called all her friends, the whole school, heck, the whole town knew about it, and she got teased like you wouldn't believe. But instead of laughing along with it like most folks do, like your grandmother did, she stood by it, sayin' that she *had* seen the haint, maybe not that time, but other times."

"Now that does sound like Aunt Cornelia." Jillian wondered if this was the incident that set her aunt on her offbeat path.

"So, now you know," said Burton. "I'm the reason Cornelia hates Moss Holloween. Lot of times I wished I'd never done it, but I reckon it's too late now to make amends."

Jillian wanted to say something to make it better, but she couldn't think of anything. Maybe if she could talk to Cornelia about it . . .

"Now, you tell me about yourself, young lady. I'm glad to see you're helping out your grandma at the bakery. That's what family does. My children and grandkids have been a blessing to me, there's no doubt. Now, you, you're not married yet, are you?"

"Um, no sir, I'm not," answered Jillian.

"Well you ought to think about it. I can highly recommend it. My Doris and I were married for fifty-one years before she passed on, and I loved her every day of it. Oh, we had our ups and downs like everyone else, but in the end we were always there for each other. And I don't know what I'd do without my children and grandchildren now she's gone." His eyes seemed to get a bit misty, but he sniffed and carried on. "I saw you dancing earlier with that blond fella—who's he?"

Jillian had almost forgotten about that "blond fella" and wished she could forget him. She explained about his connection to the Padgetts, and then explained who they were. The Puckett family attended the Episcopalian church instead of Moss Hollow Fellowship Church, so they hadn't met.

The conversation lagged as Jillian watched Burton scan the room, stopping at the dais as "Moon River" began to play. Jillian followed his gaze, but her eyes landed on Hunter, who was still talking to the mayor nearby. She looked back at Burton to see that he was watching her.

"Now there's a song a man can dance to." Burton stood and offered Jillian his hand. "May I have this dance?"

"Of course," said Jillian, standing, "I would be honored."

Taking his hand, they walked sedately to the dance floor, or as sedately as one could walk in stocking feet. Jillian was surprised as Burton took the lead. He was an excellent dancer. With his back perfectly straight and his chin up, he placed his right hand on her back just below her shoulder blade and held out her right hand at shoulder height. They took long graceful strides and turns across the floor. He seemed to have a destination in mind, moving them steadily across the floor.

It wasn't long until Burton stopped. "You know, I'm getting tired already. Maybe that young fella over there will help me out." Then he said louder, "Hunter Greyson—come here and help out an old man."

Jillian looked over her shoulder to see Hunter walking their way.

"What can I do for you, Burton?"

"Take over this dance for me. I think I'm plain tuckered out." Without waiting for an answer, he passed Jillian's hand to Hunter's and stepped aside.

"With pleasure." Hunter said it directly to Jillian.

They began to waltz as Andy Williams sang, "Two drifters, off to see the world . . ."

The song ended much too quickly. Jillian wished the DJ would play it again, or something like it, but instead he put on a psychedelic-rock song from the late sixties that soon brought more of the younger people to the floor to dance in the frenzied manner of that time. Jillian and Hunter just stood there, still locked in their waltz embrace. It never crossed her mind to mention Troy or Raeanne. But apparently, it did cross Hunter's.

"Jillian, about Raeanne—"

Someone bumped into them. It was Oliver Kent, still in his Nosferatu costume, and he was dancing with Amber French, still in her damsel-in-distress costume from the haunted house.

"Oh, excuse me, Mr. Greyson." Oliver had to practically shout over the heavy drone of electric guitars.

Hunter's forehead furrowed, and he paused a few seconds before he said, "Is that you, Oliver?"

Oliver grinned. Fortunately, he must have decided the fake teeth were too much trouble, so it was his own white teeth that showed. He still looked creepy. "Yes. What do you think?"

Hunter shook his head. "I never would have believed it."

Amber spoke up. "I know, isn't he amazing?" She looked at Oliver with obvious admiration.

Another young man bumped into them. Hunter put his arm around Jillian's shoulders. "I think we're going to move out of the danger zone. You two have a good evening."

"Thanks!" With that, Oliver and Amber returned to their dance which seemed to mostly involve jumping up and down.

Hunter guided Jillian toward the outer edge of the gym floor.

She couldn't help but wonder what he had been about to say about Raeanne. Was he trying to break it to her gently that they were soon to be engaged? And if they were, could she keep silent about what she had seen in the classroom? Would saying something destroy their friendship? But how could she not tell him? Her mind was batting it back and forth when she saw James and Savannah sitting alone at a table. She simply pointed in their direction, and he understood she meant that they should join their friends.

As they approached, Savannah said, "Hey, you two. Will you join us? I see your dates are still dancing together."

Jillian and Hunter both turned and followed Savannah's gaze toward the place where Troy and Raeanne were enjoying the raucous atmosphere of the dance floor. The hoop skirt didn't seem to be giving Raeanne any difficulty. Jillian wondered when they had returned to the gym. She looked up at Hunter. She couldn't read his expression, but he didn't seem angry that his date had abandoned him.

After they sat down, James and Hunter began talking about the current World Series, nearly always a safe subject for two men who appeared to have little else in common. Jillian was next to Savannah and turned her head away from the men to whisper, "I have something to tell you later."

Savannah looked puzzled and whispered back, "What?"

Jillian turned her head even further and repeated her statement, but in a slightly louder tone of voice.

"Can't you tell me now?" Savannah answered in an equal voice level. But just as she spoke, the music stopped and her words seemed to echo in the room.

James and Hunter stopped their conversation and looked at the women. Jillian saw them out of the corner of her eye and turned her face toward them, trying to put on the most innocent face she could muster.

She was saved from saying anything when Troy and Raeanne walked up to the table. Hunter and James stood up, and Hunter offered his chair to Raeanne, which would move him into the chair next to James. Troy grabbed one of the chairs lined up against the wall and placed it between Raeanne and Jillian, requiring that the others at the table scoot their chairs closer together. Jillian noted that Raeanne needed some extra room to accommodate her hoop skirt, but she sat down expertly, making sure she didn't sit on one of the hoops, which would have resulted in a rather embarrassing show.

"I declare, I am just burnin' up in here," said Raeanne, opening her fan and fluttering it just below her chin.

Jillian thought she did look quite flushed, *What with the crowd, the dancing, and the kissing. Mustn't forget the kissing.*

Raeanne put her hand on Troy's arm. "But that was such great fun. Thank you so much, Mr. Hansford, for being my partner. Hunter isn't so fond of that sort of dance. Isn't that right, Hunter?"

Hunter nodded. "That is true. Where have you two been? I looked for you when I came back into the gym."

Raeanne answered, "Oh, I needed to take a trip to the little girls' room and then we got something to drink. We must have just missed each other."

Jillian's face must have betrayed something of the fact that she knew that was a lie, or at least a white lie. Raeanne may have done both those things, but Jillian knew the reason they had missed each other had nothing to do with either of those activities.

Troy looked at Jillian and leaned over to take her hand, "Hey, you're not mad because I danced with Raeanne are you?"

Jillian tried to smile as genuinely as she could. "Of course not. That wasn't really my sort of dance either."

The table was quiet for a moment, during which time Jillian

yawned before she could stop herself. Everyone noticed. "I'm so sorry. I'm afraid it's been a long day for me."

Savannah said, "I don't know how you do it. I hope you can get some rest tomorrow."

"I'm planning to. After church, I'm stopping at the Padgett's house to water their plants once more before they get home, and then, I'm going to take a nice long nap."

"But what about the meeting at the li—" Savannah just stopped herself before she said "library." She recovered. "I mean, the bakery, for the baking club meeting." She knew full well the meeting had been canceled.

Jillian played along. "Oh, I guess I forgot to tell you it was canceled."

"Well, then, I hope you can get a good nap in."

As Savannah spoke, Jillian saw Ike Puckett approaching their table from the direction of the foyer. She couldn't help but think, *Now what?*

When he'd reached them he started right in. "Hey, I'm just trying to remind people—all y'all should make sure you buy a ticket or ten for the drawing at the end of the dance. Have to be here to win, but it's for a weekend for two at the Château Élan Winery and Resort over in Braselton during their Vineyard Fest. Jean and I stayed there once, and it was top-notch. Puckett's Hardware is donating the weekend, so all the proceeds will go to the hospital."

Hunter answered, "Thanks, Ike, but I don't think I'll make it to eleven tonight. I'd be happy to buy a few tickets anyway, though."

Ike slapped him on the back. "That's the spirit!"

"Oh, Hunter, can't we stay?" Raeanne said in a plaintive voice. "This has turned out to be so much more fun than I expected."

Jillian bit her lip to keep from saying, "I'll bet it has."

"Well, I—"

Troy interrupted Hunter, "I'd be happy to take you home, Ms. Foster." He looked around at Jillian, "If you don't mind of course."

Had he forgotten that he drove a two-seater? She had a moment of enjoyment picturing Raeanne trying to get into the small sports car in her hoop skirt. "No, I don't mind. I don't think I can make it to eleven either. I'll get another ride home."

"I can drop you off, Jillian," said Hunter.

"There, that's all settled," said Troy, obviously pleased with the outcome. Raeanne didn't look entirely pleased herself, but she took a dismissive look at Jillian and the smile returned to her face.

Ike spoke to Jillian, "So, are those the earrings?"

Puzzled, she reached up to touch one of the black pendants hanging from her ears.

"You know, the ones you and Savannah were looking for in the dumpster earlier this evening."

Seriously, Ike? Do men just have no clue? "Um, no, that was a different one," she answered.

"Oh." He looked up. "Hey, there's the mayor. I need to ask him to make an announcement about the drawing. See y'all later."

After Ike moved on, it was Troy who asked about it. "Were you two actually in the dumpster?" There was a slight chuckle to his voice.

"No." Jillian was trying to decide what to tell and what to conceal. She didn't much care for the snide look on Raeanne's face. "It was just me."

Savannah spoke up. "And it wasn't really for an earring."

"Savannah!" Jillian gave her a severe look.

Savannah's expression showed she spoke without thinking.

Troy asked, "So, what could induce you to climb into a dumpster?"

Jillian hesitated. "I just needed to check on something. It's a long story." She faked a yawn this time, placing her hand over her mouth. "Oh, I'm so sorry. Hunter, are you ready to go?"

In the foyer, they all bought a few tickets for the drawing, which Hunter gave to Raeanne and Jillian gave to Savannah after Troy refused them, saying he would buy some for himself.

After James and Savannah had returned to the gym, and while Hunter and Raeanne were saying good night, Jillian thought good manners dictated she should say something to Troy even though she was still feeling more than a little miffed at him.

"Well, thanks for bringing me to the dance. I'm sorry I can't stay for the whole thing. I hope you understand." She tried to say it with as much sincerity as she could.

Troy smiled. It was just so darned appealing when he did, and of course, he knew it. "It was my pleasure, Jillian. And I want to thank you. I really have enjoyed my time with you. I'm afraid this will have to be our good-bye."

"Aren't you staying for the bonfire tomorrow?"

"I'm afraid not. This has been a fun break, but I had a call from a driver who wants to unload a trailer of cars tomorrow afternoon, and I need to be there. I was going to tell you on our way back to Belle Haven. I'll head on home tomorrow morning. I hope you'll express my gratitude to your grandmother and aunt for their hospitality." He looked down at his clothing. "I'll have these things cleaned and send them back to you."

"That would be fine, and I'll certainly pass along your message to Bertie and Aunt Cornelia." She held out her hand, "Well, it's been fun, and maybe I'll see you again when you come to visit Tara. I assume you'll be back to take care of that family business you mentioned."

"Yes, I will be back for that," he said, taking her hand. He pulled her hand to his mouth, planted a kiss on it, and then said, "Au revoir, Jillian."

She avoided looking into his eyes. "Good-bye, Troy."

She turned and walked away. She took a moment to tell Hunter that she was heading to the gym to retrieve her boots and clutch.

Burton was sitting alone at the table where she had left her things, and she thought he was looking a bit tired too. "I'm glad we had a chance to talk tonight, Burton," said Jillian. "Thanks for telling me about you and Aunt Cornelia. If I can do anything to fix that situation, I will. And thank you for the dance. We'll have to do that again sometime. It's nice to dance with someone who really knows how it should be done."

He smiled. "I will look forward to that."

She hesitated. "Look, I'm heading home. Can we drop you off? I'm sure Hunter won't mind."

Burton's eyebrows rose. "So, young Mr. Greyson is taking you home instead of that fella you came with?"

"Yes. It's just that we're both tired, and our dates wanted to stay to the end. Hunter was kind enough to offer me a ride, and I'm sure he'd be glad to give you one too."

Burton looked around until he saw his son. Jillian saw him too. He was obviously telling a humorous story to a group of fellow Thrashers. She only hoped her name and the word "dumpster" weren't being mentioned.

"Well, if you're sure it's not an inconvenience. I am ready to go home, but I hate to take Ike away when he's having such a good time."

Hunter walked up to the table, carrying his shoes. "What's that?"

"You wouldn't mind giving Burton a lift home too, would you?"

"Of course not." Hunter sized up the level of Burton's tiredness. "Let me just run over and let Ike know that I'm taking you home."

A few minutes later, all three were headed out the door. Jillian was extremely tired, but when she stepped out into the brisk night air, she felt like she gained a little bit of a second wind. Even so, she was glad to see that Hunter had driven his dark-silver Lexus instead of the old, bordering on antique, sedan that he drove for business. She wouldn't mind a bit of luxury on the way home.

She insisted that Burton sit in the front with Hunter and was content to let them carry on a conversation. Leaning her head back against the seat, she realized she must have been asleep when it only seemed like a moment had passed when they arrived at Burton's house. Burton got out and opened the back door, ushering her into the front seat before saying good night. Hunter waited until he saw that Burton was safely inside his house.

"That's a nice old man," said Hunter.

"He is that. Tonight's the most I've ever spoken with him. Sorry about him maneuvering our dance together. I didn't know he was going to do that."

"Well, I'm not sorry. I had planned to ask you for the next slow dance, but when 'Moon River' started playing, I couldn't make a graceful exit from the mayor until Burton gave me an excuse. Didn't you hear me thank him a few minutes ago?"

"No, I think I must have fallen asleep."

"What time were you up this morning?"

"Oh, you know, dark-thirty. That's the baker's life, which is my life now."

"You're not sorry are you? I mean to be back in Moss Hollow after the glamorous life in California."

Jillian laughed. "Well, some people may have the glamorous life out there, but not me. Mind you, it wasn't bad, except near the end, but no, I'm not sorry to be home. How about you? Do you miss Atlanta? After all, that's where you grew up."

"I'll admit that living here has been an adjustment. Of course, I'd been to Moss Hollow to visit family all my life. I even worked a couple of summers for my grandfather when I was in college, so it wasn't a complete mystery to me. And I've come to appreciate that a small town has its advantages."

"Such as?"

"Nice people, like you."

Jillian smiled, but didn't say anything.

"One thing I could live without is the gossip mill. I've wanted to tell you, Jillian, that despite any rumors you may have heard, there is nothing between Raeanne and me. It's true that we were engaged, but that was years ago, and when it ended, that was it for me. And it was for the best. We were never well-suited. I'm saying that from my perspective now. I didn't know it then, of course. The fact that she broke our engagement to marry someone else was undoubtedly a blessing in disguise. My aunt Gertrude likes to tell people that I haven't married because I've been pining for Raeanne, but it's not true. I just want to make sure I marry the right person when I finally do make that commitment."

"It's not easy, is it—to find someone who is compatible and trustworthy. I thought I found that once. We were compatible, but he wasn't trustworthy. I completely understand."

"When Raeanne called and said she needed to get away because her marriage was falling apart, I was just doing a favor for an old friend. Nothing more."

They had reached Belle Haven, and Hunter turned the car into the driveway. He stopped in front of the old mansion, turned off the car and got out to walk around to open the car door for Jillian, lending his hand to help her out of the car. The house was not alight as it had been the last time she'd arrived home after dark with a date. The lights were on in the foyer, and at each side of the door on the outside, but that was all. However, the moon was now high overhead and lit the landscape in grayscale, making Jillian feel like they had stepped through some sort of gateway to become characters in a film noir.

As they walked toward the front door Hunter said, "Did I mention that you look very fetching this evening?"

"I don't believe you did. Thank you. Did I mention that you look very handsome this evening?"

"I don't believe you did. Thank you. Is that because of the facial hair or in spite of it?"

She stopped, and they turned to face one another. "I think I kind of like it. It makes you look slightly dangerous, but in a good way. I should tell you, I have heard certain people threaten to take their funerary business over to Painter's Ridge because of your excess hair."

"Those certain people wouldn't happen to include Wanda Jean Maplewood or Maudie Honeycutt, would it?" Hunter said, smiling.

"I don't think I should name names." She returned his smile.

"It's neither here nor there. I already have an appointment at the barber shop first thing on Monday morning for a shave and haircut." He ran his index finger and thumb from the center of his mustache and down the sides of his chin. "It's been rather different not to be clean shaven. It takes some getting used to. I might do this every year for Moss Holloween." He grinned. "Have you ever been kissed by a man with a mustache?"

Jillian thought for just a moment. "No, I don't believe I ever have."

"Well, this is your chance."

After that, nothing was said for several minutes.

Jillian went to bed on Saturday night with the intention of sleeping in until nine o'clock Sunday morning since church didn't begin until ten thirty. The very idea seemed absolutely decadent compared to her workdays. The problem was, her mind didn't want to cooperate. At first she was only dreaming, but she was gradually waking as she subconsciously replayed the events of last night's dance, from the moment she arrived at the high school with Troy until she walked up the front steps of Belle Haven with Hunter and he kissed her good night.

That kiss. With that memory, she was wide awake. She opened her eyes but there was only darkness in the room. Her mind began to toss about the question of whether Hunter's kiss meant something more than just good night. If it was something more, was that a good thing or not? Was this a turning point, or just another bump in the road?

She turned her head to look at the red numbers on her alarm clock and groaned in frustration. It was five o'clock. She pulled the covers over her head. She tried to relax and push everything from her mind, but sleep would not return. Finally, she pushed back the covers and got out of bed.

Downstairs, she put on a pot of coffee, and while she waited, she split an English muffin, toasted it, and then spread Aunt Cornelia's peach preserves over the top. Armed with a large mug of coffee and the muffin on a blue willow dessert plate, she padded to her office intending to do some social media surfing, an activity she tried not to indulge in too often.

Sitting at her desk, she began scrolling through the various posts. There were recipes, political statements, cute videos of cats and dogs and babies, and on and on. After several minutes she shook her head and closed the tab.

She took a bite of muffin and turned her mind to the problem of the Mayan vase. When she first brought it home, she had only done enough of a search on the Internet to figure out what the tree motif on it meant. Then, she had been certain that it was just a reproduction, but it occurred to her, what if it was the real thing? But that didn't seem possible. Tara and Troy had both said that their uncle had been an archeologist and a professor at Harvard—therefore, he must have been a respected member in his field. If the vase had been the real thing, wouldn't he have given it to a museum? Or could a person purchase something like that? She had no idea. But what if none of what they had said about him was true? The problem was, she didn't really know his name except as "Uncle Denny."

In a search-engine box, she typed in *Tara Padgett*, *Troy Hansford*, and *Harvard*. Looking through the results she found an obituary for a Denholm Whitfield in the *Harvard Gazette*. Words describing the Maya scholar included "gifted," "avid conversationalist," "intellectual," and "dedicated." His birth year was given as 1918, and only Tara and Troy were listed as his "surviving family."

Jillian sighed. So he was the real deal. Where did that leave her? She typed *Quinten Straub* into the search box. There was a link to an obituary in a Washington, D.C., newspaper. It stated that he was the curator of one of the preeminent collections of Mayan artifacts in the country, and other facts about his life that she hadn't known, including his family—a wife and two sons. She said a little prayer for them.

She wondered what he might have been able to tell her about the vase if he had lived to meet her at the restaurant. She tried to recall his last words to her. He had called the vase "interesting." It seemed a rather banal description for something worth . . . worth what? She'd paid three dollars for it. Was it worth more? She wished he had just come out and told her then what he knew. But then he wasn't expecting to be murdered.

She had one more person to try. She typed in *Dr. Middleton.* She couldn't remember his first name except that it had been something unusual. The search wasn't helpful as she got a list of everything from pediatricians to dentists. He could be any one of those. She tried again, adding the word, *Maya.*

Bingo! There were few results, but she clicked on one which took her to a webpage for a research library in D.C. where she found Hunahpu Middleton listed as a research fellow. Following his name were, "PhD, Oxford University, UK, Pre-Columbian Studies, Maya Epigraphy: A Study of Knowledge in the Making."

She looked at the name of the library listed at the top of the page—Rothesay Pines. Where had she seen that name before? She opened a new tab and then opened her browsing history. She clicked on Quinten Straub's obituary and quickly scanned it until her eyes fell on the name of the museum he worked for: Rothesay Pines.

She sat back stunned. Here was the link that had been missing. Two men had come to Moss Hollow who both worked within the same organization, albeit in different areas. Could it be a case of professional jealousy? Perhaps Dr. Middleton had followed Quinten and an argument had ensued. Maybe it was an accident. Did Dr. Middleton really have something he wanted to tell her, or could it be that he was tying up loose ends? But he said he had spoken to the authorities—the killer wouldn't do that. Unless it was a lie meant to reassure her that it was safe to meet with him.

Possibilities whirled around in her brain. She wondered if she should call Agent Calloway, but what could she say? She had no real evidence of anything. *No, that's not true. There is one thing,* she told herself. She had evidence in the back of her car that the vase had not been destroyed.

The sound of something breaking coming from the direction of the kitchen brought Jillian to her feet. She rushed there only to find Bertie heading to the corner where the broom and dustpan were kept.

"What happened?" It was out of her mouth before she could stop herself. She could see scattered pieces of a coffee mug on the floor, so she already knew what the answer would be, and the tone in which it would be delivered.

"What does it look like? I dropped a mug."

"Here, let me sweep that up for you." Jillian reached out to take the broom from Bertie's hand.

Bertie wasn't about to give it to her. "I'm not on death's door yet. I'm perfectly capable of cleaning up my own messes."

"That's not what I meant. I just wanted to help, and I think you know that." Jillian tried to keep the frustration out of her voice.

Bertie's tone softened. "I do know that." She handed the broom to Jillian. "Have at it. I guess I got out of bed on the wrong side this morning." As Jillian proceeded to sweep up, Bertie said, "You're up early. I thought you'd sleep in."

"I intended to, but my brain decided otherwise."

"Yes, once early rising becomes a habit, it's hard to overcome, even if you want to. How was your evening?"

"Well, I have to say, it was a mixed bag. It started out good, and then it was not so good, and then it was good again, and at the end, it was very good."

To avoid any chance that Bertie might see her blush at the thought of Hunter's good-night kiss, Jillian took the dustpan from her and bent over to brush the pieces into it. She hoped that her answer wouldn't raise questions. She wasn't ready to tell Bertie that she had been right to be leery of Troy Hansford. But she needn't have worried. When she stood upright, Bertie just raised her eyebrows and smiled. Jillian wondered if she'd looked out last night and seen that it was Hunter who brought her home. She wouldn't put it past her. Better to divert.

"I talked to Burton Puckett last evening."

"How is Burton? I don't see him in the bakery as often since he retired."

"He seemed to be fine." Jillian hesitated, dumping the contents of the dustpan into the trash can. "I asked him what he had to do with Aunt Cornelia's dislike of Moss Holloween."

Bertie unexpectedly laughed. "Did you now? And what did he say?"

"Well, he didn't want to say anything at first, but then he decided to tell me."

"I've never understood why Cornelia continues to hold on to that to this day. I've tried to talk to her about it different times through the years, but she just won't have it. You heard her when I just mention Burton's name. I don't know where she gets her stubbornness."

Jillian resisted the urge to say that was a case of the pot calling the kettle black as she put the broom and dustpan back in their places. "Maybe I can get Aunt Cornelia to talk about it."

"Talk about what?" It was Cornelia, walking toward the doorway to the kitchen.

"Uh . . ." Jillian wasn't sure if this was the right time.

While Jillian was looking for the words to say, Bertie reached up into the cabinet, retrieved a mug, and then filled it with coffee. She walked past Cornelia, heading toward the living room. "I'll leave you two to it."

Thanks, Bertie. Out loud she said, "May I get you a cup of coffee?"

"That would be lovely, dear. And would you put a little of that hazelnut-flavored creamer in it?"

While Cornelia headed for the breakfast nook, Jillian grabbed two mugs—she'd left hers next to her computer—and fixed two coffees and carried them to the table.

Cornelia seemed to have woken up in a better mood than Bertie had. She patted Jillian on the hand. "Now, what would you like to talk about?"

Jillian almost said "About Burton Puckett," but stopped herself remembering that the very name had pretty much stopped all conversation the last time it was mentioned. She decided on a different tack. "I saw an old friend of yours at the dance last night who said that you used to like to dress up for Moss Holloween."

Cornelia stopped mid-sip. "Oh? Who was that?"

"This person said that he used to have a crush on you."

Cornelia scoffed. "You mean Burton Puckett, don't you? He was a horrible boy, and I'll never forgive him for what he and that group of hooligans he ran around with did. I suppose he told you what they did?"

Jillian nodded. "He wasn't going to at first, and he only told me because I wanted to know so that I could help you get past this grudge you've been hanging onto for all these years."

"I don't think I can Jillian. I'll never forget seeing Burton and that Tom Wilkes sneering at me for believing. Before that evening, I had never told anyone about my gift of being able to contact the spirit world. Not even Bertie. She was always the down-to-earth one who wouldn't believe in a ghost if one came and sat on her lap. But when she saw it too, I thought it was safe—that she would back me up. But when it turned out to be just a trick, I couldn't take it back."

"And no one's asking you to. But it's been over sixty years now, Aunt Cornelia, and whatever Burton Puckett may have done in the past, he's just a nice old man now. He still has a sense of humor, but . . ."

Cornelia interrupted. "Ha! You call that a sense of humor? See, you're just like the rest. 'Just laugh about it and let it go.' Well, I can't and I won't, not if I live to be a hundred!" She picked up her mug and swept out of the room.

Normally, the three residents of Belle Haven drove to church together, but Jillian made the excuse that she needed to stop at the Padgett's house on the way home, so she was going to drive separately. Cornelia, for one, didn't object.

Later, after the church service was over, Jillian walked with Savannah to her car and told her about the information she had found on the Internet. The conversation rolled around to her two o'clock meeting with Dr. Middleton at the library.

"Listen, I'm going to be at the library too, keeping an eye on you and him," said Savannah. "Maybe we should notify the police."

"And possibly end up with Gooder Jones on the scene? No thank you."

Savannah looked up toward the steps of the church where Laura Lee was in conversation with Bertie. "We could tell Laura Lee. She's off duty today, but I know she'd come and help with, well, whatever needs helping with."

"I don't think it will be necessary. It's a public place. And you'll be there. If it turns out he threatens me or something, I'll give you a signal and you can call the police."

"What sort of signal?"

"I don't know." She considered. "I'll pull on my ear like this, I guess." She demonstrated.

"I still think we need to let law enforcement know. Will you at least call Agent Calloway before you meet this man?"

"Yes—I promise I'll give her a call as soon as I get home," answered Jillian. "I'll probably just get her voicemail today, but I'll tell her about the vase too. It won't take me long at the Padgett's,

177

and then I'll go home for lunch and make some excuse to Bertie and Cornelia about going to the library."

"Don't you think you should tell them?"

"I don't want to worry them. It will be perfectly safe."

Savannah looked unconvinced.

"Look, if I can just meet this man and find out what he knows without involving them, especially Bertie, all the better. I think the break-in is still weighing on her mind, though she doesn't say so. You know Bertie."

Savannah laughed. "Yes, I do."

"Well, I'll see you about a quarter to two then?"

"I'll be there."

Jillian got in her car, and once she left the church parking lot, it wasn't long until she turned into the Padgett's driveway. She got out of the car and looked around. The grass had gotten a little shaggy, but other than that, things looked the same. She unlocked the front door, and inside, she pressed numbers on a keypad to disable the alarm. She would have to remember to punch them in again to reset the alarm when she left.

The entry of the brand-new house led into an open-concept living area and dining room, with the kitchen connected just beyond by a butler's pantry. The kitchen was equipped with all the latest styles and gadgets, and there was an adjacent family room with a big-screen TV and furniture that looked like it was made for people who were nine feet tall.

The Padgett's post-modern decor reminded her somewhat of her apartment in California. When she lived there, she had preferred that style, but being back at Belle Haven, and with all the redecorating and updates they'd achieved so far, she was satisfied that not everything had to be sleek and new. There was something to be said for the Southern elegance of lush fabrics and antiques.

She checked the plants, finding only one that had gotten

a bit dry. She took care of it and had just put away the small watering can under the kitchen sink when she heard a click and the sound of the front door opening. Then she heard Troy's voice saying, "Hello?"

Jillian put her hand over her heart in relief. "I'm in here, Troy."

She heard his steps and then saw him in just a few moments, wearing that same smile that had first won her over when she met him. Even though she had been upset with him for basically throwing her over for Raeanne last night, she couldn't really be angry with him. She had only asked him out on a whim, and maybe there was an attraction between those two that just couldn't be denied. As it was, she was quite content with how the evening had ended.

"I didn't expect to see you again," said Jillian. "I thought you were on your way home."

"I am. I got a late start. But, anyway, I decided to drop off the clothes I borrowed at Belle Haven on the way, so I don't have to mail them to you, but then I saw your car here. I'll pay you for the dry cleaning."

"Oh, that's not necessary. I appreciate your willingness to go with me to our little fancy-dress ball. I hope you had fun."

"I did." He hesitated. "Look, I wanted to apologize about last night. I just . . . I mean, there's always been kind of an attraction between Raeanne and me, but, believe me, I never did anything about it before, and I guess when I found out she was getting divorced I just . . . Well, anyway, I guess we'll all be getting back to reality now."

Jillian smiled. "I guess so."

He made a move to leave, but hesitated. "Oh, I was wondering about the dumpster thing that guy from last night asked about."

"That was Ike Puckett. He owns the hardware store next to the bakery."

"Yeah, he asked about an earring, but then your friend said you weren't looking for that. You said you were checking on something. What was it? You mentioned the bakery had been broken into. Did you find some sort of evidence?"

"Well, sort of. It may turn out that your uncle's vase wasn't broken after all. I guess I really shouldn't talk about it until I've turned it over to the police."

"Oh, you haven't called them yet?"

She was about to say no, when she heard the front door click again. She and Troy exchanged a puzzled look. She headed through the butler's pantry and into the dining room with Troy following. She had just rounded the large dining table when she stopped suddenly, upon seeing the man who had entered the house. It was Hunahpu Middleton.

Jillian felt like her heart stopped. "What are you doing here?"

Dr. Middleton cast a cold look toward her. "This is nothing to do with you. You should leave." He pointed at Troy. "It's him I want to talk to right now."

Jillian turned around to look at Troy who had stopped on the far side of the table. He looked as confused as she felt. She said, "Look, I'm not going anywhere. You have no right to be here." She spoke with more confidence than she felt. She asked Troy. "Do you know him?"

"I never set eyes on him in my life."

Dr. Middleton sputtered, "And you'll wish you never had." With that he stepped in the direction of Troy in a threatening manner, and without even thinking, Jillian grabbed the vase of dried flowers that sat in the center of the dining table and crashed it over the back of Dr. Middleton's head.

He fell hard to the floor.

Troy looked at her, stunned. "What have you done?"

"Oh, my God." She knelt down to see if he was all right. She held her own breath until she ascertained that he was still alive. "Oh, thank God. He's breathing. It doesn't appear that it broke his skin. I think he's just knocked out."

"Maybe we should tie him up while we still can."

"Good idea. There's some twine in the kitchen. I'll get it." Jillian jumped up and practically ran into the kitchen. When she returned, Troy took the twine and while he was tying up the man, Jillian felt in her pocket for her phone. "Rats. I left my phone in the car. We should call the police. I'll go and get it." She started to move, but Troy said, "Don't bother, I've got mine. I'll call as soon as I'm sure he's not going anywhere."

After a minute, he stood up and took his phone out of his pocket and looked at the screen a moment. "You know, I think we can settle this without the police."

"What do you mean?"

"Simply this." Troy put the phone back in his pocket and stepped toward Jillian, grabbing her wrists and twisting her arms behind her. The pain traveled up her arms to her shoulders as she struggled to get loose.

"Troy! What are you doing?"

His voice was calm as he forced her into one of the dining chairs and began tying her arms and legs to the chair. "I'd hoped I wouldn't have to do this, Jillian. I like you. I really do. But apparently you're the sort who just can't leave well-enough alone. And now this gentleman, whoever he is, has provided an opportunity for me to tie up a few loose ends, if you'll pardon the pun."

"Troy, I don't under . . ." A glimmer of a thought began to come through. She remembered the open gate at the school, and the image of Troy and Raeanne in what was supposed to be a locked classroom. How did they get past those barriers, unless either Troy or Raeanne had picked the lock? She was certain it was him. "You're the one who broke into the bakery and trashed it, aren't you? And you took the vase too." She didn't wait for confirmation. She knew she was right. "But why? If you wanted it, why didn't you just ask me for it? I would have given it to you. For that matter, why didn't you just keep it in the first place? It was yours and Tara's to begin with anyway."

"It's . . . complicated. I didn't really understand its value until after I read Uncle Denny's journals. Like you, I thought it was just a reproduction."

"It's not?"

"No. It's the real thing."

"So, I suppose it's worth a lot of money. Is it really worth all this?"

"As an artifact, it's worth several thousand dollars, but it has an added value. According to one of Uncle Denny's journals, the inscriptions on it are a key to a real treasure. Something they found back in 1937."

"Troy, this is crazy. If you want the vase it's yours, and I promise we won't press charges. Just let me go, and we can talk about this."

"I wish it were that simple."

"Of course it's that simple," said Jillian. "It's not like you've mur—"

She just stopped herself from saying "murdered anyone," when the truth of the matter hit her. "You. It was you that murdered Quinten Straub."

Troy's normal façade seemed to break. "I didn't intend to. It . . . it just happened. I only knew I had to stop him. He came to see me in Athens that morning and had a signed document from Uncle Denny that postdated the will, leaving the vase and the other items he'd kept in his room, including his journals, to an associate of his. I told him that Tara had it all, just to buy some time. I knew she and Paul were away. I came to Moss Hollow, disguised and in a car that someone had traded in that was bound for auction the next day."

Jillian wondered for a moment why he was telling her so much. But it didn't take long for her to realize what it meant. He intended that she would never have the chance to tell what she knew. She would hear his confession, but instead of seeking absolution, he would compound it with two more murders. She tried to work on the knots he had tied without him noticing, but they were so tight, she didn't seem to be making any headway.

"I beat him here to Tara's house, and then from here I followed him to the town square. When I saw where he parked his car, I waited for him to return to it. I hit him from behind, hoping I could steal the document, but he hit his head on the concrete. I knew he was dead, and there was nothing to be done, so I reached in his jacket and took it."

That seemed to be the end of his tale. He looked at Jillian with something akin to regret, but it passed. He left the room without speaking, heading into the kitchen.

Jillian wondered how much of his story was for effect, to "handle" her, as he would say. Surely if he followed Quinten with the intention of stopping him, he meant to kill him all along. She could hear Troy opening drawers and the clatter as he rifled through them. Her heart sank as she wondered if he was looking for a knife to finish the job. Dr. Middleton moaned and seemed to stir a little. She felt bad about hitting him. How had she gotten this so wrong? Now it would cost them both their lives.

She was surprised to see Troy return with a box of matches and a pillar candle. He set the candle on the far end of the table away from her. He took out one of the matches and poised to strike it. "I'm afraid I'll be leaving rather abruptly after I strike this match, Jillian, so before I do, I just want you to know that I'm really sorry I have to do this."

"Then don't do it Troy. It's not too late." Did he intend to burn down the house?

"I'm afraid it is." He looked around the room. "Too bad about Tara and Paul's house too, but I'm afraid when the natural gas from the stove burners I just turned on reaches this room, there won't be much left afterward." He looked at her again. "I won't say au revoir this time, as we will never see each other again. So, this time, it's good-bye for good." He struck the match, lit the candle, and ran out the door, slamming it behind him.

20

Jillian immediately began trying to scoot the chair she was tied to nearer to the candle to blow it out. Not that it would stop the gas from suffocating them when the house filled to capacity or possibly exploding when it reached another ignition source. She had no idea how long that would take. It was a moot point unless she could blow out the candle. She had to keep trying.

Dr. Middleton stirred again. She shouted his name several times to try to rouse him. He shook his head and groaned. He lifted his head. "What happened?"

"I don't have time to explain, Dr. Middleton. The stove in the kitchen is turned on to release gas. Can you get loose?"

While he struggled on the floor, Jillian continued trying to scoot toward the candle, but it was slow going because the chair was so heavy. She felt the twine cut into her skin as she tried to move, and it felt like her arms were being pulled from their sockets. Her heart was beating so fast, she thought her chest would explode.

She was not much nearer when the front door flung open and Agent Calloway burst in.

"Blow out the candle!" Jillian shouted. "The gas in the kitchen is on!"

Agent Calloway ran to extinguish the candle, and then, with her sleeve over her mouth and nose, she went into the kitchen. Shortly, Agent Calloway reentered the room, coughing. She withdrew a folding knife from her pocket and opened it to cut Dr. Middleton's bonds first and then Jillian's. The three of them ran through the front door.

Outside, Jillian saw Troy, handcuffed with his arms around a tree. She could hear sirens, and soon, both the police and fire department arrived.

Questions swirled through Jillian's mind, but in the hubbub that ensued there was no one who had time to give her answers. While the fire department moved Jillian and Dr. Middleton a safe distance away, Agent Calloway uncuffed and re-cuffed Troy, escorting him to the back of one of the police cars parked down the road.

Jillian and Dr. Middleton stood side by side, watching but not speaking to one another. It wasn't a cold day, but Jillian shivered, her arms crossed over her chest. An EMT brought a blanket and put it over her shoulders, saying, "You're going to be okay. It's just shock." He asked Dr. Middleton a few questions and returned shortly with a cold pack, which he held to the back of his head, wincing as he did so.

Agent Calloway joined them. Jillian couldn't help herself. She flung her arms around the woman. "Thank you! You saved our lives."

The woman extracted herself from Jillian's embrace, wearing a grim smile. "You should thank Dr. Middleton. He was the one who called me."

Jillian couldn't disguise her surprise. "Thank you, Dr. Middleton. I'm so sorry that I hit you on the head."

Now it was Agent Calloway's turn to be surprised. "*You* hit him? Why?"

"I thought he was threatening Troy."

"I was threatening him, but not with violence," said Dr. Middleton. "I had intended to hold him until Agent Calloway arrived. I've been tailing him since I came to town three days ago. When I saw him follow you into the house, I had a bad feeling about it. I had asked Agent Calloway to come to our meeting at the library, since I could tell that you didn't trust me, so she was already on her way to Moss Hollow."

Jillian said, "I didn't know what Troy had done until after he tied me up. He confessed everything, thinking I would never have the chance to tell anyone."

"That's going to be helpful," said Agent Calloway. "We'll need a complete statement from you." She looked at Jillian, seeing her still-distraught state. "Tomorrow is soon enough."

Jillian looked at Dr. Middleton. "I still don't understand where you fit in all of this."

Dr. Middleton removed the ice pack from his head and began, "I'm an archeologist—an epigraphist, specifically, which is a person who studies ancient inscriptions. I was a student and a friend of Denholm Whitfield. When he passed away, I was on a dig in the Yucatán, and so it was a bit later, when I was in Belize visiting my parents, that I received word that he had died and a sealed letter from his attorney. When I read that Denny wanted me to have his collection of memorabilia and his journals, I faxed the letter to my colleague, Quinten Straub, and asked him to look into it. I had seen the vase before, and thought it would be a good addition to the museum. Quinten was my friend. I had no idea I was sending him to his death."

"You couldn't have known," said Jillian. "But why didn't Mr. Whitfield tell his lawyer that he wanted you to have those things?"

"I don't know. The letter was dated about the time he went into the nursing home. He may have intended to alter the will also, but forgot. I couldn't really say what happened."

"So, the first time I saw you in the bakery . . . ?"

"I had just come from identifying Quinten's body. That's where I met Agent Calloway. By that time, I had flown to D.C. His wife asked me if I would officially identify the body so I drove down to Atlanta."

Agent Calloway took over. "When Dr. Middleton arrived and told us his part of the story, and that Troy Hansford was involved, that sent up all sorts of red flags. We've been investigating him for black marketeering. He's very cagey. We've suspected that he's been acting as a middle man, using his dealership as a front to receive stolen artwork from overseas and then passing it on to others who sell it to private collectors, but we've never had enough evidence to arrest him."

Jillian looked to Dr. Middleton. "Troy said his uncle's old journals stated that the inscriptions on the vase were a key to a treasure. Is that true?"

Dr. Middleton shook his head. "I guess it depends on how you define 'treasure.' That particular piece eventually opened up a new pathway to the understanding of other inscriptions that had not yet been translated, or had been translated incorrectly. It was almost like finding a Rosetta stone—a treasure beyond price, but the treasure is knowledge, not gold or jewels."

"It's funny. Troy said something similar to me when I asked him if his uncle ever found treasure. I guess he thought he was covering up when, in fact, he spoke the truth without knowing it," said Jillian. "Why wasn't it in a museum if it's so valuable?"

"In the early days, artifacts that were uncovered didn't always end up where they should have. Denny saw that piece on his first expedition in 1937, but it somehow disappeared from the team's findings. He came across it again years later and bought it for a considerable price. He brought it back to Harvard, where we worked on the inscriptions together. I guess he wanted to keep it in his possession for the memories it held for him—all the way back to when he was just nineteen and on his first expedition. I think leaving it to me was a way for him to honor our friendship, knowing that I would want to see it placed in a museum where it belongs. But I guess it's too late for that since it was destroyed. Bloody shame, that."

Jillian's eyes grew large. "Oh my goodness! I completely forgot. It wasn't destroyed. At least I don't think so. I have the proof in the trunk of my car. I don't know for sure where the vase is now, but I suspect that if you search Troy's car thoroughly, you'll find it."

A bit later, after Agent Calloway found the vase intact in a secret compartment in Troy's car, Jillian was on her way home. She glanced toward the passenger seat at the top hat she had placed on top of the other clothing she had lent Troy. She told herself she would put it back in the box in the room on the third floor and hope to never set eyes on it again.

Just as she pulled into the drive at Belle Haven, her phone rang. It was Savannah.

"Where are you? I'm at the library, and it's two o'clock already. There's no sign of that guy yet."

"Oh, Savannah! I'm sorry. I should have called you to let you know."

"Know what?"

"Look, I just got home to Belle Haven. Can you come over? I've got a lot to tell you."

After Savannah arrived at Belle Haven, Jillian asked Bertie and Cornelia to join them in the living room where she explained what had happened and the reasons behind it. When she finally got to the part where the vase was found, exhaustion overtook her and she excused herself to go upstairs to take a nap.

About six o'clock Jillian heard a soft rap on her door. She stretched and sat up, leaning back on the headboard.

"Come in."

The door opened slowly, and Bertie peeked around the edge. "Supper's almost ready. Do you think you can eat something?"

Jillian breathed in deeply. "You know. I'm famished. I just realized I didn't have any lunch."

Bertie walked over and sat on the edge of the bed. "Besides that, how are you feeling?"

"Oh, like an idiot, I guess. I can't believe I fell for that act again."

"What 'act' is that?"

"Oh, I don't know, a handsome face, a personable façade, whatever."

"Did you fall for it? I saw that Hunter Greyson brought you home from the dance."

Jillian smiled. "I thought you might have. Well, all I can say is that your first reaction to Troy was spot on. I never imagined he had anything to do with—what did you call it the other day?—murder and mayhem?"

"Why would you think he was capable of all that? You only knew him a few days."

"For some reason, it seemed longer—like I'd known him a long time. I guess I'm too gullible."

"Maybe a certain amount of gullibility isn't a bad thing. What's the alternative? Do you want to be always skeptical?"

"No, but I don't want to be a doormat either."

"And you're not. Far from it. By all means follow your instincts, but don't build a wall because you think you might get hurt. That's the risk you have to take to live in this world. Someone is bound to let you down, but on the other side, you gain new friends and maybe more. Troy made his own choices, and he's going to pay for it. But you? You're going to be okay."

"You think so?"

"Of course. You have Belle blood running through your veins. And we're strong women, in case you didn't notice." Bertie stood up. "Now, before you come down, change your clothes for the bonfire. And comb your hair and fix your makeup too. We're expecting some company after dinner, so hurry up."

"I don't think I want to go to the bonfire this year."

"Nonsense. You get ready and come down to dinner." She looked at her watch. "You have fifteen minutes." With that, she left and closed the door.

Twelve minutes later, Jillian entered the breakfast nook where Bertie and Cornelia were already at the table waiting for her. Bertie smiled approvingly. "After what could have happened today, I think we need to say a special prayer of thanks that we still have our Jillian with us." They joined hands and bowed their heads.

With Possum curled at her feet, Cornelia stood washing the last few things that wouldn't fit or were never placed in the dishwasher while Jillian dried. Bertie had just finished putting away the last of the leftovers when the doorbell rang. She practically shouted, "I'll get it" and was out of the room before either Cornelia or Jillian could say anything.

Jillian heard male voices, and in just a couple of minutes, Bertie came to the door to summon her and Cornelia to the living room.

"Who's here?" asked Jillian as she hung up the drying towel.

"You'll see." Bertie looked at her sister. "You leave those things and come along too."

Cornelia shook her head, but started drying her hands anyway. "You know, just because you're two minutes older than me, you've always thought you could boss me around. It gets kind of old after eighty years."

"Oh, quit your complaining and come on."

They followed Bertie, single file: Cornelia, then Possum, and Jillian bringing up the rear.

When they reached the living room, Jillian wasn't all that surprised to see Hunter standing next to the fireplace. She suspected her grandmother might do something like that. But she was surprised to see another person. It was Burton Puckett, sitting in an armchair, a smile on his face.

Cornelia seemed to be stunned and unable to speak for a few moments, but Jillian could see that she was building up steam. Just as she was about to blow, Possum leaped past Cornelia to run and jump into Burton's lap, putting a paw on one of his shoulders and vigorously licking his face.

Cornelia was stunned. Burton laughed. "I'm sorry for not standing, ladies, but I seem to have a new friend here." He rubbed Possum's head and back, and the sound of the cat's purring could be heard by everyone in the room.

Smiling, Bertie led her sister to the sofa where she sat down slowly, still trying to process what she was seeing. The cat, whom

194 Mary M. O'Donnell

she was certain channeled her late husband's spirit, seemed to adore a man she'd despised for over sixty years.

She spoke, but it seemed to be more to herself than to the rest of them. "O dear me. It's a sign, a sign from Raymond. Could I have been wrong all these years?"

"I thought it would be nice if we could all go to the bonfire together," said Bertie. "I've fixed up a picnic basket with snacks, and I've already loaded it and some folding chairs in the van. You will join us, won't you, Cornelia?"

Cornelia seemed to snap out of her fog. "Me? Go to the Moss Holloween bonfire?" Jillian could tell she was about to say no when Possum laid down and rolled over in Burton's lap for a belly rub, which he supplied. She looked confused, but said, "Maybe it's time I did."

Burton looked up from Possum to Cornelia. "Please, Cornelia, accept my deepest apology for what I did when I was young and foolish. I never should have done it."

It seemed to take all that Cornelia could muster to say it, but she rose to the occasion. "I accept your apology, Burton. We'll put the past behind us and never speak of it again."

"Agreed," said Burton.

"Well, now, that's all settled," said Bertie, all but clapping her hands. "I say we should get going so we can get a good spot before they light the fire."

After they put on their coats, they went out the back door, heading for the porte cochere where the van was parked. Hunter led the way with Aunt Cornelia's arm looped through his, followed by Bertie. Jillian was walking next to Burton. When she leaned close to Burton and whispered, "How did you do it?" she smelled the strong odor of bacon grease on his cheek. He just winked at her. "But how did—" She didn't have to finish the question with "you know?" because before she could say it, Bertie turned around to wink at her too.

Bittersweet Demise
Book Six Recipe

Spicy Cinnamon Truffles

½ cup heavy whipping cream
1 teaspoon cinnamon
⅛ -¼ teaspoon cayenne pepper
   (to taste)
½ teaspoon vanilla

8 ounces milk chocolate,
   chopped
Dark chocolate or cocoa
   powder for coating

Instructions

1. To make the ganache, combine cream, cinnamon, cayenne, and vanilla in a saucepan. Bring to a simmer over medium heat. Remove from heat.

2. Stir in 8 ounces chopped chocolate until melted and smooth.

3. Place mixture in a small bowl and cover. Refrigerate for at least four hours.

4. Line a tray with waxed paper. Working rapidly, form ganache into approximately 1-inch balls, setting on waxed paper. Chill at least one hour.

5. Dip balls in melted chocolate, placing on waxed paper to set, or coat with cocoa powder.

Up to this point, we've been doing all the writing. Now it's *your* turn!

Tell us what you think about this book, the characters, the bad guy, or anything else you'd like to share with us about this series. We can't wait to hear from *you!*

Log on to give us your feedback at:
https://www.surveymonkey.com/r/ChocolateShoppe

Writing the Trail

Writing the Trail

FIVE WOMEN'S FRONTIER NARRATIVES

* * * * *

Deborah Lawrence

UNIVERSITY OF IOWA PRESS, IOWA CITY

University of Iowa Press, Iowa City 52242
Copyright © 2006 by the University of Iowa Press
http://www.uiowapress.org
All rights reserved
Printed in the United States of America

Design by Kimberly Glyder

The University of Iowa Press is a member of
Green Press Initiative and is committed to
preserving natural resources.

Printed on acid-free paper

Library of Congress Cataloging-in-Publication Data
Lawrence, Deborah.
    Writing the trail: five women's frontier narratives / by
Deborah Lawrence.
        p.   cm.
    Includes bibliographical references and index.
    ISBN-13: 978-1-58729-509-6 (cloth)
    ISBN-10: 1-58729-509-1 (cloth)
        1. Frontier and pioneer life — West (U.S.) — Sour
2. Women pioneers — West (U.S.) — Biography.
3. Frontier and pioneer life in literature.   4. First person
narrative — History and criticism.   5. American literature —
Women authors — History and criticism.   6. Women — West
(U.S.) — History — 19th century — Sources.   7. Sex role
literature.   8. Sex role — West (U.S.) — History — 19th
century — Sources.   9. West (U.S.) — History — 1848–18
Sources.   10. West (U.S.) — History — 1860–1890 — Sour
I. Title.
F596.L425   2006   2006045612
978 — dc22

06   07   08   09   10   C   5   4   3   2   1

To Jon, my traveling companion

Contents

Acknowledgments

I made my first trip on the Overland Trail eight summers ago. I saw the country firsthand from Independence, Missouri, to Oregon City. Using diaries, reminiscences, and letters of women who went west between 1836 and 1857, I followed the emigrants from campsite to campsite and landmark to landmark. By the conclusion of the two-month trip, I had become a confirmed trail addict, and as a result, when I returned to my classes in Southern California, I began to teach courses in frontier and environmental literature. With the aid and encouragement of my students at California State University, Fullerton, I started the research and writing for this book.

Work on the project has been supported by many sources. The insightful suggestions of Susan Naramore Maher and Jean Chapman have enhanced the readability of this work. I have benefited from my conversations with Robert V. Hine, who graciously shared information on Sarah Bayliss Royce. I am grateful to the staff at the Cumberland County Historical Society, the St. Louis Historical Society, the Henry E. Huntington Library, the University of California–Los Angeles Library, the Nevada County Library, the Society of California Pioneers, the New-York Historical Society, the Newport Beach Public Library, and the California State Historical Library.

My thanks go to the *American Women's Prose Writers* series for granting me permission to publish here a revised version of an article that first appeared on their pages.

The four maps in this book are original works, and for these I offer my profound thanks to mapmaker Tom Jonas. I would also like to acknowledge the encouragement and assistance of Leslee Anderson, Prasenjit Gupta, Charlotte Wright, Karen Copp, and Holly Carver at the University of Iowa Press.

Finally, my most heartfelt gratitude goes to my husband, Jon Lawrence, without whose continuing support and encouragement this book never would have been completed. It is to him this book is dedicated.

Writing the Trail

Introduction

In this study, I examine five American women's narratives dealing with the westward movement and the West between 1846 and 1870. These textual journeys are involved with what Eric Leed calls "the dialectics of gendering" encountered by women trying to adapt their inherited codes of female stasis to the challenges they faced journeying to and living in the West. In taking their journeys, Susan Shelby Magoffin, Sarah Bayliss Royce, Louise Smith Clappe, Eliza Burhans Farnham, and Lydia Spencer Lane move out of their traditional position as objects of masculine culture and question the range of privileges and restrictions authorized by gendered spatial orders.

Nineteenth-century literature played an important role in the creation and maintenance of the ideology of separate masculine and feminine spatial spheres.[1] Even postmodern critics tend to consider nineteenth-century women's writings as confirmations of home and stability, supporting what Gillian Brown has called the "celebrated stillness of nineteenth-century women." Consequently, they often overlook aspects of women's textualizations of themselves that are dynamic and contingent on movement through space. As more and more women's narratives of westward expansion are being rediscovered, historians are having to reconsider earlier patriarchal interpretations of the West.[2] Women's accounts of westward expansion modify the earlier conventional boundaries of their spheres of influence.

Women can no longer be viewed as simply representatives of home, church, and constraint. The strategic deployment of motion and stasis in their narratives functions as a sign of contradiction that questions basic gender assumptions.[3] Even when westering women sought to affirm stable borders, their texts more frequently demonstrate the unstable nature of self-representation and the permeable outlines of subjectivity. Each of the five narratives in this study is a history of transculturation and subjectivity under revision. Instead of portraying "stillness," Magoffin, Royce, Clappe, Farnham, and Lane depict geographical, spiritual, and psychological movement. By tracing their journeys, we bear witness to their awakening to selfhood and to a new understanding of gender roles on the nineteenth-century frontier. These women's personas are directly related to the narrative movement: their travels invite them to think differently and to see anew. Leaving home is a rite of passage and a precursor of their inner enlightenment.

Increasingly over the last two decades, historians have found new significance in letters, diaries, and journals written by women about their experiences in the American West. Current scholarship on western women is opening up views that have long been obscured by the identification of the American West with maleness as it has been represented in both academia and popular culture.[4] In particular, historians like Julie Jeffrey, Susan Armitage, Glenda Riley, and Elizabeth Jameson believe that only by identifying the differences between a woman's and a man's perceptions of the frontier experience can women's stories be accurately told. In response, a considerable body of feminist scholarship has been developing methodologies appropriate to women's narratives.[5]

The issue of gender in western history has been articulated in Annette Kolodny's *The Land Before Her*, Lillian Schlissel's *Women's Diaries of the Westward Journey*, and John Mack Faragher's *Women and Men on the Overland Trail*. Even more recently, works such as Brigitte Georgi-Findlay's *The Frontiers of Women's Writing*, Virginia Scharff's *Twenty Thousand Roads: Women, Movement, and the West*, and Krista Comer's *Landscapes of the New West: Gender and Geography in Contemporary American Women's Writing* have elaborated on and expanded this discussion of women and the exigencies of moving west. Additionally, an increasing number of feminist scholars, geographers among them, are exploring the intricate connection of space and place with gender and the construction of gender relations. Feminist geographers—take Doreen Massey, Joanne P. Sharp, and Linda McDowell, for examples—have radically affected our understanding of the links between place and gender. By incorporating women's source materials in their discussion of the journey experience and by exploring the ways women's personal responses to the environment are different from men's, these scholars have changed our thinking about travel and geography.

Narratives by westering women depict day-to-day existence in the frontier West. They include details about the living conditions seldom found in the more formal, public writings by men, which is precisely why women's diaries, letters, memoirs, and autobiographies are continuing to be ignored by those of us in English departments. Despite recent studies on western history, women's diaries, journals, and letters are considered by literary scholars as subliterary—pieces of local color, at best. This attitude needs to change because the new western scholarship is rewriting the literary history of the United States.[6] We who teach American literature courses can no longer look to Irving, Cooper, and Parkman as the major mythographers of the nineteenth-century literature of westward expansion without also considering the alternative versions of the myth provided by writers like Magoffin, Royce, Clappe, Farnham, and Lane. This is sufficient reason for literary scholars to join the historians and examine, theoretically and critically, these works that have been outside canonical categories.

Canonical orthodoxy does not give us an adequate comprehension of the American frontier. To fully appreciate its complexity, we must look to noncanonical women's diaries and journals that have for too long been ignored by those of us in literature. When I teach my frontier literature classes, my students relate easily to men's western texts. Their challenge is with the women diarists of expansionist enterprise, women who break the stereotype promulgated by television, movies, and canonical western literature. I have written this book with these students in mind. Women's western writings create conflicting versions of the myth of the American West. And this shouldn't be disturbing: their inclusion will provide a broader perspective and a richer variety of texts than those that currently compose our standard canon. In addition, seen through the grid of women's western writings, familiar, canonical works can be explored afresh.

My subject is neither social history nor literary history, but a literary analysis of the way in which five women's westering journeys encouraged their change and the way their growth is related to the narrative movement of their texts. My decision to treat only five narratives derived from my desire to focus the lens more closely on a few women rather than provide the reader with a broader and consequently less detailed glimpse. Examining only five writers, I don't pretend to give any kind of comprehensive overview of women's responses to the frontier, but I will give my readers an idea of the richness of these narratives that are waiting to be examined stylistically. All five of the women in my study are compelling writers, and I feel certain their words will find resonance with today's students of western literature.

Historian Gayle Davis maintains that American frontier women's diary writing illustrates the use of writing as "a significant coping mechanism" (5). Arguing that their diaries helped them adjust to the demands of frontier travel, Davis suggests that the act of writing offered women a feeling of reassurance in environments that were new and frightening and in situations where they felt powerless. Additionally, women travelers wrote to reinforce their connection with family and friends, thereby maintaining their self-image as eastern women despite the new geographical environment. The texts in this study dramatize the changes women made in order to comprehend and negotiate frontier conditions in the mid-nineteenth century.

As a researcher with literary interests, I am particularly intrigued by the stylistics that Magoffin, Royce, Clappe, Farnham, and Lane use in their writing to confront challenging frontier environments. Mid-nineteenth-century women who traveled west faced an environment that challenged their self-understanding. Their own sense of who they were was closely connected to the place they had left. Lillian Schlissel points out that the diaries of westering women are a special kind of text because they record the authors' attempts to negotiate the psychological modifications of their identity as they leave the familiar space for the unfamiliar. They used their writing to tailor their surroundings to their own meaning. As Sara Mills argues, "in the physical act of describing the landscape, the narrator is also mastering it" (78). They can't control the frontier, but they have the power of linguistical interpretation. Composing their writing, they gain a kind of self-composure. Additionally, by covering the unfamiliar with familiar interpretations, they are able to assert a form of ownership through language. What their texts reveal is the flexibility of their individual identities as their own sense of who they are changes when they face frontier conditions. In this study, I look at the written accounts of five women describing the process of being shaped by the American West. I show how their growth is directly related to the narrative movement of their texts. I explore the various ways their discourse alters and their personas shift as they are exposed to unstable and ambiguous positions in the frontier. And I explore the relational paradigms they impose on the land in order to make it less forbidding.

All five women in this study feature natural surroundings in their writings. Martha Mitten Allen argues that although men's and women's western texts represent responses to the American frontier landscape, women's romantic rhetoric was particularly eloquent (56). As Sandra Myres has suggested, these exaltations of nature mediated women's sense of dislocation as they traveled into new spaces. In the early part of their journey, travelers like Sarah Bayliss Royce and Susan Shelby Magoffin describe the scenery as inviting and in Magoffin's case, as a garden paradise. This approach helps their transition from their native state to the unfamiliar. As the landscape becomes increasingly alien and the travel more arduous, their romantic language constructions break down, and they identify their emotional and physical discomfort with the landscape. The desolation of the land reinforces their sense of dislocation. Building on studies of grieving, autobiography theory, and ecocriticism for insights into how writing about nature can become a healing act, I explore the way in which Magoffin and Royce translate terrain and self into language and form.[7] Both writers attempt to fortify themselves by turning to God and giving a spiritual interpretation to the land and to the journey itself. Their communion with God in the desert relieves their state of despair and isolation.

Clappe, Farnham, and Lane, on the other hand, discover a new sense of themselves in their frontier surroundings. Surrounded by chaotic and masculine environments, they rarely reflect on their losses. While they are clearly out of place, they discover that the wilderness clarifies and enhances their sense of self-possibility. Their writing validates their transformation and confirms their changed selves. Though seemingly disparate, these five women wrote under similar conditions. Each of them traveled west and faced an external threat to her sense of self. Each woman altered her sense of self and used her writing to confront that alteration. They chose anecdotes that offered them the best plotting possibilities and emphasized the narration rather than the representation. Their narrating personas are personable. They are not detached observers but engaged travelers with an enthusiasm for adventure. And each woman wrote for herself but with an awareness of an audience.

Chapters 1 and 2 deal with two routes west: the Santa Fe Trail and the Overland Trail. I begin my discussion with the narrative of Susan Shelby Magoffin, an eighteen-year-old bride from Kentucky who arrives in Santa Fe on the heels of Stephen Watts Kearny and the Army of the West in 1846. She ventures not only into an unknown geographic landscape of the new republic but also into an unfamiliar cultural frontier. Encountering Hispanics and Indians on the trail, Magoffin finds her attitudes challenged and her worldview enlarged. In effect, the trail becomes for her what those in the Southwest call *la frontera*, a borderland or juncture of cultures.[8] Magoffin learns Spanish, helps clerk in her husband's store, and even assumes the role of train leader during her husband's absence, a role that gives her authority over men.

Chapter 2 explores *A Frontier Lady*, Sarah Bayliss Royce's account of traveling the Overland Trail to the goldfields of California with her husband, Josiah, and her two-year-old daughter, Mary. Royce retrospectively superimposes a narrative design upon her gold rush memoir. Written at the request of her son, Josiah, and not for publication, Royce's narrative was consciously shaped with him in mind. Clearly, she wants more than to re-create her experiences in the West. She desires her words to change her reader's heart. To a son who had rejected Christian philosophy, she fashions a memorandum of God's dealing with her. Her narrative, in this sense, is reminiscent of spiritual autobiography. In the course of her account we witness her increased faith. In times of despair, Royce not only prayed to God, but she also believed she walked with him and saw him "amid the desolation of the lonely plains."

The third and fourth chapters revolve around two accounts of California in the early 1850s. Louise Smith Clappe's letters to her sister back home in the East portray the sequence of events that weans her away from the flashy-looking shops of San Francisco to the hovels and tents of Rich Bar. Driven by an insatiable curiosity and blessed with superb powers of observation, she provides us with the human side of the mining frontier. Unlike many accounts of the gold rush that repress its darker shades, Clappe, who is a witness to the beginnings of racial antagonism and increased lawlessness among the miners, details the tensions. Instead of romanticizing it as a place and time when men were self-sufficient and women were unnecessary, Clappe emphasizes the possibilities the gold rush afforded women. When the time comes to leave the mining camps, she fears that she will no longer be content to live "in a decent, proper, well-behaved house." She concludes by boasting that she has "seen the elephant." Significantly, she uses the miners' trope to suggest the enormous changes she underwent.

My fourth chapter examines the narrative of Eliza Burhans Farnham. When Farnham heard of the death of her husband in San Francisco in 1848, she set out for California by sea to settle his estate. Her ship's captain abandoned her in South America and sailed off with her children. Once in California and reunited with her children, she decides to stay and build with her own hands a two-story ranch house in Santa Cruz County. The book of her frontier experiences, *California, In-doors and Out*, emphasizes her liminal position on the threshold of two dominant ideologies: an interior, homebound domesticity and an exterior, frontier individualism. Declaring that "life in California is altogether anomalous, and that it is no more extraordinary for a woman to plow, dig, and hoe with her own hands if she have will and strength to do so," Farnham becomes a farmer, a carpenter, and a medico.

In my fifth chapter, I turn to the writing of Lydia Spencer Lane, an officer's wife who lived in the Southwest for most almost two decades. Although there are over sixty published books and articles by nineteenth-century frontier army wives, only a few of these narratives describe army life before 1865. Covering the years from 1854 to 1870, Lane's memoir is one of these rare accounts. Her memoir testifies to the roles that genteel ladies from the East played when they followed their officer husbands to primitive outposts in the Southwest. Never staying more than six months at any one place, Lane considered herself as part of her husband's regiment. "I had 'gone for a soldier,' and a soldier I determined to be," she writes. Her reminiscences underscore her transformation from young civilian bride from the East to "soldier" of the Southwest. At one point in the narrative, she even commands Fort Fillmore when her husband is called away. When the time comes to leave the Southwest and army life, Lane is filled with regret. She doesn't want to leave her "gypsy life."

The stories these women tell reveal women's involvement in every aspect of the westering process. They refute the notion that the western nineteenth-century wilderness was entirely a male domain. By examining the West through their eyes, we can begin to address the omissions of older histories of westward expansion, and as a result, we can comprehend our heritage more completely. These westering women's intimate revelations evidence the need for literary scholars to reexamine the history of the American frontier—from the feminine perspective.

Writing the Trail

> *It is the life of a wandering princess, mine.*

SUSAN SHELBY MAGOFFIN

A Wandering Princess on the Santa Fe Trail 1

In June 1846, Susan Shelby Magoffin set out from Independence, Missouri, down the Santa Fe Trail. With her husband, Samuel Magoffin, a veteran Santa Fe trader, she crossed the plains and mountains to Santa Fe and then traveled along the Rio Grande to El Paso Norte and finally south into Chihuahua. Published for the first time in 1926, *Down the Santa Fe Trail and into Mexico* is unique because it is the earliest narrative about the Santa Fe Trail by an Anglo-American woman.[1] Even a superficial reading of the diary reveals its historical significance. Magoffin's account records a crucial time in the history of the trans-Mississippi West. As a member of her husband's merchant caravan, she saw the trail in one of its busiest years of trade, a year when more than a million dollars' worth of goods was hauled over a thousand miles into the northern provinces of Mexico.[2] Additionally, her journal is significant because she entered Santa Fe only two weeks after the Americans occupied New Mexico. She was an eyewitness to Stephen W. Kearny's conquest, and she followed Colonel Alexander W. Doniphan and his Missouri Volunteers down the trail into Chihuahua.

The Santa Fe Trail was primarily a road of commerce used by merchants. Women travelers were few until after midcentury, and as a consequence, most of the stories of the Santa Fe Trail tell of the experiences of men. Mary Dodson Donoho was the first Anglo-American woman to come over the trail in 1833. She helped her husband, William, manage a

Santa Fe hotel until 1837. According to historian Marian Meyer, at least four others in addition to Donoho preceded Magoffin as the first Anglo-American women to travel the Santa Fe Trail: Rachael Plummer, Mrs. Harris, Sarah Horn—these three women were all captured and enslaved by the Comanches and rescued by William Donoho—and an unnamed woman (*Mary Donoho: New First Lady of the Santa Fe Trail*, 31). Even as late as the 1860 census, there were fewer than fifty Anglo women in Santa Fe; this total included ten nuns at the Loretto Academy.[3]

Susan Magoffin is in the vanguard of this small group of westering women. Her narrative is significant because hers is the first Anglo-American woman's perspective of the trail. Her eyewitness account is also a rarity because it is one in which women matter. Newly married and pregnant, Magoffin illuminates the domestic side of the Santa Fe Trail experience in her diary, allowing her readers to share moments of every-dayness on the trail by detailing the incidents seldom found in the more formal, public writings by men. Her account does not, however, support the stereotype of women as "gentle tamers." The assumption that women went west reluctantly, passively taming the wilderness with their civilized presence, was influenced by early works on western women, beginning with Dee Brown's *The Gentle Tamers* in 1958. Magoffin's writing counters this passive image.

Magoffin learned Spanish, helped clerk in her husband's store, and even assumed the role of train leader during her husband's absence, a role that gave her authority over Mexican men. She made many friends among the Mexicans, whom she grew to consider generally charming people. When her brother-in-law, trader James Magoffin, was jailed in Mexico and she and her husband were under threat of attack from Mexican forces, her assessment of the Mexicans remained balanced. Her spiritual alteration is evidenced by her increasing references to passages of scripture and reflections of the judgment to come. Even her attitude toward her husband changes, and before the journey is over she writes in her diary: "After all this thing of marrying is not what it is cracked up to be" (245). Magoffin's growth—psychological, emotional, and spiritual—is directly related to the narrative movement: her travels invite her to think differently, to see anew.

Unfamiliar with her new surroundings, Magoffin doesn't "know her place." As her party moves onto foreign terrain, she has to learn how to negotiate in a country that seems hostile to both her eye and her imagination. The dislocating effect of her travel is intertwined with her self-understanding. A cultivated Kentucky woman, she probably did not expect that her journey down the Santa Fe Trail would compel her to

Susan Shelby Magoffin
*in 1845, from a
daguerreotype. Courtesy
of the Missouri Historical
Society, St. Louis.*

rethink so many assumptions basic to her gender and her class. But the trip through the distinctively new environment of the Southwest required new methods of coping and adapting. Even when she uses past tense to condense the events of the days when she neglected to write in her journal, she portrays the impact of prior events on her present self. As a consequence, her narrative is not only an account of a journey completed but also a record of her ongoing process of making sense of the different landscapes and cultures as well as of her own changing self.

Magoffin is pregnant during her journey. Iris Marion Young, a feminist theorist, has suggested that "pregnancy reveals a paradigm of bodily experiences in which the transparent unity of self dissolves" (161). In pregnancy, the notion of a woman's self as integral is undermined: the boundaries of her body are in flux, and her private space is the site of another. Magoffin's changing body underscores the transformative effects of her journey down the Santa Fe Trail.

✳   ✳   ✳   ✳

Magoffin was born on July 30, 1827, at Arcadia, her family's estate, about six miles south of Danville, Kentucky. Although biographical information concerning her parents, Isaac Shelby Jr. and Maria Boswell

Warren, is sparse, it is known that her family was prominent and wealthy and that she was born into an atmosphere of ease and comfort. Her great-grandfather, Evan Shelby (1719–1794), had been a distinguished soldier and fur trader, and her grandfather, Isaac Shelby (1750–1826), was elected as Kentucky's first governor in 1792. Susan Magoffin's older sister, Anna, was married in 1840 to Beriah Magoffin, the brother of Samuel and a Kentucky governor.

Although Susan Magoffin did not write for publication, it is apparent that she was confident that her narrative would be read. She knew she was a trailblazer. Magoffin was traveling to a foreign country on which the United States had declared war only a few weeks earlier. She was only eighteen years old in 1846, and she had been married to Samuel, who was twenty-seven years her senior, less than eight months. Her writing evidences her love for her husband and her infatuation with his romantic trail career. Her narrative is filled with many personal items and references to *mi alma*, her affectionate name for him. Arguably one of the finest trail journals by a nineteenth-century westering woman, it wasn't published until 1926 when Stella M. Drumm, librarian of the Missouri Historical Society, convinced Magoffin's daughter to permit publication.[4] Although some critics have regarded the diary as "girlish" and "naïve," scholars immediately recognized its value as a significant addition to southwestern trail history. Historians like David Lavender, Howard Lamar, Marc Simmons, and Annette Kolodny have found Magoffin to be an intelligent, observant, and tolerant narrator. Even more recently, Virginia Scharff has referred to her as "an agent of the American empire, charged with the job of domesticating a series of strange places" (4). There are two historical novels based on Magoffin's narrative: Shirley Seifert's *The Turquoise Trail* (1950) and Jean M. Burroughs's *Bride of the Santa Fe Trail* (1984).

Before the summer of 1846, Magoffin's knowledge of the Southwest was confined to information from her husband and his friends and her reading of travel accounts and reports of expeditions. When she first arrives in the Southwest and responds to the actual facts of the frontier, her responses are governed by the preconceptions she brings with her, ideas that were shaped entirely by men. Among those whom Magoffin read in order to prepare herself for her trip was Josiah Gregg. In her journal entries from Independence to Bent's Fort, Magoffin used Gregg's *Commerce of the Prairies* as her model. Gregg traveled the Great Plains four times between the years 1831 and 1840. Published in 1844, his account of the overland trade between the United States and Mexico has been recognized as the classic description of the trail. Because *Commerce*

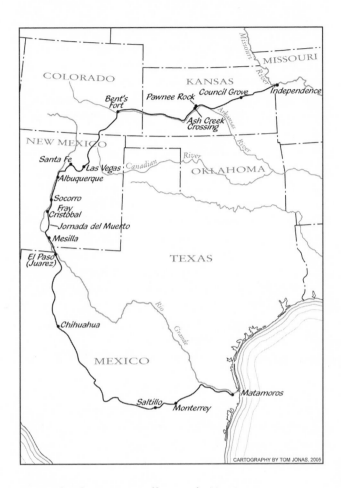

Route taken by Susan Magoffin. Map by Tom Jonas.

of the Prairies helped shape Magoffin's expectations of the frontier, Gregg's narrative is of consequence to readers of Magoffin's text.

It is especially interesting to note how Magoffin locates herself in relation to Gregg's narrative—both the aspects of their texts that are similar and the characteristics that distinguish her voice from Gregg's. Although Magoffin's experiences differed from Gregg's because of her gender and because of the conveniences she had, like Gregg, she was a keen observer, and her narrative provides one of the most accurate and detailed descriptions of life along the Santa Fe Trail. And also similar to Gregg, Magoffin begins her diary as the innocent adventurer. However, midway in her journey, she is initiated into the wilderness, loses her innocence, and as a consequence is no longer able to keep her previous adventurous, light-hearted tone. After Bent's Fort, she increasingly uses an introspective and pious voice; instead of viewing the landscape with delight, she sees it in terms of obstacles to be overcome. In contrast, Gregg's narrative is factual and neither emotional nor imaginative. And whereas Magoffin's character changes through the course of her journey, Gregg remains the innocent, albeit always curious and keen, observer throughout the trip.

Moreover, Gregg's account depicts the Southwest as a landscape that renews and revitalizes. Gregg joined the caravan of Santa Fe traders because he felt himself in need of a "tour of health." And the prairie cure worked so well for him that after two weeks of riding in his carriage as an invalid, he was able to ride the rest of the way to Santa Fe on his pony. In contrast, Magoffin's health begins to deteriorate before she arrives at Bent's Fort. To appreciate her disappointment, we have to remind ourselves that she had been led by Gregg's narrative's promises to anticipate that the journey would be physically rejuvenating: "I never should have consented to take the trip on the plains had it not been with that view and a hope that it would prove beneficial; but so far my hopes have been blasted, for I am rather going down hill than up, and it is so bad to be sick and under a physician all the time" (64). Her willingness to take the journey in her pregnant state emphasizes her anticipation of the curative effects of the landscape. Her frustration is in part a result of the discrepancy between preconception and the sobering, contrasting reality.

As Magoffin deals increasingly with the adversities of the trip, she is no longer able to use Gregg as a model. Her representation of the landscape and her persona become more and more insecure as she attempts to come to terms with an experience for which she discovers she was totally unprepared. This juncture is central to Magoffin's narrative perspective because it highlights her inability to stay within Gregg's discursive framework. And as a consequence of this move away from Gregg's text, Magoffin must revise the rhetorical strategies she had used in the earlier section of her narrative. Exchanging the authoritative stance for the tentative, she deconstructs her earlier, more clearly defined sense of self as she records her journey from Santa Fe, down the Rio Grande, and across the Jornada del Muerto.

✳   ✳   ✳   ✳

Magoffin begins her diary on June 9, 1846, in Independence, Missouri. In 1832, Independence was the main jumping-off point for the Oregon, California, and Santa Fe trails. Travelers like the Magoffins gathered here to outfit themselves with equipment and supplies, make up their companies, and take their plunge into the wilderness. The Magoffin caravan consisted of fourteen large ox-drawn wagons filled with trade goods and a baggage wagon pulled by two yoke of oxen and driven by a man named Sendevel. There was also a Dearborn—a light, four-wheeled carriage with a canvas top and adjustable canvas sides—and a Rockaway carriage, both drawn by mules. Including the three Mexican tent servants for the Magoffins, there were eighteen men and "Mr. Hall," the wagon master, Susan's maid, some two hundred oxen, nine mules, two riding horses, some chickens, and their dog Ring.

Whereas many women begin their westering journals and letters with the details of painful separations and expressions of reluctance or regret, Magoffin starts her account with a mood of celebratory anticipation. Countering the stereotype of the reluctant and frightened westering woman dragged off into the terrible frontier, Magoffin anticipates their trip to be "an extended honeymoon safari."[5] She writes that in Independence "the curtain raises now with a new scene." Although she doesn't realize it yet, Independence is the jumping-off point not just for the geographical frontier but also for a psychological wilderness where conditions will threaten to undermine her carefully constructed gendered ideologies of selfhood that home and wilderness adventure represent.

Magoffin inscribes herself as a subject constituted on a border between acts: "My journal tells a story tonight different from what it has ever done before. The curtain raises now with a new scene. This book of travels is Act 2nd, literally and truly" (1). With these opening words of her journal, Magoffin casts herself in the first of a number of poses she will assume over the next 206 pages. Here she is the greenhorn traveler about to venture into an unknown geographic landscape of the new republic. Later, as she encounters Hispanics and Indians on the trail, she will find her attitudes challenged and her worldview enlarged. In the wide, empty landscape of the Southwest, she discovers a spatial freedom that is liberating. She moves beyond recognizable geography into an unfamiliar physical and cultural terrain. This is *la frontera*, a transitional region with diverse communities and complex local and regional identities with permeable borders. The effect of *la frontera* on Magoffin is reflected in her poses. Liberated from the restrictive norms of the East, she changes from the innocent traveler and child bride to a princess and then from a princess to a pioneer and traderess. At the points in her travels when she responds to particularly difficult pressures and is no longer able to keep up the lighthearted self-distancing, she becomes the penitent seeking a stronger relationship with God and desiring his forgiveness for her "sins and transgressions."

As the curtain rises on act 2, Magoffin's persona is poised to move away from the domestic spaces and characteristics of mid-nineteenth-century womanhood with which she is familiar. Admitting that she could say what few women in civilized life could—that the first house her husband took her to after their marriage was a tent—Magoffin readily adapts to their rustic living conditions. In the opening pages of her narrative, she invites her reader inside her canvas home. She describes the tent's interior in detail, from the combs on the little dressing bureau to the carpet on the floor to the mattress and linen on her bed. The significance of her canvas home can be grasped in a variety of ways. First, the image of the tent as the immediate setting that she lives in undercuts the notion of a house as a place of stability with its well-known rhythms and norms. Here it is the emblem of frequent removals. Second, her tent home can be viewed as a symbol for Magoffin's self. No longer inhabiting the house of civilized and complacent society, she is a subject in transition. Finally, her canvas home is the metaphor for her diary, the textual container of her changed worldview. As she records her experiences in order to make sense of them, she converts verbal space into living space. In her diary, she can say what she wants "without that oppression and uneasiness felt in the gossiping circles of a settled home" (10).

Expressing impatience with the trees of eastern Kansas, which remind her of the confinement of a settled home, Magoffin responds to the open and rolling grasslands with delight: "Oh, this is a life I would not exchange for a good deal! There is such independence, so much free uncontaminated air which impregnates the mind, the feelings, nay every thought, with purity" (10). Whereas many westering women found the emptiness, the enormity of western spaces, to be daunting, Magoffin did not: she is the willing inhabitant of an idealized wilderness garden. Instead of the conventional catalogue of places and facts, her diary entries are filled with romantic descriptions of the prairies. Magoffin and her husband "noon it" along gently curving streams, under the shade of cottonwoods or locust trees. On her walks, she delights in the abundance of flowers, especially the quantities of roses. With the zeal of an amateur naturalist, she describes the wild onions, antelope, and birds. The charms of the flowered prairie expanses are sources of happiness for her. In these early pages of her narrative, her persona emerges as a frontier Eve, both adventurer in and assessor of the wilderness paradise: "It is the life of a wandering princess, mine," she concludes after five days on the trail (11).

However, after the first few weeks on the trail, Magoffin became increasingly anxious, and her depiction of the landscape reflected her fears. One of the symbolic boundaries between her old life and her new one was Council Grove: "We are now at the great rendezvous of all the traders. Council Grove many be considered the dividing ridge between the civilized and barbarous, for now we may look out for hostile Indians" (16). Like other women coming to the frontier from "civilized" society, Magoffin carried with her deeply ingrained attitudes toward the Indians, and she had been conditioned by reports of their attacks. Consequently, it is not surprising that she was fearful and at the same time fascinated by the Indians she met along the way.[6] As I will show, Magoffin crosses the line into an area of "savagery" that is totally filtered through her preconceptions, prejudices, and cultural values. But, as she experiences the Indians firsthand, her diary reveals dramatic changes in attitude.

Magoffin's trip from Lost Spring to Cottonwoods, punctuated by frequent downpours, was an ordeal: the trail became a river of mud and the wagons bogged down to their axle hubs. Although her Rockaway carriage managed to survive the quagmires, when her tent was raised, water covered the floor to a depth of several inches. She describes her bed as a boat floating on a pond. After a particularly violent storm, she writes, "As bad as it all is, I enjoy it still. I look upon it as one of the 'varieties of life,' and as that is always 'spice' of course it must be enjoyed" (23). Along the Arkansas River, the mosquitoes were intense. "Millions upon millions" of the insects, she complained, knocked against the carriage and "reminded me of a hard rain. It was the equal to any of the plagues of Egypt. I lay almost in a perfect stupor, [and] the heat and stings made me perfectly sick" (34). At Big John's Spring, she is afraid "some wily savage or hungry wolf might be lurking in the thick grape vines" (18). However, she keeps her concerns to herself because she feels that her husband would make fun of her: "I would not tell *mi alma* these foolish fears, for I knew he would ridicule them, and this was torture to me" (18). She wrestles with her fears in silence.

Magoffin struggles to regain her balance during such times by recording her experiences and describing her sense of accomplishment in her ability to cope with these unusual situations by herself. Comparing herself favorably to her westering predecessors, she adds, "If I live through this— and I think from all appearances now I shall come off the winner—I shall be fit for one of the Oregon Pioneers" (23). A few entries later, she attempts to dispel her fears by evoking the image of her pioneering grandmother, Susannah Hart Shelby. She compares her grandmother's situation in the War of 1812 with her own trials in New Mexico, and she concludes without hesitation that her own situation is the more dangerous one.

Although at times she portrays herself as the intrepid adventurer, Magoffin also on occasion presents herself as the frightened, helpless woman. However, she does this with a playfulness that undermines her fearful pose. One of her trials is snakes:

> While Jane and I were on a little stroll after dinner, I carelessly
> walking along stepped almost onto a large snake; it moved and
> frightened me very much. Of course I screamed and ran off, and
> like a ninny came back when the snake had been frightened by me
> as much as it had me, and had gone I can't tell where. (26)

Rattlesnakes were abundant on the prairies, and Josiah Gregg wrote about coming across a den of these reptiles: "I will not say 'thousands,' though this perhaps were nearer the truth—but hundreds at least were coiled or crawling in every direction" (*Commerce of the Prairies*, 46). In textual dialogue with Gregg, Magoffin writes, "And we also had a rattle-snake fracas. There were not *hundreds* killed thou', as Mr. Gregg had to do to keep his animals from suffering, but some *two* or *three* were killed in the road by our carriage driver, and these were quite enough to make me sick" (50). She plays Gregg's experience against her own, seemingly reinforcing male frontier dominance. However, on closer inspection, her tone seems to parody Gregg's version, exposing his description as an exaggeration.

With no respite from travel even on Sunday, Magoffin begins to find it difficult to differentiate one day from the other. As a consequence, on June 28, 1846, she asks God to be "pardoned" for forgetting the Sabbath:

> It was the Holy Sabbath, appointed by my heavenly father for a
> day of rest—and classed it so much with the days of the week, that
> I regularly took out my week's work, knitting [*sic*]. Oh, how could
> I ever have been so thoughtless, so unmindful of my duty and my
> eternal salvation! (31)

For Magoffin, time is no longer marked by temporal days but by spatial movement. She finds this shift in emphasis from *when* to *where* disorienting and transgressive. In this instance, she has forgotten the Sabbath, and as a consequence, she fears damnation.

To what extent is this anxiety for her soul a result of her increasing apprehension of the wilderness? We do not know. But a credible surmise is that like other travelers on the frontier, she was afraid of death on the trail and burial in a wilderness grave. Death shadowed the overland routes, and there are relatively few trail diaries that do not record the loss of human lives. Magoffin details the first casualty in their party; a Mexican youth who died of consumption: "Poor man, 'twas but yesterday that we sent him some soup from our camp, which he took with relish and today he is in his grave!" (38). She writes that the grave must be dug very deep in order to prevent the wolves from finding the body.

According to Lillian Schlissel, men tended to record trail deaths in "aggregate numbers," as opposed to the women diarists who "noted the particulars of each grave site" (*Women's Diaries of the Westward Journey*, 14). Magoffin's first exposure to death in the wilderness foreshadows her upcoming miscarriage at Bent's Fort and the death of a second child in Matamoros a year later. The loss of a child would be emotionally traumatic for a woman in the comfort of her home and with the support of traditional family and friendship systems, but the trauma would most certainly be exacerbated in a frontier setting.

The harsh conditions on the trail were frightening and dangerous for women. Women's diaries frequently express concern about the safety of family members. Magoffin increasingly worried about the safety of her husband: "It is a painful situation to be placed in, to know that the being dearest to you on earth is in momentary danger of loosing [*sic*] his life" (44). Pregnant, she must have wondered at what point on the trail her labor would begin. We know that she contemplated the precariousness of life in general—"'twas but yesterday that we sent him some soup." Certainly, she must have had fears concerning the future of her unborn child. And although she doesn't mention it, Magoffin must have had frequent thoughts about her own mortality.

Magoffin is also afraid of Indians. At Pawnee Rock, the sandstone register where passing travelers carved their names, she describes her anxieties as she leaves her inscription:

> We went up and while *mi alma* with his gun and pistols kept watch, for the wily Indian may always be apprehended here, it is a good lurking place and they are ever ready to fall upon any unfortunate trader behind his company—and it is necessary to be careful, so while *mi alma* watched on the rock above and Jane stood by to watch if any should come up on the front side of me, I cut my name, among the many hundreds inscribed on the rock and many of whom I knew. It was not done well, for fear of Indians made me tremble all over and I hurried it over in any way. (40)

Although she is afraid that Indians lurk nearby, she is nevertheless determined to leave her inscription on a rock not only for future travelers to see but also as a way to celebrate July 4, Independence Day.[7]

Magoffin's desire to leave a record of her presence in the wilderness is significant. She writes her name on the rock, and by doing so, she turns terrain into text, evidence that she had been there. Her inscribed name articulates her national origin, her geographical mobility, and her bodily presence. Midway between Missouri and New Mexico, Pawnee Rock represented the challenges overcome thus far on the trail traveler's journey.

The landscape, therefore, is both the catalyst for and the artifact of her text. By placing her protecting husband prominently in the scene ("watching on the rock above"), Magoffin intertwines her presence at the outcrop with the risks that she had to take to get there. As a textual landmark, it emphasizes the connection between where she is placed psychically and where she is placed geographically. Her description of the threatening landscape serves as metaphoric commentary on her unstable, frightened physical self.

Despite her fears and complaints, Magoffin had a relatively pampered life on the trail. Her economic situation provided her with the domestic help that protected her from the fate of many toilworn westering women. As mentioned earlier, she was accompanied by her maid Jane, at least two servant boys to carry out most of the trail chores, and an indulgent husband. During the day, she traveled in a private Rockaway carriage, and at night she slept in a conical tent that was equipped with a cedar table, stools, a camp bed, and a carpet made of "sail duck."

Whereas in many westering women's writings men are on the periphery of the action, Magoffin keeps Samuel closer to center stage. As she rides in her Rockaway, he is usually on his horse alongside, attempting to shield her from the hardships of the trail. However, regardless of her husband's presence, Magoffin's account cannot be read as the autobiography of a marriage. Her focus instead is on herself and the detrimental and beneficial effects of change wrought by the journey. And despite her husband's attempts to protect her from the rigors of frontier life, by the time their caravan reaches Ash Creek, the difficulties of the journey have taken their toll on her buoyant spirit. Her enthusiastic assessment of the frontier becomes increasingly cautionary as the landscape begins to oppress her. Magoffin dramatizes the detrimental effects of travel when she describes her fall from her carriage at Ash Creek. Descending the dangerous bank, her carriage turns over and she is thrown to the ground unconscious. This accident undermined her health and led to her later miscarriage at Bent's Fort.

Whether consciously intended or not, Ash Creek marks the turning point in her journal. As she became increasingly frail, her ability to withstand the trail's rigors declined and her spiritual faith grew. Her diary entries begin to reference passages of scripture and to contain reflections on the judgment to come and on her sinfulness, especially her failure to "keep the Sabbath," and the tone of her narrative becomes increasingly somber. Her fear of the Indians and the downpours, oppressive heat, keening winds, rattlesnakes, and mosquitoes prove too great an ordeal.

After Ash Creek, Magoffin's journal entries evidence the kind of mental exhaustion many early travelers from the lush East felt after having to face the barren stretches along this section of the trail day after day. The landscape is literally marked by the signs of her suffering. "Oh how gloomy the Plains have been to me today!" she complained on July 11. "I am sick, rather sad feelings and everything around corresponds with them" (47). Significantly, she projects her own "sick, rather sad feelings" onto the vast geography of the "gloomy" plains. This relation between her own condition and the terrain she is negotiating is instructive for its demonstration of the way in which environment frames her mood. As essayist Scott Russell Sanders has noted, the geography of the land and the geography of the spirit are one terrain (xvi). Her emotions provide, rather than forfeit, meaningful connection to the landscape.

Because of Victorian reticence regarding sexual matters, women diarists rarely mention details about pregnancy and birth. However, the "sickness" Magoffin refers to is most definitely pregnancy-related. And when her condition grows worse, Magoffin's husband sends a man to get a doctor who was traveling with a group ahead of their party. She writes:

> Now that I am with the Doctor I am satisfied. . . . He . . . is called
> an excellent physician "especially in female cases," and in brevity I
> have great confidence in his knowledge and capacity of relieving
> me, though not at once, for mine is a case to be treated gently, and
> slowly, a complication of diseases. (53)

Despite her depression and troubled pregnancy, Magoffin struggles to remain optimistic now that Dr. Masure is nearby. However, the wind-swept, rolling, and oppressively monotonous grasslands present her with emotional challenges. Enigmatically she describes her case as "a complication of diseases." What kind of "complication of diseases" is she referring to? There can be no doubt that the dislocation of the journey and the lack of female family and friends were contributors to her poor health, anxiety, and fear. The sheer emptiness of the terrain she is traveling through increases her panic. Magoffin told her journal, "The idea of being sick on the Plains is not at all pleasant to me; it is rather terrifying than otherwise" (53).

A massive mud structure on the Arkansas River, Bent's Fort was the most renowned landmark on the mountain branch of the Santa Fe Trail.[8] Built in 1834, the adobe fort was a private, not a military, post and served as a center for Indian and fur trade. However, when the Magoffin wagon train arrives at the fort on July 27, General Kearny and 1,700 soldiers from Fort Leavenworth are there preparing for their march to Santa Fe. At her first view of the complex, Magoffin declares that it looks like an ancient castle with its massive earth walls and round-bodied defensive towers. With her keen eye for detail, she provides her readers with a physical layout of the fort's interior: the wedge-shaped corral, wagon sheds, the living and work rooms that surrounded the plaza, the well, the billiard room, and the parlor. She describes sitting in the fort's parlor with the Mexican wife of George Bent and some other señoritas. Sitting on one of the cushions that lines two of the walls—apart from the other women—Magoffin comments on their habits.

Although the parlor here represents a site of potential interchange between the eastern white woman and the Mexican women, Magoffin's emphasis on her separateness highlights her distinction from them. Her comments reveal both puzzlement and derision. With an aloof and somewhat condescending attitude, she notes a bucket of water that stood on the table. To her astonishment, whenever anyone drank from the common dipper, any water remaining in it is tossed onto the dirt floor. She is revolted when one of the Mexican women begins to comb her long black hair with so much cooking grease that it dripped. "If I had not seen her at it, I never would have believed it greese [*sic*], but that she had been washing her head," Magoffin writes (62–63).

On July 30, her nineteenth birthday, Magoffin complains of being sick with strange sensations in her head, back, and hips. She grumbles about the din of blacksmith hammers, braying mules, crying children, and quarreling soldiers in the patio outside her room. The next day, she suffers a miscarriage.[9] Sadness and grief flood the poignant entries in this section of her diary. Children and motherhood are the mainstays of the domestic sphere; they provide the contrast to the unknowns of the American wilderness. But Magoffin's trail experiences are undermining the gendered ideology of feminine domesticity and masculine adventure. As the curtain raised on act 2 and she set out from Independence down the Santa Fe Trail, she crossed the boundaries of normal expectations for young women. Her miscarriage—a result of her "fall" at Ash Creek—is the price exacted.

Undercutting the sentiment of the scene, Magoffin shifts from her private distress to a description of an Indian giving birth to a healthy baby in the room below her. Perceiving a profound difference between her own and the Indian cultures, she writes, "It is truly astonishing to see what customs will do. No doubt many ladies in civilized life are ruined by too careful treatments during child-birth, for this custom of the heathen is not known to be disadvantageous, but it is a heathenish custom" (68). Magoffin's observations here are significant for two reasons. First, as Glenda Riley has noted, frontierswomen rarely record their responses to the childbirth and child-care practices of Indians, and Magoffin's observation is a rare exception (*Confronting Race*, 150). Second, Magoffin's scene challenges conventional dominant paradigms. The structural symmetry of the two women—Magoffin, in the room above, privileged by her race, class, and culture, and her Indian double, in the room below—characterizes western race relations by reinforcing the imbalance of power rankings. But instead of subscribing to the popular notion of Indians as a "dying" race because they are incapable of accommodating themselves to changed conditions, Magoffin is the one who lies passive and weak in her bed. In contrast to the ailing Magoffin, the Indian woman, half an hour after she has given birth, walks to the river to bathe herself and her baby. As if to reconcile her sense of obligation to the "civilized" social order, Magoffin refers to the Indian woman's way as "heathenish," in other words, something other than the white custom, but she is nevertheless able to recognize it as something both "natural" and advantageous.

This begins a period of extensive searching and a marked change in Magoffin's narrative stance. She can no longer position her journal in relation to Gregg's text. She gives up her imitative voice of authority and adventurous mode and turns inward. We get a glimpse of a deeply personal side, a side that shows a commitment to her Christian heritage. Increasingly she focuses on the transient aspects of human existence. Her spiritual apprehension links her with the circumspect tradition of the seventeenth-century Puritan poet Anne Bradstreet. In "To My Dear and Loving Husband," Bradstreet celebrates marriage while pointing to a love more eternal. Concerned that God has punished her for loving her husband too much, Magoffin laments, "If I could feel sure too that my idol is not on earth. That loving my dear husband as I do, I am not excluding an Image more precious to the soul of mortals, than all things earthly" (71).

Magoffin is confined to her bed until August 5. Two days later, General Kearny's troops leave the fort for Santa Fe, and the next day, August 8, the Magoffin caravan is permitted to follow. Crossing the Arkansas River, considered the boundary between Mexico and the United States, is hard for Magoffin. She comments in her diary, "I'm now entirely out of 'the States,' into a new country. The crossing of the Arkansas was an event in my life, I have never met with before; the separating me from my own dear native land" (72). Complaining of loneliness and isolation, she conjures up memories of those back home. Like most women on overland trails, as she moves into a foreign country her glance is like that of Lot's wife: backward rather than toward the road ahead. The scene is dense with symbols—the forced movement, the river, and Magoffin's grief and her concentration on the home she has left. Mourning the loss of her child, Magoffin crosses the Arkansas and enters the wilderness.

The river marks the boundary between the ordinary and the extraordinary, order and chaos. She now finds herself in a literal wilderness, a kind of geometrical nightmare of immense vistas, red sand hills and mesas, and brilliant light. She is also in a cultural wilderness, and this is especially clear in her account of Las Vegas, New Mexico.

For Magoffin, the heat and the filth magnifies the unpleasantness of the little town of Las Vegas. Unfamiliar with the New Mexican customs, she is openly dismayed by the *nuevomexicanos*, who drink copiously of *aguardiente*, smoke *cigarritas*, and stare at her as an object of curiosity.[10] But Magoffin watches them as closely as they watch her. This mutual cross-cultural gaze of curiosity is doubly significant. On the one hand, the *nuevomexicanos* are interested in Magoffin's habits and dress. Because Anglo migration to New Mexico in the first half of the nineteenth century was predominantly male, Anglo women like Magoffin were a rarity. Similar to her Mexican counterparts, Magoffin approaches them with apprehension, suspicion, and a good deal of curiosity. A number of narratives have focused on the attitudes of westering Anglo-American males toward the Mexican population of the Southwest. With few exceptions, however, these texts have not dealt with the attitudes of Anglo-American women.[11] Magoffin provides a feminine perspective on the Mexican population of the Southwest. Reflecting many of the racial sentiments of her day, the initial impressions she formed in Las Vegas were later modified and in some cases discarded as she came to know them as individuals and began to understand something of their culture.

Magoffin's initial impressions center on the New Mexican women's propensity for smoking and liquor and their lack of modesty.[12] She considers their loose, breathable clothing "truly shocking," and she is disgusted by the way they cover their faces with flour paste "when they wish to look fair and beautiful at a Fandango" (102). Their white faces gave them the "appearance of one from the tombs," she wrote. At first confusing the red paint on the women's lips for blood, she admits that she has a hard time restraining her laughter. She found the mothers to be indolent and morally lax. Embarrassed by the naked children, she kept her veil drawn to "protect her blushes" (95). And, as might be expected, Magoffin thought that the food was inedible. At their dinner in Las Vegas, she complains about the dirty tablecloth and the lack of knives, forks, and spoons. The food itself is completely "unaccustomed" to her palate (94), and the only thing she finds edible is a little soup and a fried egg.

A stark contrast emerges when one compares Magoffin's contact with the Hispanic residents of the Southwest at this point in her narrative with her attitudes toward them during and after her stay in Santa Fe when she views them with a more sympathetic eye. According to Glenda Riley, although Anglo frontierswomen showed an ability to change their view of Indians, they did not often extend their sympathies toward other racial, ethnic, and religious groups, and "they continued to deprecate most 'others'" (*Confronting Race*, 212). Magoffin will prove the exception, developing amicable feelings toward Hispanic men and women. By the time she is in Mexico, she will even censure American soldiers for their misuse of Mexican property.

James Wiley Magoffin's successful negotiations with General Manuel Armijo, governor of New Mexico, enabled the Magoffins' caravan to enter Santa Fe on August 30, 1846, only twelve days after General Kearny's occupation. Basking in the pleasure of her accomplishment, Susan boasts that she is the "first American, who has come under such auspices," and that some people claim she was "the first under any circumstances that ever crossed the Plains." Evidently it did not occur to her to include her servant Jane as another American woman to first "come under such auspices." Most likely Jane was black; however, there is no verification of this in Magoffin's narrative. Two fictional accounts of Magoffin's journey do say that she was black.[13] If this were the case, Jane may have been the first woman of her race to travel the Santa Fe Trail to its end, and Magoffin's inability to credit Jane's presence reflects her resistance to crossing racial lines. Representing herself from the onset of her narrative as a subject in transition between acts, Magoffin is able to slip outside the boundaries of women's sphere, but she is not yet capable of crossing the boundaries separating racial and cultural identities. It is only when she takes up housekeeping in Santa Fe that her entries begin to evidence her increased empathy toward the racial and ethnic "others" she encounters on the frontier.

The Magoffin caravan reached Santa Fe on August 30, 1846, twelve days behind Kearny's troops. Samuel Magoffin rented a four-room adobe under the shadow of the church, two blocks from the plaza that marked the trail's end.[14] Glad to be once again in a temporary stopping place on the frontier, Susan began to settle in. Enthusiastically, she embraces the domestic toils about which men's writings are so consistently silent. She describes her daily tasks as "superintending" her housekeepers and haggling for vegetables and fruit in the Santa Fe market. Her bartering in the marketplace creates a relationship between herself and the New Mexicans. To negotiate she had to use their language, in both the literal and figural senses: she had to speak Spanish and participate in their pattern of economy. She boasts: "One must look out for themselves, I find if they do not wish to be cheated though only of a few cents, and called *tonta* [stupid], into the bargain" (112). Although she claimed she was simply doing her duty to please her husband, it is obvious that she derived a great deal of personal satisfaction from her successful interactions in the marketplace and in her ability to fit into the community.

Although Magoffin's Santa Fe entries are filled with sad yearnings for home and family, they are juxtaposed with her new delight for New Mexico life. She began to revise her opinion about Mexican food and describes the soups, meats, and desserts that she finds to her liking. Additionally, she enjoyed Santa Fe society. She recorded the informal social visits with Santa Fe women, the formal dinners and dances she attended, and the people she met, their clothes, and their manners. General Kearny's troops were preparing to leave for California, and at their farewell ball at the Palace of the Governors, Magoffin decked herself out in a scarlet Canton crape shawl so that she would "be in trim with the natives." Briefly forgetting her miscarriage at Bent's Fort, she could even call the native *cuna* a beautiful dance.

Also at this farewell ball, Magoffin met Doña Gertrudis de Barcelos, familiarly known as La Tules.[15] One of the most expert monte dealers of her time, Barcelos is an enigmatic figure in New Mexican history. She had amassed a fortune as a proprietor of a prosperous Santa Fe gambling saloon and bordello and was rumored to have been the former mistress of Armijo. Unable to appreciate a woman of such extraordinary independence as Barcelos, Magoffin perpetuates the Anglo perception of her as a promiscuous rabble-rouser. She describes Barcelos as "a stately dame of a certain age, the possessor of a portion of that shrewd sense and fascinating manner necessary to allure the wayward, inexperienced youth to the hall of final ruin" (17).

On October 7, the Magoffin caravan leaves Santa Fe. It will travel down the Rio Grande and across the Jornada del Muerto to El Paso del Norte, and then it will head toward Chihuahua City and Saltillo, where Samuel Magoffin and his brothers had established markets.[16] Magoffin writes that she is impatient to be on her way. In contrast to her feelings at their journey's start in Independence, she is not enthusiastic for the travel itself. Instead, now she is anxious to get on the road that will lead to Matamoros and the ship to New Orleans and ultimately her return to Kentucky. Her thoughts are directed toward the future: the establishment of a permanent Kentucky home with her husband and the reconnection with the family and friends she has left behind.

Although the final section of *Down the Santa Fe Trail and into Mexico* reveals Magoffin's increased empathy for the Mexicans and their customs, it also emphasizes her growing dislike for the barren landscape.

The buoyant and romantic enthusiasm that she expressed at her first sight of the prairies is replaced by a realistic assessment of the sterile stretches of desert in the south. In addition, this final section of the journal reflects Magoffin's renewed appreciation for God's mercy in sustaining her through the perils of the road.

Magoffin's journal does not offer a self-conscious account of the process of her initiation into southwestern life, but it does bear witness to the evolution of her consciousness in several revealing ways. The more she learns about the New Mexicans, the more tolerant she is in her evaluations of the Hispanic culture. This does not mean that by the time they arrive in Chihuahua she has developed an egalitarian view of humanity; for example, as evidenced in Santa Fe by her impression of Doña Barcelos, she is unable to appreciate a woman who doesn't conform to eastern standards of "feminine place." But her diary does demonstrate an increased empathy toward people different from herself and hence suggests that she underwent a considerable growth of mind and perspective during her journey. In Santa Fe she was able to make friends and improve her Spanish. She discovered most of the people to be charming and delightful. And she is able to break through the prejudices that she brought with her. For example, although the northern Mexicans were branded with the stigma of cowardice, Magoffin found this charge to be inaccurate: "It is a strange people this. They are not to be called cowards; take them in a mass they are brave, and if they have the right kind of a leader they will stem any tide" (177).

On their trip to Chihuahua, even though the Magoffin caravan was under constant threat of attack from Mexican forces and her brother-in-law, James, was in jail in Mexico, Magoffin's assessment of the Mexicans remained balanced. In El Paso, they took lodging in the house of Señor Cura, a priest who was a prisoner of Colonel Doniphan.[17] Magoffin expressed her love for her host family:

> Our situations are truly singular; we have a brother prisoner in
> Chi.[huhua], while they have one *el Señor* Cura [the priest] held as
> hostage by our army for his safety, and we are here in the same
> house and as I trust, friends. . . . I shall regret deeply when we have
> to leave them; twould be injustice to say that I like one more than
> another for I love them all. (215)

Her friendship with the Curas is thematically significant. Her "knowledge of these people," she writes, "has been extended." Whereas in the parlor at Bent's Fort and in Las Vegas, she had observed the Mexican people with disapproval, her opinion of them now has changed: she is impressed by the Mexican warmth, hospitality, and cleanliness. Magoffin's increased empathy is also illustrated by her altered attitude toward their food. As she made clear during her dinner in Las Vegas, the southwestern dishes were at first "unaccustomed" to her palate. However, by the time she leaves Santa Fe and is on the trail toward Chihuahua, not only does she find the food palatable, but also it is so delicious to her that she wants to learn how to cook it for herself.

On November 26, the wife and daughter of the owner of the San Gabriel house the Magoffins take lodging in come with their *mola* stone and corn and teach her how to make tortillas. Later during the visit, the women exchange knitting techniques. Magoffin writes, "On showing her [the landlady] the much easier mode of the U.S. she seemed much surprised and delighted" (168).

Cooking and knitting—uniquely feminine activities—draw these women together and become a form of discourse for them. Although Magoffin judges the tortilla-making and Mexican way of knitting to be "tedious," her involvement evidences her growing facility to bridge the divisions between herself and the women around her by taking part in their activities.

As she grew to appreciate the hospitality and kindness of the Mexicans, Magoffin became increasingly critical of the manner of her own countrymen. In Chihuahua, for example, she is openly sympathetic to the plight of the residents during the American occupation. She comments on how Colonel Doniphan and his regiment of Missouri volunteers have complete disregard for the property of the town's citizens: "Instead of seeing it [Chihuahua] in its original beauty as I thought to have done twelve months since, I saw it filled with Missouri volunteers who though good to fight are not careful how much they soil the property of a friend much less an enemy" (228–29).

Magoffin's changed view is paired with a gradual change in her status. As she begins to speak Spanish, to learn how to marshal their caravan's camp in her husband's absence, and to haggle successfully in the Santa Fe marketplace, she moves into a southwestern realm of experience and knowledge that is fundamentally different from her previous eastern ways of thinking. Instead of distinguishing herself from the Southwest, she begins to associate herself with her surroundings. For example, whereas she was furious when she thought she had been cheated in the Santa Fe markets, she portrays herself now as a shrewd and experienced businesswoman with the knowledge and skills necessary for successful bartering. While her husband is away, she takes his place behind the counter. Entering the masculine realm of merchant trader, she once again is clearly outside the limited sphere of woman's place as it was so carefully defined by the cult of True Womanhood. In her entry for December 15, she describes one customer as particularly challenging—however, Magoffin the shopkeeper is her equal and refuses to yield even one *pedzao* (bit) in the price. She refers to herself as a "traderess," emphasizing her role in the Magoffin family's business affairs and in the enlarged sphere of social and economic activity as well.

Despite her new status and her changing attitude toward the people and their customs, Magoffin's diary is increasingly filled with manifestations of her trepidation as they head toward Chihuahua. The Apaches surrounded them, coming into their camp and driving off their stock. The Mexicans were advancing on them from the south. Daily she and her husband heard conflicting rumors about American military defeat. And, on January 28, they received news that the Taos people had revolted and murdered American citizens, including the governor, Charles Bent.[18]

Puritan captivity narratives use the Old Testament type of *Judea capta*, the image of Israel suffering in Babylonian captivity, to illustrate the captive's submission to God's rightful chastening. Consciously or unconsciously, Magoffin appeals to this image. Mary Rowlandson's narrative, *A True History of Captivity and Restoration of Mrs. Mary Rowlandson* (1682), begins the public record of American women's encounters with the New World wilderness landscape. Rowlandson presents herself as the meek and frightened white woman, suffering in the wilderness.[19] She has lost a child, and her physical frailty makes it difficult for her to travel. On her own, Rowlandson's narrative suggests, she could not survive, and she submits to God. Similarly, by dwelling on her increased physical and emotional frailty and the barrenness of the landscape, Magoffin lays both the emotional and the pictorial groundwork for the biblical type she is about to invoke.

On February 1, the Magoffin caravan was at the mouth of the Jornada del Muerto.[20] Susan had been eight months on the road. The combination of hazards faced on the strenuous trail, the months of anxiety, the loss of her child, the constant fear of Indian and Mexican hostility, and the guilt in not attending regularly to her religious obligations gave her a continuous sense of fear. And now she is pregnant again. Wondering whether she will ever get home and surely fearing for the survival of her unborn child, she begins a sober reflection upon the extent and seriousness of her sins, revealing a consciousness of her unworthiness. She compares herself to the biblical prodigal son, and she quotes the words of the prodigal when he came to himself.

Like Rowlandson, Magoffin is physically and psychologically exhausted, and she can no longer enjoy the sights that she admits are beautiful but barren. The river bottoms with their lush green vegetation had provided her imagination some respite from the barren landscape during their trip from Independence to Santa Fe, but from Santa Fe to Chihuahua, they were no comfort. Arriving in Fray Cristobal on February 2, Magoffin writes that she can say nothing of its beauty. She tries to imagine what the river bottom would look like in summer: "The River bottom is then green; the cottonwoods are leaved; the stream, though at all times dark and ugly, is more brisk and lively in its flow" (195–96). She has been too long away from the green hills of Kentucky to which she is accustomed. The "green" recalls pastoral comfort, home. She greens the landscape in her imagination in order to come to terms with it and to find an equilibrium within herself. A combination of mental and physical exhaustion brought on by the ordeal of traveling in the starkness of the New Mexico desert have soured Magoffin's perception of the Southwest.

Magoffin attempts to shut herself off from the arid New Mexico landscape. Her diary entries become brief and noncommittal. She makes an entry on February 5 at the Laguna del Muerto, and then she does not write again until February 8, at their river camp somewhere near Robledo and Dona Ana. In her entry of February 14, she admits that the road has ceased to engage her attention. Her closed eyes are invitations to the imagination: her mind is freed from the immediacy of her present condition and a kind of miracle takes place. She writes that God "in his infinite mercy has come near unto [her] when she was far off, and called [her] when [she] sought not after him." She feels him reaching out to her, and she says, "Though I am now in darkness, the Lord has said 'Awake thou that sleepest, and arise from the dead, and Christ shall give thee light'" (204–5). The darkness she feels in the Jornada is indistinguishable from the darkness of the soul that has turned from God. Similar to the captive in the Puritan captivity narrative, Magoffin has now been called from the darkness, and as a consequence the tone of her narrative changes from here on out as she moves into the final entries of her journal. Magoffin is performing grief work.

In *Refiguring the Map of Sorrow*, Mark Allister discusses the relationship between autobiography, nature writing, and grief narrative. He uses the ecological term *ecotone* to apply to works in which the human and natural worlds meet and, more specifically, to books that are about people who move through their mourning by turning to observations of nature. Allister suggests that for authors like Gretel Ehrlich, William Least-Heat Moon, and Peter Matthiessen, the landscape can become a spiritual geography that enables healing. This is the case for Magoffin. As Magoffin intertwines the unfamiliar Jornada with her own inner desolation, she is able dramatize her struggle in metaphors and insights that allow her to work through her grief. In short, at this point, Magoffin retreats into a world created for her by the religious traditions of Christianity. Moving slowly through the spare, raw country of the Southwest, she is the suffering and equally bare protagonist who wants desperately to go home. Although her Kentucky home as she left it cannot be regained, she can return to her starting point — God's eternity.

Despite El Paso's good accommodations, the presence of women, and opportunities for her to attend church, Magoffin feels like a captive. She writes: "We may be seized and murdered in a moment for we are Americans, and though disposed to be peaceable, are here entirely against our own will, judgment and inclination" (215). In Saltillo, she continues to complain of loneliness and isolation. Watching a company of Virginians passing through town on their way to war, "some destined never to return," she notes that one of them was a "youth of apparently eighteen years: his face was pale, young and innocent" (235). There is an implicit protest here against innocence or naiveté lost. Perhaps in this youth she recognizes her own transformation from the trusting wandering princess on the Santa Fe Trail to the suffering, homesick traveler on the road to Matamoros.

On August 1, 1847, she receives a letter from her sister Letty in which she learns that her sister Anna has had a baby. Instead of a joyful response, Magoffin confides to her journal: "I do think a woman *emberaso* [*embarazada*, pregnant] has a hard time of it, some sickness all the time, heart-burn, head-ache, cramp etc. after all this thing of marrying is not what it is cracked up to be" (245). Indeed, Magoffin is not thinking about her sister here. She is addressing her own situation. Although this comment should not be construed to mean that she is not happy in her marriage, she is exposing the gap between her expectations and the reality.

In Monterrey, Magoffin eats cake and drinks champagne with General Zachary Taylor in his tent. She concludes that he is nothing like the stories had led her to believe. Instead of "the uncouth back-woodsman I expected to have seen I find him polite, affable and altogether agreeable" (253), she notes. Magoffin seems even more excited to meet Mrs. Hunter, the American wife of the army quartermaster. She writes, "I can well say that two women meeting after an entire sepperation [*sic*] of twelve months from female society, are certainly a curiosity" (251). Excited to share their adventures and anxieties, she says that they talked nonstop. According to Magoffin, their "tongues were as incessantly in motion as bell clappers in Mexico" (251). The reason for Magoffin's enthusiasm is obvious: she is starved for female companionship. Removed from her family and friends, she has had to rely only on the relationship with her husband. And that has not been enough.

The trip to Mier is distressing, and Magoffin's writing changes in this section of the journal. It comes in short, clear spurts. There is more going on here than her party's haste: Magoffin has lost her reserve. Her journal entries reveal not only glimpses of the war-torn countryside but also her increased anguish: "Till now I've done nothing but travel, every morning up by 1 o'clock and on the road by 3 o'clock jolting over stumps, stones and ditches, half asleep, expecting an attack from Mexicans constantly" (258–59). This description is in profound contrast to the opening "act" of her journey and her anticipation of the trip prior to setting out, where she saw good health as intrinsically linked to travel. Events have proved more complicated than she anticipated at the outset. In particular, there can be little doubt that Magoffin's psychological despair is connected to the hellish terrain. Some details are riveting. For example, she observes that they "passed the bones of murdered countrymen, remains of burned wagons, all destroyed by Mexicans" (259). In order to get potable water, they had to travel three miles "to the burned town of Marine" (259). Here Magoffin reports that she met an old woman who asked to be taken to America. Given Magoffin's attitude toward the landscape, it is telling that she refers to the woman as a "witch."

Nevertheless, her cheerfulness and fortitude in adversity return, and Magoffin concludes her diary with a sense of humor. Although Mier, she writes, is "the most miserable hole imaginable" (259), she is able to make light of their sleeping accommodations. The Magoffins have to share quarters with servants, visitors, boarders, and a Captain Thompson. She writes, "There is no door shut between us, and it is all as *common as one room*" (260). Magoffin says that if she ever has "the pleasure of seeing Mrs. Thompson," she will "make her laugh with the scenes of this night" (260). This is the last episode of her diary. The sentence that comes after—"We have said goodbye to land travel and tomorrow shall take a steamboat for Comargo"—brings her narrative to an abrupt end.

One would like to conclude the story of Magoffin's journal with images of normalcy and stasis—the return to Kentucky and family and friends—but Magoffin ended her journal on September 8, 1847, just before she caught yellow fever at Matamoros, during which time she gave birth to a son. The child died shortly afterward. The Magoffins took a vessel from the Mexican coast to New Orleans and returned to Kentucky to live in Lexington. However, the rigors of the Mexican trip had ruined her health. She bore another son they named James, but he died soon after birth. A fourth child, Jane, was born in 1851 without mishap.[21] In the spring of 1852, the Magoffins moved to St. Louis County, Missouri, and built a home at Barrett's Station, a short distance from Kirkwood. Here Susan gave birth to another daughter, Susan.

Susan Shelby Magoffin died in 1855 at the age of twenty-eight. She was buried in Bellefontaine Cemetery in St. Louis, Missouri.

I seemed to see Hagar, in the wilderness walking wearily away from her fainting child among the dried up bushes, and seating herself in the hot sand. I seemed to become Hagar myself.

SARAH BAYLISS ROYCE
A Narrative of Frontier Housekeeping

The California-Oregon Trail is a 2,000-mile trace across the country by which an estimated 250,000 to 500,000 emigrants traveled to settle California and Oregon between 1840 and 1870. The crossing usually took five to six months with the pioneers traveling between ten and fifteen miles each day. They departed from the Middle West between mid-April and the first of May, just after the spring thaw, when there was usually enough grass on the prairies to feed the livestock.

Approximately 25,450 emigrants traveled overland to the West Coast in 1849.[1] In Wyoming, at a place known as the Parting of the Ways, the trail divided. Only 450 emigrants took the northwesterly Oregon route, also known as the family trail, and as many as 25,000 followed the southwestern route that led to California. Most of the forty-niners on the California trail were young men: these early prospectors rarely brought their families, and they usually didn't intend to stay. No one knows for certain how many women went to California in 1849. Estimates vary from less than 2 percent to as many as 12 percent. One of these rare women to participate in the early years of the California Gold Rush was Sarah Bayliss Royce.

Born in England, at Stratford-on-Avon on March 2, 1819, Sarah Eleanor Bayliss arrived in Philadelphia with her parents, two brothers, and three sisters when she was three months old.[2] After a brief residence in Germantown, Pennsylvania, and New York City, her family moved to

Rochester, New York, when she was nine. Royce graduated from the Phipps Union Female Seminary of Albion, New York, where she studied the liberal and domestic arts along with religion. After graduation, she taught school. Royce's love of books is evidenced on the trip to California. Faced with the need to lighten their wagon's load in the Nevada desert, she never discards her books. Rummaging through jettisoned items from previous wagons, she wisely passes over many treasures, but she selects one book, *Little Ella*, which she reads to her daughter. Royce had a strong religious commitment and was a member of the Church of Disciples of Christ. The observance of the Sabbath was so important to her that on the Overland Trail when they were in Indian country the Royces let the main body of the wagon train go ahead while she and her family "held a social meeting for prayer, reading, and singing."

In May 1845, Sarah Bayliss married Josiah Royce, a Rochester clerk or small tradesman. She was seven years his junior. Their daughter, Mary Eleanor, was born two years later. Shortly afterward, the Royces decided to emigrate, and in 1849, they joined thousands of others and traveled the Overland Trail to the goldfields of California.

When she was sixty years old, Sarah Royce revised and edited her "Pilgrimage Diary" in which she had jotted notes of her life on the frontier, thirty years after most of the episodes had transpired. Published posthumously in 1932 as *A Frontier Lady*, it was written at the request of her son, Josiah Royce, and not for publication. Royce consciously created and shaped her narrative with him in mind. To a son who had rejected Christian philosophy, she fashioned a memorandum of God's dealing with her. Her narrative, in this sense, is reminiscent of spiritual autobiography. This context accounts for the fact that in Royce's memoir the discourse of marital relations is less prominent than in Susan Shelby Magoffin's account. Additionally, whereas Magoffin's narrative authority in the first section of her diary comes from her text's linkage to Josiah Gregg's *Commerce of the Prairies*, Royce's reminiscence gets its authority from her dealings with God.

Magoffin's and Royce's accounts are similar, however, in the way in which they configure the trails in terms of sacrifices to be made and obstacles to be overcome. Like Magoffin in her entries after Ash Creek, Royce presents the discomforts of the journey as aggravated by dangerous river crossings, bad weather conditions, and anxiety about the Indians. What makes Royce's account special among contemporary writings about the West is that she records details about the trail experience that other writers, especially men, tended either to miss or ignore. And whereas most of the story of the mining West tells of the efforts of men,

Sarah Royce,
taken after her husband's death. Courtesy of the Department of Special Collections, Charles E. Young Research Library, University of California–Los Angeles.

Royce's eyewitness account of the gold rush is unusual because it is one in which women matter. Her narrative illuminates the domestic side of the mining camp experience and the active role women played in building new frontier communities.

Royce was a cultivated eastern woman. Like Magoffin, she probably did not anticipate that her journey would compel her to rethink so many of her white, middle-class assumptions. Each of the first three chapters of *A Frontier Lady*—"Plains," "Desert," and "Mountains"—takes her one remove away from the settlements of the East and into the darkness of the western wilderness. Repeatedly, Royce recounts the times she loses hope and resorts to prayer. Often the landscape echoes her physical state. Her complaints of thirst and hunger become a refrain. Threatened by physical hardships she turns to God, and it is this image that becomes the predominant undercurrent of her text. Similar to the second half of Magoffin's narrative, Royce writes in the tradition of the Puritan captivity narratives of the late seventeenth and early eighteenth centuries.[3] Her journey through the wilderness is both literal and symbolic: her physical suffering mirrors her spiritual affliction. In her move from plains, through desert, over mountains, and into El Dorado, she journeys simultaneously toward submission and self-sufficiency.

The persona Royce creates in her narrative is that of a hardy woman of great courage and fortitude. Her writing reveals her daily routine on the frontier and the ways in which she asserts herself. But her daily tasks do not divert her from her relationship with God, and during the course of her account, we witness her increased faith. In times of despair, she not only prayed to God, but she believed she walked with him "amid the jagged, broken, and barren peaks," and saw him literally, "amid the desolation of the lonely plains—for who else was there but God in the desert to be seen?" For Royce, God is not an abstraction, an entity detached from time. She feels his presence during her frontier experiences—the trip west, the life in the primitive California settlements, and moments of loss, grief, and fear. As a result, Royce is never wholly alone: she comes to realize that God dwells where she dwells.

While much has been written of men's changing self-definition brought about by their experience in the frontier West, change in women's definition has seldom been addressed. Royce's narrative dramatizes her alteration. Always on the move, she is constantly modifying her own perspective toward what she encounters. Although Royce honors the codes of domesticity, she radically redefines traditional domestic arts in order to adjust to the challenges of frontier housekeeping. And she uses travel—not domesticity—as the central defining cause of her transformation. Significantly, her narrative begins in motion and concludes with Royce still unsettled. At no time in her story is there any stability of the home place, even though Royce is writing her reminiscence from a stable location. Finally, she uses the title of her narrative to reinforce her change. It is an eastern-reared woman who sets out for California on April 30, 1849, but it is *a frontier lady* who recounts her westering experience.

*   *   *   *

Like thousands of other families, the Royces were lured westward by James Marshall's fateful discovery of gold in January 1848. They left their home in Rochester, New York, for eastern Iowa and moved to a farming village three miles from Tipton where they began preparing for their trip to California. From there, on April 30, 1849, they set out for the goldfields. Although the weather looked threatening, Royce didn't want to delay their departure: "Had I not made up my mind to encounter many storms? If we were going, let us go, and meet what we were to meet, bravely" (3). In contrast to Magoffin's youthful excitement in her

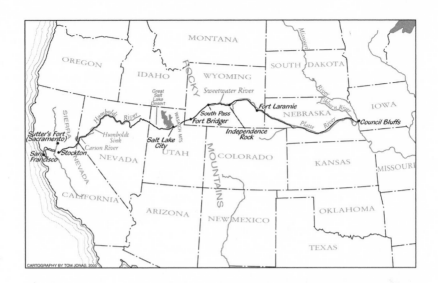

California trail traveled by Sarah Royce. Map by Tom Jonas.

first entry, Royce's leave-taking, even in reminiscence, is painful. Unlike Magoffin who was simply traveling through the frontier and returning home, Royce was journeying west to take up residence. She was leaving behind household goods, symbols of comfortable domesticity. Most important, she was bidding farewell to family and friends who in all likelihood she would never see again. Her "leaving" is, therefore, a home-leaving, a drastic cutting loose from a way of acting and relating that had been handed down to her from generation to generation. It was not just a physical removal.

After holding in her emotion during the first night of homesickness, Royce wrote that "in the morning there was a mildly exultant feeling which comes from having kept silent through a cowardly fit, and finding the fit gone off" (5). The emotional restraint that Royce evidences here sets the pattern of her self-representation. From the outset, she casts herself as a woman who is able to adapt with equanimity to the unusual situations of western travel.

It took the Royces one month and four days to reach Council Bluffs, Iowa, their jumping-off place[4] for "the grand pilgrimage" (3). Rain, wind, and mud accompanied their trip to Council Bluffs, but it was "merely introductory to the journey proper to California," she writes (3). The Kanesville/Council Bluffs outfitting town had begun as a Mormon way station on the emigration route to the Salt Lake Valley. For

Royce, the town was the last taste of civilization before setting out for the wilderness. As she crossed its threshold, she began to slip out of social relationships and familiar spaces that formed her stable, eastern identity.

It is not at all surprising that we hear the ambivalence in Royce's narrative voice. Like Magoffin, Royce is venturing into an unknown literal landscape and into an unfamiliar psychological wilderness. She is carrying with her deeply engrained nineteenth-century gendered ideologies, which include assertions that women should stay in the domestic sphere and protect traditional values. Although men also care for the values of home and family, they are socialized in ways that allow them to function in the public sphere. Clearly, then, migrating women faced conditions that threatened to undermine their constructions of self-identity that the home front represented. In this chapter, I argue that Royce's journey forces her to reexamine the concept of "home" in the context of travel. For her, the space marked "home" is no longer determined by a geographic place. Her narrative chronicles the ways in which she articulates a more abstracted sense of home amid a condition of homelessness. When she encounters the unfamiliar environment of the West, her sense of self is altered. An effect of this alteration is a reassessment of her understanding of belonging and a reestablishment of her familial, communal, and spiritual ties.

Royce describes Council Bluffs as a "city of wagons" (8).[5] She remarks on the scarcity of women and notes that when men were accompanied by wives and children, "their wagons were easily distinguished by the greater number of conveniences" and the "household articles they carried." According to Royce, these wagons had a more "home-like" look (8–9). Similar to Magoffin's canvas home, this image of the "moving" houses undercuts the notion of a house as a familiar place of stability. Royce's wagon home was carrying her into a foreign country and away from all things familiar.

Even the presence of women travelers gives her little comfort and consolation. Although the few women who caught glimpses of each other were in general very kind, she remembers that "there was no motive for any particular mutual interest" because they were about to travel in different companies (9). Indeed, their existence highlights Royce's feelings of estrangement. They do not reach out or express welcome. They simply stand there.

As discussed in chapter 1, in the Hispanic villages and pueblos, Magoffin notes the reciprocal gaze between the women and herself as one of extreme interest in the exotic nature of the other. They shared a mutual curiosity. In these scenes Magoffin is both subject and object: as Magoffin was looking at them, so they were looking at her. To each, the other was exquisitely strange. On several occasions she becomes extremely uncomfortable under their gaze, and she has to draw her veil.

The westering women that Royce sees, on the other hand, are not exotic. They are forty-niners like herself. And yet, despite their similarity, Royce casts these women into an iconic "they." Instead of focusing on their commonality, she portrays the women still within sight of each other, yet already outside the sphere of their previous connections of female solidarity and under the pall of the trip's isolation. In Royce's scrutiny of the women watching each other and their recognition of not only their prior kinship but of a new kind of separation from each other occasioned by the trip they were about to undertake, she is suggesting the variable nature of both home, relations, and identity. The westward journey involves the modification of ordinary relations. Just as the home itself cannot be transferred undisturbed, so Royce and her relationships are complicated by travel.

Usually in early May, after the grass ripened into forage, the overlanders began their formidable journey across half a continent. Ominously, Royce's company leaves June 10, much too late in the season to be setting out. As they pull out of the Missouri River frontier town with their "little all," an Indian agent bids them goodbye. Royce writes that it was her "farewell to the fag-end of civilization on the Atlantic side of the continent" (10). This rupture with the home country, similar to Magoffin's feelings of separation from her "dear native land" as she crosses the Arkansas, is the last glance at familiar terrain before heading into the uncharted wilderness. Interestingly, Royce is at the start of her trip when she feels this break, while Magoffin is well into her journey. One way to account for their difference is that Magoffin is an on-the-scene chronicler and is oblivious to the hardships that await her. Royce, on the other hand, is writing an account years after the fact and from the perspective of the entire trip and its psychological costs. Another difference is their class. In the early stages of the journey, Magoffin is a tourist traveling in luxury and for pleasure. Royce is middle class, and she travels with no servants to carry out the trail duties. Additionally, she has a two-year-old child to care for, and when we do get an occasional glimpse of her husband, he is nothing like the doting and concerned Samuel Magoffin.[6]

Royce remarks that they were "guided only by the light of Frémont's *Travels,* and the suggestions, often conflicting, of the many who, like ourselves, utter strangers to camping life, were setting out for the 'Golden Gate'" (3). Virtually all the major overland guidebooks prior to the 1860s were written by men and for men.[7] As a consequence, they were not particularly useful for women emigrants. As Lillian Schlissel notes, one of the reasons women kept diaries of their overland travel was to share their experiences with the westering women who would come after them (82). They felt the need to compensate for the lack of information women had about the ordeal of traveling for five or six months with children. The guidebooks written by men didn't detail how to cook for entire families, or how to make beds in tents, or how to keep infants clean when water was too scarce to be used for washing. The guides' advice to travel with only the absolute essentials reinforced the notion that women and their domestic world were an unnecessary encumbrance on the trail. Although Royce challenges the conception of woman as irrelevant and separate from the realm of movement, she realizes the lack of appropriate "light" for women traveling outside the boundaries of instituted roles.

Almost everyone going west on the overland route joined a company. Communal efforts were significant in helping to avoid tragedy: the goal was to ensure that sufficient manpower would be available for whatever contingency might arise along the way. When emigrants set foot on the right bank of the Missouri River, they were in Indian country and outside the pale of civil law. The companies were surrogate societies, designed to carry a sense of law and government along with them. After they crossed the Missouri River, the men in Royce's group began to organize into a "regular company" by appointing a captain and subordinate officers. Participants usually signed a document that spelled out the rules of conduct, but disagreements and deviations often occurred before the first bend in the road. Royce notes that a few members of their group, including herself, tried to incorporate in the bylaws a rule that Sundays would be a day of rest. However, the majority disagreed, insisting that the lateness of the season made it imperative that there be no interruption in the travel.

Some overlanders wanted to abandon the journey and return home. The contemptuous term "backed-out Californians" referred to those who did so. Royce writes that there were some in her party who desired to turn back, but they stayed because they were involved in family or business relations. The term "backed-out" is telling. It suggests that the emigrants were facing west, both literally and psychologically. Their backs were to the home country. Their journey, then, called for turning their faces toward the unknown rather than aligning themselves with what was fixed, rooted, and stable. There is the sense, too, that their linkage to social relations will become increasingly critical as they move farther away from their geographical home space.

Whereas those who took the ocean route to the goldfields suffered from boredom, the Overland Trail emigrants wrote of their journey as characterized by the exhausting grind of unaccustomed duties that soon became routine work.[8] Royce reported that everyone on the trail pitched in to do what had to be done. According to John Mack Faragher, men and women had different trail responsibilities. Men dominated the leadership process and their work focused on keeping the party moving: getting the wagons, stock, and family safely through to California. Women's duties consisted of cooking, washing, and caring for children. Royce observed that in "the few cases where there were women they were, without exception, seen doing their full share of the work" (12). She recalled that while the men met to organize their train, "the few women in the company were busy meantime in cooking, washing, mending up clothes, etc." Although these chores done by the women fall under the category of domestic and within the realm of housework done by women in general in this period, on the trail they were accomplished under difficult conditions. Many women in their diaries, Royce and Magoffin included, applaud themselves for their inventiveness in producing a semblance of domestic order out of meager resources and in primitive conditions.

What makes up the detailed pattern or rhythm of westering women's diaries varies. Some women simply recount the daily tasks. Other diarists comment on the scenery, naming the flowers, herbs, and varieties of grass, especially during the beginning of the trip. Others detail the tensions that build up among the party members. The predictable characteristic of women's trail narratives is their concern with death. There is hardly an overland diary of the 1840s that does not record the death, usually a result of disease, of a family member along the way. According to historian John Unruh, disease was responsible for nine out of every ten overland emigrant deaths en route (408). Of all the illnesses the emigrants encountered, cholera was the most common.[9] Introduced by way of the port of New Orleans, it traveled up the Mississippi to St. Louis, where four thousand people died in 1849. From that time on, cholera was endemic on the trail. It would strike suddenly, often killing the victim within hours of the first symptoms. Death was imminent, Royce wrote, and "made our wagon his first point of attack."

The oldest of the men in Royce's company died of cholera not long after they left Council Bluffs. Royce describes the body of the deceased "stretched upon a rudely, constructed bier" beside their wagon (14). Her family having been exposed to the contagion, Royce contemplates the prospect of having to leave her child or husband in an unmarked wilderness grave. Three days later, two more of their company die, and Royce recalls the gloom that hung over their group as they contemplated their own mortality. Praying to God, she meekly submits to his will, and immediately a "peace took possession of [her] soul, and spite of threaten-ing ills, [she] felt strong for duty and endurance" (17). Her submission and God's consolation are reminiscent of the Puritan captivity narratives' use of the Old Testament type of *Judea capta*, the image of Israel suffer-ing in Babylonian captivity, as discussed in chapter 1 with regard to Magoffin's presentation of her narrative self in the Jornada del Muerto. Whereas it isn't clear whether Magoffin employs this image consciously or unconsciously, Royce is purposefully using the biblical type to invoke the image of the frightened and lost soul suffering in a spiritual wilder-ness away from God. Royce's literal and spiritual conditions rest in a Job-like submission, and her adaptability to suffering on the trail comes from this position of acceptance.

As the trail passes through the Black Hills, Royce eyes the countryside with curiosity and comments on the beauty and variety of the scenery: the mountain stream, the sparkling waters of a babbling brook, and the pleas-ant surroundings of the tall grasses. However, this perspective changes abruptly on July 16, when the region becomes destitute of vegetation. Royce notes that because they had started late out of Council Bluffs, the cattle preceding them had eaten all the grass near the road. Now in the evenings the stock had to be driven a distance to graze, so the company divided in two. The older men stayed with the wagons, and the others drove the cattle up the valley; on one occasion, they had to take the cattle fifteen miles away from the trail before they could find enough grass. This juxtaposition of the praise of the wilderness beauty with the sudden deso-lation is pointed. What was hours ago the garden of plenty has become a rugged wilderness whose physical hardships might well destroy them. Royce disabuses her readers of their pastoral fantasies and depicts instead an unpredictable and, therefore, inhospitable landscape that ominously foreshadows events to come. Her wagon home is no secure haven, and the terrain itself is alien and constantly changing. The only "solid ground" under the traveler's feet is provided by her faith in God.

If concern with death is the most prominent characteristic in women's trail narratives, the second predictable trait is their record of the geological trail markers along the way. Even though most overlanders, including Royce, configured the land as a foreign place, it was not totally unfamiliar. A series of landmarks—Courthouse Rock, Chimney Rock, Scott's Bluff, and Devil's Gate—had been meticulously described and named by such earlier travelers as John Charles Frémont. These descrip-tions of geologic formations break the gloomy tabulations of graves. Most important for the emigrants, they served as markers of the remain-ing distance to the journey's end and as gauges of their progress. They knew, for example, that if they arrived at Independence Rock, the most famous landmark west of Fort Laramie, later than July 4, they would have an increased risk of snows in the mountains later on.

The Royces reached Independence Rock on July 26. John C. Frémont encamped near here in 1842. He engraved his name on the rock and made a lengthy description of the place in his *Report of the Exploring Expedition*. In contrast to the scientific discourse that Frémont uses to describe the rock, Royce writes that "at a distance one might fancy it an enormous elephant kneeling down" (25). She describes the granite outcrop as a "bare mass of rock, without vegetation, rising directly from the flat, sandy land bordering the river." Widely known as the site that marked the approximate halfway point of the overland journey, the rock was famous for the emigrants' proclivity for carving their names on it so that travelers who followed in their footsteps would know they had passed that way. Determined to ascend the famous landmark, Royce takes her daughter with her—"that she might have it to remember, and tell of" (25). Recalling that the view she enjoyed from the top "fully paid for the labor" of the climb, Royce experiences, enjoys even, her success. Her struggle up the granite outcrop—the antithesis of the issues of home and private sphere usually found in discourses by women—is rewarded by the view.

Similar to Pawnee Rock, the sandstone register where Magoffin leaves her inscription, Independence Rock is a place where writing occurs. Like Frémont, Royce will carve her name into the rock so that others will acknowledge her presence in this frontier space. However, because she brings her daughter with her, she marks her presence, not as a rugged and masculine individual, but as a woman and a mother. From the top, she has a sweeping view of the surrounding country. Although it is a terrain that she is merely passing through, she still takes the time to make her connection with it, to textualize it, both by writing on the rock and by writing in her narrative about its significance.

Royce renders her landscape with an enthusiastic eye. She describes not only the scene but also her own involvement with it. Her personal response brings her society's values to bear on the wild country. Barbara Bender notes that when we "perceive" landscapes, "we are the point from which the 'seeing' occurs," and as a consequence, it becomes an "ego-centered landscape, a perspectival landscape" (1). According to Bender, this engagement may be a way of "laying claims, or justifying and legitimating a particular place in the world" (2). Nineteenth-century westering diarists, like Royce, used their writing to negotiate the unfamiliar and to position themselves in their unknown surroundings. Similar to Royce, they both reinforce and control their own sense of self and make the unfamiliar place more knowable by placing their names on the rock.

Like most forty-niners, Royce failed to describe the ecological implications of the overland migrations or concern for the Indians who they were displacing. Although her predominant characterization of the Indians was as an ever-present threat, in actuality they did not pose a serious danger for the emigrants.[10] According to John Unruh, from 1840 to 1860, Indians killed approximately 362 emigrants. However, during this same time period, 462 Indians were killed by emigrants (185). In the 1840s and early 1850s, the few Indians the overlanders did encounter demanded tribute in exchange for passage through their territory. When the Indians asked for a token gift for traveling across their land, the men of Royce's company refused to comply with the "unreasonable" demand (13). Instead of attempting to understand the Indian customs of hospitality, Royce was annoyed by what she viewed as their begging and pilfering. Although many women who went west changed their minds to a more positive view of Indians, Royce does not. She becomes anxious and overwrought at each encounter. While there is a recognition in her narrative that the emigrants are unwelcome in territory that is not theirs, she perceives the Indians according to stereotypes customarily used to dehumanize people so as to make it easier on the trespassers' consciousness.

Crossing the Rocky Mountains, Royce takes her last look "at the waters that flowed eastward, to mingle with the streams and wash the shores where childhood and early youth had been spent" and where all she loved, "save, O, so small a number, lived" (26–27). The pass was so easy and gradual that it would have gone unnoticed if it had not been for their guidebook's directions. Royce desires to mark the spot with a pillar of rocks and to write on one of the stones Samuel's words of gratitude: "Ebenezer, hitherto hath the Lord helped us." However, the place was so desolate that she could not find branches, sticks, or pebbles with which to fashion her roadside altar. She "stood still upon the spot till the two wagons and the little company had passed out of hearing; and when [she] left not a visible sign marked the place" (27). Her attempt to commemorate the site with an altar of stones is thwarted because of the barrenness of the place, but her language in this passage—"I stood still upon the spot"— suggests that she has forged a link with the site on a spiritual level. Royce describes this moment of thanksgiving as utter stillness. She is outwardly motionless but inwardly moved.

Looking toward an unknown future in the West, Royce remembers to thank God for the help he has provided in their journey thus far. If for Royce, home is where God is, she reminds herself that God is here in this "desolate" place, and, therefore, even in such wild terrain, she can re-create a semblance of the idea of home. The sacred is not an aspect of a particular place: it is created and maintained by intentional human effort. Royce's affirmation of the sacredness of the occasion alters her percep-tion of the hostile and isolated area, and as such it is a gesture that fosters her connection to the physical space. This empowering knowledge that Royce claims for herself and her family reinforces her narrative's thesis. Set in motion with the act of leave-taking, Royce's text evidences the ways in which her feelings of homelessness encourage her to foster new and more flexible definitions of home, definitions not linked to a specific location.

The Wasatch Mountains offered the wildest scenery their party had as yet seen. The dust was so excessive that it was like "wading in a bed of fine ashes." At the entrance of Great Salt Lake Valley, members of Royce's party "faced each other with mutual looks of wonder" because they were unrecognizable to each other under their dust coverings. This image of the dust-covered emigrants reveals the transforming effects of the trail. The emigrants are so altered from their former selves that they don't recognize themselves or their companions. The hem of her skirt with its perpetual ring of caked mud, her hair dulled by the alkali, and her skin burned to the color of hazelnuts, Royce—her cleanliness and dress symbols of her gendered and cultural difference—is literally and symbol-ically altered from her eastern self.[11] And this alteration is a direct result of the rigors of the journey. Consider them: the physical indignities of trail life, especially for a young woman in the company of mostly men; the constant mental and emotional strain; the irrevocable separation from friends and family; and not least of all, the knowledge that they were stragglers and that the trail saved some of the harshest trials until the end when both oxen and travelers were exhausted.

Most overlanders who took the route through Salt Lake City stayed at least a week, reorganizing companies, eating fresh vegetables, and sat-isfying their curiosity about the Mormons. Arriving in Salt Lake City on August 18, the Royces spend eleven days resting and questioning what to do. A party was being organized to take a southern route through Los Angeles, but Josiah Royce decides to cross the Sierras, even though it was considered too late in the season.[12] Royce gives no reason as to what prompts her husband's decision. Although she remembers that they "coolly talked it over," she labels their final decision "perverse" (33). Per-haps he was impatient to arrive at the goldfields. Maybe he was confident he would be able to handle the arduous country ahead of them. Whatever convinced him to attempt the Sierras at such a late date without other experienced travelers, it was apparently enough to persuade only one person: an elderly man in poor health agrees to accompany them (34). On August 30, the Royce party with their solitary wagon and three yoke of oxen start over the Salt Lake cutoff. Their only guide is two small sheets of notepaper entitled "Best Guide to the Gold Mines, 816 miles, by Ira J. Willes, GSL City."[13]

After the Royces had traveled a few days, two "shiftless" young men approached and asked to join their group. It was common on the trail for single men to travel within the family system: young men would often approach a family or party leader with an offer of assistance in exchange for board. As Royce notes, the extra men meant more protection, but the situation also had its drawbacks. Their wagon was packed with a very small margin of provisions for contingencies, and food and water for the desert crossing were crucial. Now they would be forced to share the little that they had with these new members of their group. Here Royce illustrates how accommodations to frontier life involved having to place trust in strangers from diverse backgrounds on short acquaintance. Whereas the traditional notion of home is built on a sense of purely private space and a membership based on blood ties, overland travel required an expansion of the familial community. Instead of relationships held together by bonds of love and natal culture, overlanders like the Royces formed bonds with others as a necessary means of survival in the frontier. The tie between the members is made because they are traveling outside their legitimate ("home") space. Frontier travel, therefore, encourages Royce not only to enlarge her definition of home but also to adjust to reconfigurations of her family unit and to reassess her understanding of belonging.

Perhaps Frederick Jackson Turner's early emphasis on the heroic individual confronting the environment is responsible for the lack of scholarly attention to the role of kinship networks in the westering migration. However, the importance of group relationships, as evidenced by westering women's diaries, can no longer be ignored. Royce's narrative is not about the rugged, lone frontier traveler. It is about the complex series of interrelationships that are essential to survival in the West. The army outposts, the creation of wagon train companies, the Mormon guidance in Salt Lake City, the Sierra relief parties, and the San Francisco Benevolent Society establish this important motif in her narrative.

On October 2, somewhere on the alkali plains between the Humboldt Sink and the Carson River, the inexperienced party makes a disastrous mistake. Setting out before daybreak in order to avoid the heat, they take the wrong branch of the trail and enter the desert crossing instead of taking a side road and stopping at the meadows to feed their oxen on the precious grass and to fill their containers with water. Not realizing their error until they are far upon the desert, they have to turn back. Royce remembers her terror:

> Turn back! What a chill the words sent through one. Turn back, on a journey like that; in which every mile had been gained by most earnest labor, growing more and more intense, until, or late, it had seemed that the certainty of advance with every step, was all that made the next step possible. And now for miles we were to go back. In all that long journey no steps ever seemed so heavy, so hard to take, as those with which I turned my back to the sun that afternoon of October 4, 1849. (45)

Retracing their steps, they meet another little party of stragglers en route to the California goldfields. This group was short of supplies and hurrying to cross the Sierras before the onset of the winter season. Josiah asks for grass and water to get their team over the desert, but the reply is a unanimous no. However, the one woman in their group pities the Royces' situation, and Royce notes that had the decision been up to this woman, she would have insisted on sharing their feed and water.

Significantly, Royce depicts their predicament through the sympathizing eyes of the emigrant housewife. The land has overpowered the Royces, and they cannot even expect relief from their fellow man. However, she does not clearly condemn the group's lack of charity. There is no accusation or recrimination. Instead, her text points to their only source of hope: God.

This reliance on God becomes even clearer in the scene that follows. As Royce recalls the days of their march back toward the Humboldt Sink, she dwells on their discouragement. The little water they had with them is nearly gone and their oxen are in danger of dying. With something approaching desperation, she prays as she walks. Moving slowly through the heavy sand, she finds her imagination acting intensely. Royce remembers: "I seemed to see Hagar, in the wilderness walking wearily away from her fainting child among the dried up bushes, and seating herself in the hot sand. I seemed to become Hagar myself" (49). Hagar, Abraham's outcast slave, wandered alone and pregnant in the desert. An angel appeared to her and promised that her offspring would be "too many to count" (Gen. 16:10). The first woman since Eve to have a vision of divinity, Hagar knows both that she is watched over by God and that even though she is a slave, she can behold the Light. Contemplating Hagar, Royce feels time slide away, as if Hagar's perceptions have become her own. Time and eternity intersect. Royce, the reminiscing narrator, uses Hagar to instruct her reader. Hagar knows that God hears her weeping. Similar to Hagar,

Royce's persona is homeless and wandering in the desert. She must learn to rely on God as Hagar did.

That noon, Royce's group came to a cluster of sage bushes and a fire left by some campers. Smoke was still visible. Suddenly before Royce "a bright flame sprang up at the foot of a small bush." Feeling the presence of God in this burning sage bush, she began to speak to Him and felt in response a strange illogical peace, which gave her the illusion "of being a wanderer in a far off, old time desert" (50). These mystical experiences free her mind from the immediacy of her present condition and make possible a regenerative and transforming connection with both Hagar and Moses, other persons in another time and place. They reinspire her trust in God for his protection and provision. Significantly, Royce's visions involve both Hagar and Moses, thus illustrating her ability to closely connect with both female and male biblical personas.

God is not only the God of Abraham—he is the God of Sarah. In the desert Royce experiences God directly. Her emphasis is as much on herself as on God. Trusting that God will watch over her and her family in the wilderness and grateful for his loving presence, Royce is not passive. As she retells her experience to her son for his conversion, she emphasizes the need for trust and gratitude. Both are choices that require effort and leaps of faith for Royce, given her perilous situation.

After three days at the Humboldt Sink, Royce's party once again faces the Forty-Mile Desert gauntlet and the vicious heat of the unrelenting sun. Two of their travel-weary oxen die of exhaustion. And the party's reward for braving the rigors of the desert is the seventy-mile trek up the eastern slope of the Sierra Nevada. Emigrants at this point on the trail often found that their wagons had to be lightened so the remaining animals would survive. Royce comments on the array of discarded supplies along the road. Most gold rushers in 1849 overpacked for the journey and were forced to leave many of their supplies along the trail. Royce describes the trunks, papers, boxes, and even deserted wagons littering their path. She notes that although there were many things among the discarded goods that would have been valuable in a civilized scene, she could see few items—given her present condition—worthy of picking up. The rugged necessities of the trail have fractured her old ways of seeing. Now the seasoned frontier woman, Royce reminds her readers to travel light. Dresses, trunks, and boxes count for nothing when crossing a life-threatening desert or climbing the daunting Sierra Nevada. The metaphor of baggage is both material and psychological: excess luggage retards movement. Royce's "little all," a phrase that she repeatedly uses, suggests the regard she has for what can be salvaged from the past and taken with her to the new location. But her emphasis is on the lightness of her load.

The two men the Royces had picked up outside Salt Lake City begin to whisper together about how much easier it would be to leave the slower-moving Royces behind. Shortly after, they move on ahead. With the loss of the two men, Royce begins to despair and again resorts to prayer. Similar to the desert section of her narrative, Royce acts as her reader's spiritual guide: she assures him or her that although the literal wilderness continually threatens her, she is mistress of the symbolic one.

As Royce prays for help, the party notices dust rising in the hills ahead. Suddenly out of the dust ride two horsemen, each leading a pack mule. Their loose garments flap at their sides like wings, and the thought runs through Royce's mind that the men look "heaven-sent" (63). Miraculously, the first words from one of the strangers are "Well, sir, you are the man we are after!" The men are from a military party that had been sent out by the U.S. government to bring in the last of the emigrants, and the emigrants they had just relieved were those whom the Royces had seen in the desert.[14] The sympathetic woman in the party had pleaded with the relief committee to rescue the straggling wagon. The relief expedition's assistance of the overland emigrants who had found themselves in dire straits further epitomizes the concept of overland community. Royce writes that she stood "in adoration, breathing, in [her] inmost heart, thanksgiving to that Providential Hand . . . which had wrought out for [them] so unlooked for a deliverance" (64).

As a spiritual autobiography, Royce's account has its roots in Puritan beliefs and the Puritan practice of conversion narratives.[15] Designed to be read for evidence of God's dealings with the soul, these narratives were to be viewed in relation to the scriptural metatext. Furthermore, while they recorded individual experiences, they were also communal events: Puritan congregations listened to the conversion narratives in order to be spiritually strengthened. Just as the cooperative efforts of the emigrants involved cohesive interdependence among those who were traveling the Overland Trail, Royce's autobiography acts within a social context in its expectation that her life story will be spiritually useful to others and will strengthen the community. Her narrative has, to borrow Jane Tompkins's insight about nineteenth-century women's fiction, designs upon the reader, primarily upon her son—a lapsed Christian.

Mounted on a mule, Royce made her way with the rest of her party across the Sierra Nevada by the Mormon Trail–Carson Pass route. This trail had been opened in mid-1848 by a group of Mormon Battalion veterans. It comes up the Carson River Valley to the area of what is today Genoa and then heads up the narrow canyon of the West Carson River, westward across Hope Valley and around Red Lake. The emigrants then climbed Devil's Ladder and crossed the first summit in the Carson Pass area. On October 19, they crossed the highest ridge and viewed what Royce called "the promised land." As she looked down into the Sacramento Valley and into California's "smiling face," she wrote, "I loved you from that moment, for you seemed to welcome me with loving look into rest and safety" (72).

Despite her romanticism, her first glance must have tested her psychological fortitude. After their 2,000-mile trek from Council Bluffs, they had nothing to welcome them but a raw frontier. And if she had harbored any dreams of immediately establishing a permanent home, she would be disappointed in the years ahead because their arrival in California initiated a nomadic existence of successive removals to mining camps and to the burgeoning gold rush centers of Sacramento and San Francisco.

The Royces arrived in the Sierra foothill mining camp of Weaverville, better known as Webertown or Weberville, a few miles outside Placerville. They set up a tent alongside a creek bed and began panning for gold. As a covered wagon woman, Royce must have craved the comforts of a grounded home. She remembers that she was at first "like a child fixing a play-house" (79), but with a "lurking feeling of want of security from having only a cloth wall" between her family and the "out of doors." Her anxiety rested not only on an appreciation of the physical danger, but on a far deeper fear of the loss of civilization. Despite the fact that her home is now a tent, her narrative is careful to emphasize that Royce herself still exhibits the unmistakable features of the stereotypical middle-class eastern woman. She sings while she fixes her "play-house," and she is the gracious hostess when miners drop by for a visit. In other words, she emphasizes her feminine self as she domesticates her wilderness dwelling through her homemaking activity. And just as she had to learn new techniques to do familiar and unfamiliar chores on the trail, so now she has to devise new domestic techniques to meet the challenge of living in a tent.

The California gold seekers were not settlers or pioneers in the tradition of America's westward migration.[16] They were a disparate assortment of transients and strangers, ready to take and not to build. "All were absorbed in washing out gold, or hunting for some to wash, that they could not think of doing anything else," Royce wrote (84). Concerned with how to make the greatest amount of money in the shortest time, they shared an indifference toward California and its future. Most did not want to be tied down or burdened by social responsibility. There were few jails; vigilante justice was often violent, brutal, and inflicted quickly so as not to delay those called upon to pass judgment. One story Royce tells is of three thieves in a nearby town who had been tried by a vigilante committee and hanged, thus giving the name "Hang-Town" to the place. In 1849, however, there was still little crime in the camps, and Royce admits that the Hang-Town incident was the exception.

For example, she observed "buck-skin purses half full of gold-dust, lying on a rock near the road side, while the owners were working some distance off" (80). She writes that "before long [she] felt as secure in [her] tent with curtain tied in front, as [she] had formerly felt with locked and bolted doors" (81). Royce's sense of self-confidence is clearly evidenced in this passage. She associates her feeling of safety with her new house, but significantly, she works within a wilderness construction—a cloth tie instead of a bolt and canvas walls instead of wood or brick. Her concept of home has been pared down. Her self-confidence comes not from a home in the traditional sense, but from a dwelling that is not as secure and is less seclusionary.

In 1850 less than 8 percent of the total inhabitants of California were women. Including Royce, there were three women forming the female population at Weaverville. The miners considered it a privilege just to look at a member of the opposite sex. Royce tells of one forty-niner who asked to speak to her daughter Mary because he had seen "so few ladies and children in California" (80). As a consequence of this gender crisis, women had the opportunity to be paid for the domestic duties they had always performed for free in the past. Many goldrushing women worked—and not just as prostitutes or schoolteachers, as some histories suggest. They were boardinghouse keepers, missionaries, and cooks. These women mined their gold by working for others. Royce reports that one of the Weaverville women was exultant because she had just received an offer of a hundred dollars a month to cook three meals a day for a hotel owner's boarders. Plain and "acquainted only with country life," this woman felt that "her prospect of making money was very enviable" (82). Even her husband was "highly pleased that his wife could earn so much." Royce observes that when she saw the woman again after some time, she was "much changed in style." With a new hairstyle and a fancy gown, she came to invite Royce to an upcoming dance. Amused, Royce notes that it was her first invitation to "society" in California: "It gave me a glimpse of the ease with which the homeliest if not the oldest, might become a 'belle' in those early days, if she only had the ambition; and was willing to accept the honor, in the offered way" (84).

Julie Roy Jeffrey, in *Frontier Women*, argues that pioneer women brought eastern sex-role standards west with them. In her study, which was based on a broad geographical area, she contends that pioneer women were affected by nineteenth-century ideals of gentility—that a "true woman" should be obedient, pious, and pure. However, although evidence from women's narratives does suggest that female respectability was a means of self-protection and a way to attain status in a strange, new environment, the diaries, journals, and letters from California goldrushing women indicate that a woman's ultimate power in the mining camps came not from male deference, but from her own productive responsibilities. The working women who cooked, sewed, and washed frequently earned more from their efforts than their mining husbands. Contrary to the nineteenth-century stereotype of feminine helplessness, narratives like Royce's indicate that pioneer women took action to manage their lives, and they were often the breadwinners and wage earners.

Ninety-nine out of a hundred men in the California placer diggings were lucky to make expenses, and the Royces soon discovered that "mining was a lottery" (113). Unsuccessful, Josiah formed a partnership with two or three acquaintances and opened a store to serve the miners. Sarah worked behind the counter, selling supplies to the residents of Weaverville. Although she remains traditional enough to see her income as family funds, she is once again outside the proscribed private, domestic female sphere. Similar to her experience on the trail, the difference between women's and men's work in the mining camps is blurred. Standing alongside her husband behind the store counter, Royce is able to take on responsibilities that were considered to be masculine and public. Like the trail, the store represents the site where the gendered ideologies of masculine adventurous enterprise and the sheltered world of women and home intersect. Even though she is no longer in the wagon and on the journey west, Royce continues to locate herself outside conventional notions of home and community.

Many critics, among them Gaston Bachelard, Yi-Fu Tuan, and J. Douglas Porteous, stress the connection of home and self-identity. The association of home and the female can be applied easily to Royce's narrative because her continual reconfiguration of home and self are central to her thesis. Her wagon and canvas tent identify her as transient and unstable. As I mentioned earlier, Royce's narrative begins in movement, not from the secure position of her home in the East. She propels her readers through her text by taking them from one location to another, never allowing them to stay for long in any spot. And significantly, she doesn't end her text from a position of conventional home and security. Even in the final chapter of her memoir, she does not have a permanent, stable, and traditional home. Her narrative remains open-ended; home and self-identity remain unsettled. She is, in the biblical phrase, a "stranger in a strange land." A pilgrim on earth, her real home is to be found with God after her death. Part of her intention seems to be to make her readers question their own feelings about self and home.

Royce advocates struggle and change. She counters the stereotype of westering as a male enterprise in which women played a largely inconspicuous role. She is the central character in her text. From her vantage point in the wagon or behind the counter of the Weaverville store, she is able to comment on the men and women she meets who are different from her middle-class, eastern self. Her continual removals encourage her to see in less exclusionary ways. For example, as a well-bred easterner, it would have been easy for her to approach the Weaverville gold rushers with a critical eye. Instead, not only does she readily admit to the prejudices she brought with her, but she also displays a surprisingly fluid or "relational" understanding of the miners. She alternates between comments on their new-found excesses and forgiving much of their coarse behavior for the privations they suffered in the "semi-barbarous" life in the camps. Not one miner stared at her "obtrusively," she remembers. They watched out for her and her child, and in the evening they gathered on the creek bank to listen to her play hymns on her melodeon.

On December 27, two months after they entered Weaverville, the Royces, still recovering from an attack of cholera, made their way to Sacramento, a mining supply center brimming with new settlers—in less than a year it had grown from a four-tent outpost to a city of more than ten thousand. The Royces bought a plot of land on which to build a home and store. Perhaps this section of her narrative is yet another attempt by Royce to lure the reader toward an expectation of the Royces' realization of a safe home and community. However, they enjoyed only two weeks of calm January days before the onset of the Great Flood of 1850.[17] The flood turned the town into a lake, and citizens had to retreat to the second stories of their houses—if they had them.

Along with fifty other Sacramento residents, the Royces escaped to the second floor of a house on a hill. Finally, on January 15, they descended into a boat moored under their window. Eventually the Royces along with hordes of other refugees took the steamer *McKim* and were carried away to San Francisco. Royce noted that "once, and I think only once, a woman and a child or two, were seen with the men" (98).

With a population that expanded daily, San Francisco was a true boomtown. It had burgeoned from a hamlet of 812 in the spring of 1848, to a town of 5,000 in the summer of 1849. By mid-1850, it would boast 25,000 residents. The Royces take up temporary lodging in the Montgomery House on Montgomery Street between California and Pine. Unable to create even the semblance of a home in lodging so uninhabitable, Royce details their cramped conditions for the reader. The hotel's small, uncarpeted sitting room had a single window, one table, and a few chairs. A length of calico partitioned it from the dining room. Upstairs, a hall extended the length of the building. On each side, cloth partitions framed narrow doorways to the hotel's rooms. These rooms Royce described as "a space two and a half feet wide and six feet long, at the farther end of which was a shelf or stand, on which you could place a candlestick, while you had just room to stand and dress or undress. At the side of this space were two berths, one above the other; and these berths, so situated, were the only sleeping accommodations afforded by this hotel" (100). Royce didn't comment on the ceiling, but even the ones in the finest accommodations were of canvas.

Shortly afterward, the Royces left the hotel and moved to slightly better lodgings, but it was still only a temporary relocation. With their "little comforts" piled about her, Royce addresses the reader:

> The conveniences of civilized life, the comforts of home, can not
> be keenly appreciated, or even fully seen, by those who have never
> been, for a time, shut out from them. Repeatedly in the days that
> now followed, did I find myself feeling that I had never before
> known the brightness of the evening lamp-light, nor the cheeriness
> of the morning breakfast room, with all their orderly accompani-
> ments; that I had never before realized the worth of quiet domestic
> life, unworried by ever-threatening dangers. (103)

Instead of harboring feelings of longing for the "conveniences of civilized life," she appreciates them now in ways she did not when she had them. In other words, she had to leave home to recognize "the worth of quiet domestic life." While Royce finds these memories comforting, they serve primarily to force a rethinking of her present home. Here in a San Francisco tenement, her "little all" that she has brought with her overland has the transformative capacity of sentimental possession to make their residence a home. But she cannot replicate the home she had in the East. In her contentment with her new lodgings—"more comfortable than any place we had occupied for many months"—Royce signifies a reformist rather than conformist ethos: she brings the home under the aegis of adventurous enterprise. The domestic values she celebrates here involve removal—her domestic sanctuary is temporary one-room lodging in the tumultuous, western metropolis of San Francisco. Wagon, tent, hotel, one-room tenement—what is striking about these lodgings is their association with *nomadism*, a term Royce invites the reader to associate with *unstable*. She continues to represent herself as a homemaker, but a homemaker who is emphatically outside the confines of the conventional, stationary house.

On May 4, 1850, Royce was an eyewitness to San Francisco's second major fire. In addition to the resulting fear of arson and widespread violence, a pall of corruption hung over the city.[18] One response to the danger was the rise of the Committee on Vigilance. This group administered the corporal punishment necessary to provide the order and stability required of a respectable city. The women's response was the Benevolent Society, a group of respectable women whose objective was to change the town's social atmosphere, particularly its open acceptance of sexual immorality.

Royce tells of one man who brought his "disreputable companion" to a Benevolent Society's function. The Society ladies told them to leave. Royce reports that the incident "proved to him, as well as to others, that while Christian women would forego ease and endure much labor, in order to benefit any who suffered, they would not welcome into friendly association any who trampled upon institutions which lie at the foundation of morality and civilization" (114). Royce and the other Society ladies' notion of community stability becomes a set of ideological determinants they consider necessary for civilized living. Similar to the exclusion/inclusion principle around which the concept of home is structured, the Benevolent Society provides a sense of belonging to those who share the same philosophy. These public connections, while not private and intimate, are affiliations that could loosely be called "family." Additionally, they mediate the ladies' self-perception as "ladies" and their feared loss of identity. By applying eastern morality to new circumstances, the women could maintain a comforting familiarity in their new environment.

Although Royce emphasizes Christian women's responsibility to maintain "morality and civilization" in the public sphere, she does not simply perpetuate the cliché that women alone are the civilizing force on the frontier. She claims that men, women, marriage, and family are at the heart of this process. Royce's assessment of the men and women in California, however, is that their "shallow, weak natures" do not "furnish depth of soil for the growth of life-long affection." Another problem she recognizes is the ease with which marriages can be dissolved. Guaranteed their right to own property by the constitutional convention at Monterey in 1849, women were freed from an economic dependency that in many cases kept them in undesirable marriages. This right, coupled with their scarcity and the entrepreneurial opportunities for them, contributed to the high divorce rate.[19] For an unsatisfied wife, there was plenty of opportunity for her to find another husband. A major theme of Royce's narrative is revealed in the choice of her title for the final chapter of her text: "Fortitude." Royce argues that the men and women in the frontier need moral strength and courage to manage the instability and freedom that the region offers.

In her concluding chapter, Royce describes her family's removals to a series of tents in various mining camps after their stay in San Francisco. This making and unmaking of homes in the final pages of her text further undermines the notion of a stable and fixed house. Significantly, at the point in which she is writing her reminiscence, Royce is in a permanent home, a place she purposefully never mentions in her account. What is important to the theme of her text is that home is always in the process of becoming a home, but never arriving at a fixed point.

Near the end of her narrative, Royce describes moving into one tent home that was in a beautiful but lonely location; the nearest house was a half mile away. Arranging her furniture and spreading her carpet, she makes her place "quite aristocratic." But this absorption in home-building is undercut when she rips the cloth wall of her tent in order to create two diamond-shaped windows. The home that Royce is trying so hard to establish is now exposed to the outside. Royce uses the domestic trope of her wilderness canvas house to suggest that while the home is the social ideal of women, it cannot be moved across space unchanged. And like the California homes she has inhabited, Royce herself is persistently transient. Her change is not only geographical but also psychological. Travel has altered the very nature of her being. As both domesticating woman and self-moving individual, Royce's self-construction as a liminal subject reveals the artifice of "separate spheres."

In the lonely nights when her husband is away on business, Royce sits at the diamond-shaped windows of her canvas home and looks out into the night. The two windows are in a sense her eyes that have been opened as a result of her experience in the West. At times, she admits she was so fearful and the tension of her nerves so great, "the reaction was inexpressible." And Royce writes that she never relaxed her guard. Consider her anxieties: she has left behind her emotional supports, including a large kin network and her associates in close religious fellowship. She does monotonous work in primitive and isolated frontier conditions.[20] Her husband is often away. And, consistent with the majority of frontier women's narratives, when he enters the narrative, he is only on the periphery of the action.

Royce portrays her husband as kind but not particularly successful, resourceful, or aggressive. Her text illustrates personal transformation rather than a dependent wife-husband relationship. Nor does she emphasize the family unit. The Royces had three daughters, Mary Eleanor, Hattie, and Ruth, and one son, Josiah. Another son, John Samuel, died in infancy. Royce's son Josiah was a leading American intellectual of the late nineteenth and early twentieth centuries.[21] His works in theology, metaphysics, logic, history, psychology, epistemology, social policy, and ethics are still widely read and discussed. But her children are rarely mentioned. Royce's focus instead is on herself and her journey as a means of change.

In her narrative, Royce presents herself as a frontier lady on the threshold of two dominant ideologies: a homebound domesticity and an adventurous individualism. Potentially able to slip outside the borders of the culturally defined spaces of womanhood, she challenges the cultural definition of "woman" as domestic and separate from the realm of adventurous enterprise. During her first five years in California, Royce set up housekeeping in eight different places. A subject in transition, she is realized in the very act of movement.

* * * *

Royce's journal concludes when the family arrives in Grass Valley, but her relocations do not. After twelve years in Grass Valley, where the Royces were founding members of the Disciples of Christ church, they moved to the Bay Area to provide a better education for their children. The couple spent their later years in Los Gatos where Josiah died of heart disease in 1888. Following her husband's death, Royce returned briefly to the East, her first visit since she arrived in California in 1849. In 1891 in a San Jose post office, a man collided with her, sending the seventy-two-year-old Royce reeling against a wall. She suffered a large gash and fell into an illness from which she never recovered. Royce died on November 24, 1891. She and her husband are buried in Oak Hill Cemetery in San Jose.

> *I think that I may without vanity affirm*
> *that I have "seen the elephant."*

LOUISE SMITH CLAPPE

A Feminine View of the Elephant **3**

A s Sarah Bayliss Royce discovered, the gold rush was predominantly an all-male enterprise. The federal census of 1850 reflected that the population of California was 92.5 percent male. Two years later there was little change: California continued to be one of the most male-inhabited places not only of the nation, but of the world.[1] In his sermon "The Duties of Females in Reference to the California Gold Excitement," the Reverend James H. Davis admonished women to perform their "duty" and persuade men to stay at home instead of succumbing to the gold mania.[2] Not only was it unseemly for women to go to the goldfields, but it also was their responsibility to oppose men's undertaking of the gold rush adventure. Louise Smith Clappe, a woman reared in the East, was told that "it was absolutely indelicate to think of living in such a large population of men" (3).[3] Nevertheless, she came west with her physician husband in 1849.

Clappe's *The Shirley Letters* is a revealing account of gold rush life along the Feather River. Although she unfortunately has been nearly forgotten as a writer significant to the development of American frontier literature, Clappe ought to be remembered for her graphic accounts of the California mining camps. In the 1850s and 60s, San Francisco was the West Coast base for publishing houses, boasting such journals as the *Pioneer*, the *Golden Era*, the *Hesperian*, the *Californian*, and the *Overland Monthly*. Writers like Mark Twain, Bret Harte, Joaquin Miller, Charles

Warren Stoddard, and Prentice Mulford mixed an exaggerated reality with a little western mythology and literalized the California Gold Rush.[4] Their selections were frequently episodic, humorous, and sometimes detailed aberrations that were intimately connected to that state. Sagebrush realism survived only twenty-five years, ending abruptly with the arrival of the transcontinental railroad in 1869 and the consequent desire of Californians for a literature that replicated eastern styles and traditions. Filled with the particulars of frontier life, Clappe's letters are excellent examples of this short-lived California genre.

In the process of composition, however, Clappe's detailed account grew into something more than simply fine examples of sagebrush realism. My thesis contends that by tracing Clappe's experience in the multicultural California frontier, we bear witness to her awakening to divided cultural loyalties, to radically rearranged family relations, and to a new understanding of gender roles as she witnesses goldrushing women creating new alternatives to conventional notions of nineteenth-century female behavior. Her letters record the transformation she undergoes as a result of these new perceptions. Referring to herself at the onset of her trip as a "shivering, frail, home-loving little thistle," she slowly begins to take root in California's "barbarous soil" (1). On her arrival, Clappe is an outsider whose marginality gives her fresh insight. Casting herself as the central character in her own story, she establishes a place in the male-dominated landscape. Her persona is directly related to the narrative movement: her travels invite her to think differently, to see anew. Her writing provided her with a psychological release for the tension she must have felt as one of the few women among so many men. It also gave her a sense of empowerment: in the inflammable atmosphere of the camps, she was able to control textual reality with pen and ink.

Finally, I argue here that *The Shirley Letters* is significant because, like the narrative of Sarah Royce, it provides a feminine interpretation of the California Gold Rush. However, unlike Royce's narrative, which details the journey westward and the turbulence of San Francisco, Clappe's text concentrates on a smaller slice of geography: the mining camps of Rich and Indian Bars. Her letters illuminate California's interior and the private, domestic side of the mining camp experience. By narrowing her focus, Clappe is able to concentrate on what Mary Louise Pratt refers to as the contact zone, the social space where disparate cultures meet.[5] California's mining frontier becomes for Clappe a liminal landscape of changing meanings, and consequently her text encodes these encounters with "otherness" and her attempts to accommodate them through language. Her letters to her eastern audience about life in the

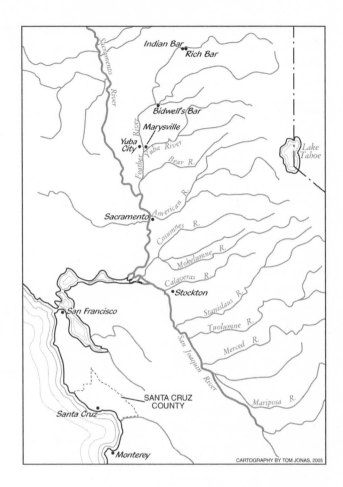

The California goldfields. Map by Tom Jonas.

West link her to home—they are the site in which her changing narrator self meets her eastern "sister" who is the constant reminder of the woman Clappe was prior to her journey. Her cabin in Indian Bar serves as a governing metaphor for her narrative. The openness of the house with only curtains as room partitions, windows without glass, and little furniture is penetrable and gives her the maneuvering room she needs to reconsider and redefine the frontier preconceptions and eastern attitudes she brought with her to California.

Louise Amelia Knapp Smith Clappe was born in Elizabeth, New Jersey, on July 28, 1819, the same year as Sarah Royce. She was the oldest of the seven children of Moses and Lois Smith.[6] At fourteen she left home to attend the Female Seminary in Keene, New Hampshire, whose founder, Catherine Fiske, was a pioneer in education. Orphaned at eighteen, Louise and her siblings were placed under the guardianship of Osmyn Baker, an attorney and later a state senator from Amherst, Massachusetts. She was further educated at the Female Seminary at Charlestown, Massachusetts, in 1837 and at Amherst Academy for the following two years. Clappe became an instructor of French and traveled regularly throughout New England.

In the summer of 1839, on a trip back from Chester, Vermont, to Amherst, she met a fellow stagecoach passenger, Alexander Hill Everett.[7] Everett was a diplomat, author, editor, and major contributor to the *North American Review*, the literary journal of the American "renaissance." He was also the private secretary to John Quincy Adams. Clappe's meeting with Everett initiated an exchange of letters that continued until his death in 1847. Housed at the California State Library, the correspondence survives as a collection of forty-seven letters from him to her. The letters reflect Everett's concern for Clappe, and the value she placed on them is evidenced by the care with which she preserved them until her death at ninety-three. Their nine-year correspondence must have made her conscientious about producing her best writing and consequently would have provided the writing practice and habit that she would be able to draw upon when she was working on her journalistic letters from the mining camps. As early as 1839, she had confided to Everett of her plans to journey to the Far West (September 13, 1839, *Shirley Papers*). Unlike her friend Emily Dickinson, she boasted of her appetite for adventure and referred to herself as "a regular Nomad in [her] passion for wandering."

In Northampton, Massachusetts, on September 10, 1848, the thirty-year-old Louise Smith married Fayette Clapp, a physician five years her junior. (She added the terminal "e.") Both husband and wife suffered from ill health and gold fever. Almost a year later, on August 20, 1849, the newlyweds, together with her sisters Isabella and Henrietta Smith and his uncle Sylvanus Clapp, sailed out of New York harbor on the schooner *Manilla* bound for California.[8] They reached the Golden Gate on January 11, 1850.[9]

The fog and the damp weather of San Francisco's bay area quickly persuaded the Clappes to move to Marysville, a town at the confluence of the Feather and Yuba rivers. Either in San Francisco or Marysville, Louise met Stephen Massett, the young co-owner and coeditor of the *Herald*, the earliest newspaper north of Sacramento.[10] In addition to editing the newspaper, Massett wrote under the pseudonym "Col. Jeems Pipes of Pipesville." He offered Louise an opportunity to write for the *Herald*. Adopting the pen name "Shirley," she submitted three epistolary essays and two poems to Massett. Although this early writing is verbose and stiff, it gave her the opportunity to establish her identity as a writer. In the spring, she returned to San Francisco and made plans with Fayette to leave for the mines.

Between September 1851 and November 1852, Clappe wrote twenty-three letters, purportedly to her sister Molly in Massachusetts. Now she used the pseudonym "Dame Shirley," creating an image of an educated woman of authority. By writing to explain her perceptions of the West to her sister who had never been there, she could speak as the voice of experience and address an audience of innocents about the possibilities of life in the camps. The letter format allowed Clappe the opportunity to be both public and private. Because writing for publication was an activity still viewed by many as inappropriate for women, she was able to escape the imposed literary confines by posing her narrative as a series of letters. Additionally, she was able to disclose the intimate side of herself because, ostensibly, she was writing not to a general audience but to her sister. She immediately addresses the egotism of the epistolary format by reminding her sister that "you have often flattered me by saying that epistles were only interesting when profusely illuminated . . . by a great I" (18).

From the beginning of 1854 to the end of 1855, the letters were published in every issue of the short-lived *Pioneer*, San Francisco's literary monthly.[11] Titled "California in 1851 and 1852, A Trip into the Mines," her stories received enthusiastic response.

* * * *

Clappe's portrayal of the sequence of events that wean her away from the "flashy-looking shops and showy houses" (24) of San Francisco to the hovels and tents of Rich Bar emphasizes her break from her past eastern life. This severance leaves her open to redefine herself through her exposure to the California frontier. Highlighting the connections between the representation of landscape and the formation of identity, she is keenly aware of the symbolic potential of this opening section of her text. Clappe describes the first thirty miles above Marysville as a smooth and easy ride. She casts herself as a tourist, enjoying the beautiful countryside. Suddenly, ten miles below Bidwell's Bar, the road begins to run along a precipice, and according to Clappe, "should the horses deviate a hair's breadth from their usual track, [they] would be dashed into eternity" (7).[12] At Bidwell's she discovers that "there was nothing to sleep in but a tent, and nothing to sleep on but the ground, and the air was black with fleas hopping about in every direction" (8). Exchanging their "excruciatingly springless wagon" for mules, Clappe and her husband set out for Berry Creek House, but twice they find themselves lost in the woods and forced to go without food and to sleep on the ground.

Clappe is not only introducing the character of the land she is passing through, but she is also emphasizing her response to the country. Her narrative position becomes unstable: she is in constant fear that she will never be able to find the main trail, that she will be taken captive by Indians or eaten by grizzlies. Her husband said that she "looked like a dying person" (10). Indeed, this symbolic dying of her old self leaves her open to her identity reformation, the central action of her text.

Cut off from the security of home, Clappe entertains feelings of isolation and vulnerability. Nevertheless, despite her fearful pose, she presents herself as good-natured and able to find beauty in the surrounding wilderness. The antithesis of the hopeless, worn-out drudges that populated men's writing about frontier women, she demonstrates that she has at least the seeds of independence, energy, capability, and resilience. Finally, in symbolic anticipation of the reversal of social hierarchies she will experience in the mining camps, the Clappes as tenderfeet must rely on frontier men and women to provide accommodations. They make their way to Berry Creek House, and after a good night's sleep, they continue north to Wild Yankee Ranch, where they breakfast on "dainties, fresh butter and cream" (11).

Clappe's first residence was the aptly named mining camp of Rich Bar, the site of the richest gold strike along the Feather River. Discovered in the summer of 1850, the narrow bar produced nearly four million dollars in gold during its brief existence. It was so productive that a limit of ten square feet was established as the maximum size of a claim. A horde of prospectors arrived to the area during the summer of 1851, including storekeepers, gamblers, and doctors. According to Clappe, when her husband reached Rich Bar in 1851, there were only two or three physicians, but in less than three weeks, there were twenty-nine (3). By the time Louise arrived, Rich Bar was a community of nearly two thousand miners, five women, and a few children. On the main street there were about forty structures: tents, "plank hovels," several log cabins, one unique tenement "formed of pine boughs, and covered with old calico shirts" (26), and the two-story Empire Saloon and Rooming House.

Further indication of the impermanent character of the mining communities was the number of boardinghouses or hotels.[13] In 1850, for every one thousand gainfully employed Californians, over nine were in the boardinghouse trade. Astounded at the inundation of lodgings, Clappe refers to the whole of California as the "hotel state." Even the finest hotels, however, were primitive, as she discovered when she became a resident of the Empire Rooming House.

In *The Lay of the Land*, Annette Kolodny states that while the prevailing male view of the land was of a "virginal Paradise," women rhetorically domesticated the landscape. Scholars consider this concern with the domestic to be the distinguishing characteristic between women's and men's gold rush narratives. At the onset of her California experience, Clappe spends more time detailing the interiors of buildings than unspoiled nature, but the deflationary tone she uses in her descriptions runs counter to notions of privileging the domestic. For example, she devotes the second letter almost entirely to a description of the Empire, with details ranging from its canvas roof to the deck of cards on a corner table in the barroom. Despite the expense—it cost eight thousand dollars to build because the materials had to be freighted from Marysville at a price of forty cents a pound—"nothing was ever more awkward and unworkmanlike than the whole tenement," disparaged Clappe.

Clappe's fascination with interior spaces continues as she walks her reader down the main street of Rich Bar and into her husband's office, the only office on the river. "When I entered this place," she wrote, "the shock to my optic nerves was so great that I sank, helplessly, upon one of the benches . . . and laughed until I cried" (26). Fayette was appalled by her response, and his partner "looked prussic acid." The partner hadn't been out of the mine for years, and to him their office was "a thing sacred and set apart for almost admiring worship." Here, read in the context of "empire" building, Clappe exposes the awkwardness of social establishments in the West. As indicators of cultural domestication, the obtrusive and in most cases hastily constructed buildings present a humorous comment on the complex process of the destructive inroads of American culture and expansionism.

In October 1851, Clappe and her husband move into their new twenty-foot-square log cabin in nearby Indian Bar. Smaller than Rich Bar, Indian Bar has only twenty tents and cabins, including "those formed of calico shirts and pine boughs" (49). She begins the first letter from Indian Bar by inviting the reader into her rustic home: "Enter my dear; you are perfectly welcome; besides, we could not keep you out if we would, as there is not even a latch on the canvas door" (50). Clappe describes the details of each room, down to the rosewood workbox that sits on her toilet table, which is actually a trunk elevated upon two cases of wine. Whereas women in the camps often complained that they missed the amenities and comforts of eastern cities, Clappe concludes the tour by admitting that despite the "oddity" of most of her furniture, she is "in reality as thoroughly comfortable as [she] could be in the most elegant palace" (53).

The openness of her dwelling with only curtains as room partitions, windows "as yet guiltless of glass," and spare furniture suggests the "breathing room" that she will experience on the bar. Ultimately, the cabin, having served its purpose, will be left behind when Clappe leaves. It is the life that is engendered in the cabin that she will embrace and take with her. Furthermore, as mentioned at the onset of this chapter, her house serves as a governing metaphor for her text. Within, there is maneuvering room. Clappe addresses themes that are not partitioned off into structured chapters, but instead appear almost haphazardly ordered at first glance. As there is no latch on the door, readers move from one vignette to another with no formal thresholds to cross. Just as her one-room house allows for an interpenetration of private and public life, so the contents of her letters blend domestic and private matters with the public issues that were peculiar to the situation in the camps. And her letters unite an increasingly simple colloquial style with the sophisticated perceptions of an educated easterner.

As Clappe becomes comfortable with the physical freedom provided by her Indian Bar cabin, she moves outdoors to explore her surroundings. She represents her narrating self as a woman who takes great delight in nature above the conventions of feminine behavior. From the beauty of the white lilies to the crisp mountain air and the splendor of the pines, she tells the reader, "I take pains to describe things exactly as I see them, hoping that thus you will obtain an idea of life in the mines, as it is" (38). Instead of configuring the terrain as strange and alienating as many women's narratives of westward expansion did, Clappe's account presents the landscape as inviting. Insects, birds, even lizards make their way into her narrative. Unlike many women travelers who conceive of the land's beauty as linked necessarily with practical considerations—for example, the land's suitability for future agriculture—Clappe's sense of nature's beauty is aesthetic. Her adaptive familiarization with the terrain, first physically and then imaginatively with her pen, gives her an increasingly privileged view.

In Clappe's textual reconstruction of her aesthetic experiences with the land, she is able to invoke the fascination of her original discovery. Her pose as an adventurous explorer suggests that enjoyment of nature is not restricted to men. Clappe's discourse is immediate and personal, grounded in an embodied and gendered self. As Bruce Greenfield has illuminated, the traveling observer whose narrative strategies appropriate the landscape aesthetically is nevertheless affirming his or her authority and therefore implicating himself or herself in the politics of expansion and losing his or her innocence in the process. Her perspective no longer bound by her eastern origins, Clappe contrasts the murky New England skies to the blue skies of California. In order to view the "prettiest little rivulet," she is willing to walk for miles, ruin a pair of silk velvet slippers, lame her ankles for a week, and draw a "browner horror" over her already sunburned face (117). However, although she emphasizes the uplifting aspects of California's wilderness, which includes a healthy salubrity, she does not suggest that California is Edenic, and she turns her lens from the beauties of nature to the overwhelming fact of winter in the mines.

Like Royce's narrative, *The Shirley Letters* provides the rare glimpse of the loneliness and boredom confronting prospectors during the winter season that put an end to their mining activities and confined them on a place "about as large as a poor widow's potato-patch."[14] Accustomed to continuous labor, the Indian Bar miners were suddenly thrust into winter months of inactivity, little or no income, and when deep snow prevented wagons of food supplies into the camps, famine. Clappe describes the miners' attempts to keep themselves amused during the winter of 1851 with a three-week "saturnalia." They started on Christmas Eve with an oyster and champagne dinner in the Humboldt Hotel. Clappe heard them dancing in the hotel as she fell asleep in her cabin, and the next morning when she woke, they were still dancing. They partied for four days straight until they got beyond dancing, "lying in drunken heaps about the barroom, commenced a most unearthly howling" (93). Those who kept themselves away from the revelries were taken before a kangaroo court and sentenced to "treat the crowd." Whereas when she was a recent arrival, Clappe was "enchanted" with the opportunity to spend winter in the mountains (3), the bacchanals of 1851 changed her attitude. In her letter of November 1852, she admits her concern at the "dreadful prospect of being compelled to spend the winter here, which, on every account, is undesirable" (190).

Clappe further deflects her reader's attention away from the beauty of the frontier by confessing her fears of dying in California and having to be buried in a wilderness grave. In doing so, Clappe locates herself within a tradition of women's frontier writing. In contrast to the narratives by men that frequently viewed Indians as enemies, women diarists of the frontier more often than not saw the real enemies of the wilderness as death and disease. As traditional caretakers of the sick and dying, gold rush women soon saw death as commonplace. Jacob D. B. Stillman, a gold rush physician, estimated that as many as 20 percent of the miners died from illness within the first six months of their arrival.[15] The cholera epidemic of 1850 killed 15 percent of Sacramento's population, 5 percent of San Francisco's citizens, and 10 percent of San Jose's. In their accounts of frontier life, women diarists, Royce and Magoffin included, frequently admitted to being afraid of a wilderness burial. Clappe is no exception.

In her letter of September 22, 1851, Clappe describes the funeral of Nancy Ann Bailey, a proprietor of the Empire Hotel. As the procession leaves for the hillside graveyard, a "dark cloth cover, borrowed from a neighboring monte-table, was flung over the coffin." Shocked by the sound of the nails as they were driven with a hammer into the coffin, Clappe is confronted with her own mortality. Somberly she contemplates that if she were to die in the camps, she, too, would be taken to her "mountain grave beneath the same monte-table cover pall, which shrouded the coffin of poor Mrs. B" (38–39). Clappe's elaboration of detail in this entry suggests not only the solemnity of the occasion, but more important, her personal fears. Despite the fact that previously she was able to identify charm and beauty in the unfamiliar landscape of California, it is entirely disquieting for her to think of spending eternity here. As she does so, she tempers her romantic attitude toward the place with its desolate and uninhabited qualities.

The charge has been made that Clappe spent much of her time writing about the lowbrow manners of her frontier neighbors. Nothing is further from the truth. The openness of her Indian Bar cabin expresses her sense of self as linked to the attitudes she carried with her. She recognized her own pretenses for what they were and the folly of holding to them in a frontier community: her lovely china tureen made a good chamber pot and a cotton cloth sufficed for glass in the window opening. And although she was amused by an Irishman's down couch, which "consisted of a single feather laid upon a rock," when it came to reconciling fashionable taste to backwoods conditions, she was willing to confess that the practical notions outweighed the fanciful ideas with which she came west. In fact, she was equally quick to acknowledge the error of other romantic notions she had, including her romantic notions of Indians, mining, women, and prospectors.

Clappe's first encounter with Indians comes on her ride to Rich Bar.[16] A number of Indian women are harvesting grass seeds. She is moved not by fear, but by sympathy for their impoverished condition. Although Clappe's narrative does not comment directly on the connection between the suffering of the Indians and the effects of white expansion and the gold rush, it is there for the reader as subtext. Her observations make it clear to the reader that the Indians' condition is a result of the negative cultural and environmental consequences of American intrusion. Her discourse, however, concentrates on the discrepancy between the reality of Indians and her literary expectation of them. She describes an Indian woman she meets as a "wildwood Cleopatra" with "those large, magnificently lustrous, yet at the same time soft eyes, so common in novels, so rare in real life" (12). She admits that a "stern regard for truth" forces her to acknowledge that the Indian she described as a "wildwood Cleopatra" was the "only even moderately pretty squaw" that she had ever seen. Clappe discovers that the Indians "have little resemblance to the glorious forest heroes that live in the Leather Stocking Tales." While she does reveal ambivalence toward them in her depiction of an eight-year-old Indian boy they called Wild Bird—she describes him as both a beautiful little boy and a "barbarous little villain" (135)—it is tempered by the fact that she is describing a child.

Although Clappe was told that the Indians weren't safe, she let them into her house with a view of gaining more knowledge about them and their culture. She is interested in capturing the "real Indian" with her pen, not the Cooperesque, imaginative version that she came west with. This close-up gives her a degree of authority not available to her eastern stay-at-home readers. By allowing the Indians into her one-room cabin, Clappe invests this section of her narrative with symbolic meaning. Reversing the historical process of California native people's dispossession, she configures a personal and individual inclusion of their presence by inviting them into her "open" house. Although she remains in control as the white, genteel hostess, she is able to expose as flawed the notion that Indians are to be feared as a threat or excluded. She offers her own cabin as a site of contact and incorporation. The fear of the Indians she had expressed during her trip from San Francisco to the mines is now gone. Based on the authority of experience, she finds them to be sympathetic and docile. As with the writing of her female contemporaries, most of Clappe's descriptions of the Indians are of women and children. This focus further encourages her readers to relinquish their own prejudices and directs their attention to the impoverished condition of California's indigenous people instead.

In addition to her changed perception of the Indians, Clappe's eastern attitude toward prospecting changed. Her anticipation of easy wealth gave way to the realization that mining is a dirty, hard, and precarious operation. The idea of mining that she brought with her was that one sauntered "gracefully along romantic streamlets, on sunny afternoons, with a parasol and white kid gloves" (75), stopping every so often to rinse out a panful of yellow sand. "Since I have been here I have discovered my mistake," she confides to the reader. She also discovers that science is no guide to gold. Miners who used geological calculations were frequently disappointed, while those who dug "just for the sake of digging" were as apt to be successful. "Gold mining is Nature's great lottery scheme," Clappe wrote. "A man may work in a claim for many months, and be poorer at the end of the time than when he commenced; or he may 'take out' thousands in a few hours" (123).

In letter three, Clappe confesses that her knowledge of the earth sciences is limited, and her attention to the geology lectures she attended at Amherst College had more to do with her admiration for Dr. Edward Hitchcock, her instructor (and later president of Amherst), than her enthusiasm for the subject. However, by the fifteenth letter, not only is she able to discuss the science of locating gold deposits and the method of staking a claim, but she also captures the changes in mining techniques as the lone prospector excavating the foothills with his pick and shovel gives way to companies of men and elaborate and costly mining techniques. She describes the coyote holes extending hundreds of feet into the hill, "until air is so impure as to extinguish lights" (121).

The most important changes dramatized by her letters involve water. One of her "sleep murderers" is the flume that she depicts as an immense trough, which "with the aid of a dam, compels [the river] to run in another channel, leaving the vacated bed of the stream ready for mining purposes" (43). She describes the long tom, an enlarged rocker: eight to fifteen feet in length, it is attached at its upper end to a flume or ditch that delivered a constant stream of water. Building dams, flumes, and races to divert rivers involved men's using sophisticated technologies and working cooperatively. Clappe gives an account of the increase in the number of extensive operations that were cropping up along the river. Within a five-year period, miners built five thousand miles of ditches and flumes. Although Clappe doesn't address the environmental repercussions, her reader can easily appreciate the devastation of California's physical ecology caused by the gold rush.[17] Entire mountains were washed away. Loosened debris choked the river channels and caused flooding downstream, rivers changed course, leaving dry channels behind, and hillsides were stripped of all vegetation. In *Assembling California*, John McPhee notes that within the space of a year and a half, hydraulic mining had washed "enough material into the Yuba River to fill the Erie Canal" (66).

Although Clappe doesn't comment directly on the massive destruction of the California landscape or the dispossession of the Indians, she does provide a detailed account of the crisis of gender in the mining camps. It was a society of young, lonely men, most of marrying age. Even the gold towns of San Francisco, Sacramento, and Stockton had few women. In 1850, William Brown commented from Stockton that "a woman is a curiosity in this country" (letter to his father, July 25, 1850). Luzena Stanley Wilson arrived in Sacramento to discover that a miner was willing to pay her ten dollars for a biscuit made by a woman. From Nevada City, Joseph Crackbon "got nearer to a female this evening than I have been for six months. Came near fainting." Clappe reported that one Rich Bar man had not spoken to a woman for two years, and when he saw her his heart became so elated "at the joyful event, he rushed out and invested capital in some excellent champagne" (27). There was even a dog at the camp that barked at the very sight of her because it was its first glimpse of a woman (45). Whereas in the East, women of the "better sort" became definers of respectability, the female presence was so scarce in California that the gold rushers used any woman to measure the civilization of a camp. They viewed someone as refined and fashionable as Clappe as a "petticoated astonishment."

As a further consequence of this gender crisis, women yearned for female companionship, and their letters and diaries express this need. Georgiana Bruce, an educated, sophisticated friend of Eliza Burhans Farnham, had lived for three years at the transcendentalist community of Brook Farm near Boston. She came to California in 1850 and wrote home to her friends in the East: "Every good woman needs a companion of her own sex, no matter now numerous or valuable her male acquaintances, no matter how close the union between herself and husband; if she have a genial, loving nature, the want of a female friend is a sad void."[18] In the absence of friends left behind, Clappe eagerly sought new attachments with other women in the camp. There were four women forming the female population at Rich Bar, and in the fourth letter, she records the death of one of them, a major loss for the remaining three women.

Unlike her camp sisters, however, Clappe led a pampered life. She refers to herself as a "mere cumberer of the ground; inasmuch as [she] toiled not, neither did [she] wash" (39). But she concludes that "as all men cannot be Napoleon Bonapartes, so all women cannot be *manglers*; the majority of the sex must be satisfied with simply being *mangled*." It was precisely because she was freed from most of her domestic chores by a cook and a laundress that she was able to spend her days strolling around the bars and indulging in what she referred to as the "excessive egotism" of being a writer. Her fascination with the interior space of the Indian Bar cabin paralleled her acknowledged luxury of being able to indulge in an inner life.

As mentioned in chapter 2, the diaries, journals, and letters from California goldrushing women like Sarah Bayliss Royce indicate that a woman's ultimate power in the mining camps came not from male honor or favor, but from her own self-sufficiency.[19] In their letters home, women frequently commented on the economic advantages created in the context of the gold rush.[20] The women who Clappe made friends with were not "idlers" like herself, but working women who cooked, sewed, and washed and frequently earned more from their efforts than their mining husbands. One enterprising forty-niner, Mary Jane Caples, began to make and sell pies when her miner husband, James, fell ill. Selling fruit pies for $1.25 each and mince pies for $1.50, she found her business to be so profitable that the following spring when the couple left the creek, she left with regret: "Sorry I was to lose my customers."[21]

Clappe hated the chore of washing, but she admired Mrs. R., Rich Bar's washerwoman. Mrs. R. earned a hundred dollars a week washing clothes. Clappe heard one unnamed miner heap praises on Mrs. R. for her industry: "Such women ain't common, I tell you; if they were, a man might marry and make money by the operation" (39). At first glance, Clappe might appear to distance herself from an open approval of the liberated mining women by an endorsement of the home and nest as the proper sphere for women. An apt example is her quoted line of poetry: "He sings to the wide world, she to the nest." She claims this sentiment is an illustration of the "beautifully-varied spheres of man and woman" (80). However, Clappe immediately counters her submissive rhetoric with an abrupt transition: "Speaking of birds, reminds me of a misfortune that I have lately experienced." She then proceeds to tell her reader a story of a wild pheasant that she takes as a pet and attempts to tame. The "free, beautiful, happy" pheasant dies as soon as its free and wild nature becomes housebound (80–81). It dies of "home-sickness" because it has been "shut up in a dark, gloomy cabin" (81). Her underlying argument, that women need the freedom to leave the confines of the "nest," is telling. Clappe concludes the passage by enjoining her female reader to speculate on the frontier's potential for liberation from the stultifying confines of the domestic sphere.

Clappe's frontier is a multicultural social space.[22] And as exciting and picturesque as it might be, she learns that it is inhabited by some dangerous and vulgar people. She doesn't leave these darker shades of mountain life out of her text, as so many commentators on the mines tended to do. The search for gold reincarnated the American dream by promising anyone—regardless of social standing, education, or money—the possibility of striking it rich. During the first year and a half of the gold rush, many of the miners had more money than they had ever had before, but there was very little to spend it on. As a consequence, they lived in similar types of housing, ate the same kind of food, and dressed in common shapeless hats, baggy pants, flannel shirts, and high boots. Because it was hard to judge another's circumstance by his appearance, social distinctions—except in the case of Indians—were almost obliterated. Yankees, Californios, Mexicans, Chinese, French, and Chileans mined side by side. The California mining camps became one of the most diverse societies of the world. Bret Harte used the word *commotion* to describe the tenor of the social conditions on the bars, but by the summer of 1850, his term was entirely too lighthearted. The competition had increased and the number of hostilities grew, especially against outsiders. Petitions began to circulate, asking for the exclusion of foreigners from the mines.

Clappe's letters evidence the beginning manifestations of the racial antagonisms harbored by her fellow Americans. In her letter of May 1, 1852, she writes that at Rich Bar they passed a resolution to forbid any foreigner from working the mines on the bar. She describes the resolution as "selfish, cruel and narrow-minded in the extreme" (127). The Rich Bar expulsion results in an influx of Mexicans at Indian Bar, which increases the tensions, especially on Sundays, when Clappe describes the fights as "truly horrible." In her letter of August 4, 1852, she gives an account of one Sunday race riot that was more serious than usual. It started when a rumor went through Indian Bar that the Mexicans had conspired to kill all the Americans on the river. Hearing the cries of "Down with the Spaniards," the Mexicans barricaded themselves in the saloon. "The Rich Barians, who had heard a most exaggerated account of the rising of the Spaniards against the Americans, armed with rifles, pistols, clubs, dirks, etc., were running down the hill by the hundreds" (147). The bar was a "sea of heads." During a "lull in the storm," Clappe's husband came into their cabin and pleaded with her to retreat to the hill so that she wouldn't be accidentally wounded. She argued that she didn't fear "anything of the kind" and begged to be allowed to stay, but in the end, "like a dutiful wife, [she] went on to the hill." There she joined the other two women of the community, and the three of them, "left entirely alone, seated [themselves] upon a log, overlooking the strange scene below." Referring to this race riot between the Spaniards and the Americans as "the entire catastrophe," Clappe laments the changing temperament and expresses her disgust at the treatment doled out to others who are deemed different.

From her vantage point on the hill, Clappe observes the riot. In the midst of the "fray" is a Mexican woman, and a vigilance committee is authorized to apprehend her.

> The first act of the Committee was to try a *Mejicana*, who had
> been foremost in the fray. She has always worn male attire, and on
> this occasion, armed with a pair of pistols, she fought like a
> fury.... Some went so far as to say, she ought to be hung, for she
> was the indirect cause of the fight. You see always, it is the old,
> cowardly excuse of Adam in Paradise. (150)

The Mexican woman is the marginalized other on two counts: she is a person of color and she is a woman. By considering race and gender in tandem, Clappe invites her reader to reexamine how the force of gendering has interacted with racial violence. Furthermore, the *Mejicana* is a crossdresser. Like her masculine actions—"armed with a pair of pistols" and fighting "like a fury"—her clothing blurs the lines between masculinity and femininity. Her adoption of masculine attire can be seen as the nineteenth-century woman's attempt to escape out of the contexts defined by the patriarchy into the open spaces of her own authority. Clappe depicts herself and the other two female observers as white and feminine. Whereas the *Mejicana* was in the midst of the fray, Clappe and the other two women have been removed from the action-filled streets below. Their removal highlights their position as victims of an oppressive and censorious patriarchal social system that restricts women and prevents their functioning as full human beings. The *Mejicana* represents Clappe's new knowledge that is in the process of undermining her attempts to be a "dutiful wife" and sit safely on a hill looking down on the fray below. This passage also reveals what is at stake if she challenges the limits of traditional notions of feminine behavior: "Some went so far as to say, she ought to be hung."

Clappe's letters are particularly interesting at this point because they record a significant change in her narrative positioning. In the first letters of her account, she was the cultivated outsider, safely rooted in her eastern background. She fashioned herself as a tenderfoot lost in the woods between San Francisco and Rich Bar. In the course of her increasing sense of command over the terrain, her marginal pose is dropped. No longer is she able to remain aloof from the human and cultural tensions she is witnessing in the camps. Now, as the experienced western dweller, she not only feels compassion for the foreign miners who are being unfairly treated by the Americans, but she is also able to condemn lynch-mob violence and the vigilance committees as a gross abuse and a contradiction of justice and order. And she is learning to look at the interconnections between race and gender through a multicultural lens: she exposes the eastern-based nineteenth-century ideology of domesticity that restricted women's freedom at the same time as she establishes an identification with the figure of the *Mejicana*.

Compare Clappe's change with Magoffin's transformation. During her trip from Las Vegas to Santa Fe, Magoffin shields herself from the gaze of the Mexican villagers and shuns their customs. Later, after she leaves Santa Fe and follows the trail down into Chihuahua, she becomes increasingly interested and involved in them and in their way of life. Consequently, as she does this, she also becomes more aware of the American soldiers' mistreatment of the native people, and she finds it increasingly difficult to maintain her national loyalty. Similar to Magoffin, Clappe's cultural contact complicates her earlier notions of self and "other": she is even able to envision a female solidarity that undermines ethnic demarcations.

In addition to the incidents of discrimination, prejudice, and hierarchies of privilege that elicit her anger, Clappe is also disconcerted by the increase in lawlessness. The first year of the gold rush brought 250,000 excited and optimistic argonauts. But as the surface gold was panned out, the initial enthusiasm began to give way. By the early 1850s, the average miner was making only three dollars a day. Clappe's letters witness this change in the atmosphere. Whereas the first eight letters portray a mood of celebration, marred by few deaths and little violence, by the ninth letter, the temper is darker. Rich Bar and Indian Bar suffered increased lawlessness as gold fever attracted more unsavory characters. "In the short space of twenty-four days, we have had murders, fearful accidents, bloody deaths, a mob, whippings, a hanging, an attempted suicide, and a fatal duel," she writes (145).

The gold seekers were not settlers or pioneers in the tradition of America's westward migration. They were a disparate assortment of transients and strangers, ready to take and not to contribute, whose main concern was how to make the greatest amount of money in the shortest time. With that common motive, they also shared an indifference toward California and its future. Most did not want to be tied down or burdened by social responsibility. There were few jails; vigilante justice was often violent, brutal, and inflicted quickly so as not to delay those called upon to pass judgment.[23] Clappe's letter of December 15, 1851, details the mob's decision to hang a miner suspected of stealing gold. The miner's execution occurred less than three hours after the sentence was pronounced. The preparations for the hanging were done so hurriedly that the writhing body had to be hauled up and down several times before the miner was pronounced dead. Another "barbarous deed" she records is that of a miner who had accumulated eight hundred dollars and was returning to the States. He left Rich Bar with two "friends" who later returned with the miner's money and blankets. They claimed that the cold weather had been too much for the miner, and they had to leave him in his dying state or they would have perished with him. Unable to distance herself from the violence, at one point, in a gesture similar to Magoffin's in Las Vegas, Clappe has to bury her face in her shawl to escape the "disgust and horror" of the vigilance committee's whipping of several Spaniards. After the lashing, one of the young men "swore a most solemn oath that he would murder every American he should chance to meet alone." Clappe can appreciate the young man's curse at her own countrymen.

As a delicate, well-bred eastern observer, Clappe could have easily approached the miners with a critical eye. Instead, she is a sympathetic observer: she doesn't preach, and she rarely condemns. Her residence in the mining camps has given her an understanding of the frontier and a sensitivity to the reality of the place that she realizes her eastern reader doesn't have. The presence of the fundamental drives of man, and the sympathy and understanding evoked from her by that awareness, causes her to admonish her reader not to "think too severely of our good Mountains. . . . It requires not only a large intellect, but a large heart, to judge with becoming charity of the peculiar temptations to riches" (91).

In the eighteenth letter, Clappe describes the Fourth of July celebration. The ladies (four total: two women recently arrived from the States, Mrs. B., and Clappe) and the men of the upper Feather were enjoying an elegant dinner at the hotel. Clappe observes the two fashionable newcomers and compares them with Mrs. B. and herself, dressed in their old, unstylish garb. On one level, Clappe is being self-critical: she is contrasting her past polished and sociable self with her present western condition. Subtly, however, she uses the comparison to display her new self to its advantage. As they are eating dinner, a small fight erupts in the barroom below, and two men rush into the dining room with "blood-bespattered shirt bosoms" (141). At the sight of the blood, the "pretty wearer of the Pamella hat" faints, and the festivities wane. Clappe, who has grown strong from her adaptation to the land, is given a glimpse of her former delicate, upper-class New Englander condition.

Clappe describes her transformation in terms of dwelling in and making a textual claim on the land through her writing. This notion is linked to a view advanced by Nina Baym that the essential quality of America rests in unsettled wilderness and the opportunities it gives as a medium through which an individual can make his own destiny and his own nature.[24] Just as Clappe's sophisticated veneer is stripped away, so too are her words and syntax simplified and revitalized. In the beginning letters, her eastern language predominates. It is literary, traditional, reflective, abstract, and sprinkled with French and Latin phrases. In the camps, Clappe is confused by the cacophony of foreign tongues. She doesn't comprehend the unfamiliar mining terms, she dislikes the miners' slang, and she finds their constant use of profanity revolting: "I am told that here, it is absolutely the fashion, and that people who never uttered an oath in their lives while in the 'States,' now Clothe themselves with curses as with a garment" (42). The longer Clappe is in the mines, however, the more used to the miners' language she becomes. Gradually she appropriates it and fashions a new language for herself that includes their slang and geo-rhetoric. Almost subversively she embraces a more masculine discourse—an increasingly active, explicit language—to create her story.

Frequently Clappe uses humor to portray the range of behaviors she observes. She has a cheerful disposition and is able to see the ridiculous or the ludicrous in a situation. Although, like Royce, Clappe does not foreground her husband, he is not exempt from her witty characterizations. Clappe exposes his incompetence and conversely promotes her own resilience and adaptability. Whereas her physical and emotional health improve markedly during her stay in the camps, Fayette grows increasingly ill and incompetent. He is constantly concerned about his health. He easily loses his way on trips, his plans work out for the worst, and his impractical investments include spending a thousand dollars on a worthless mining claim. Entertaining their guests, she becomes the intellectual pivot of their social life. In the fourth letter, Clappe describes her husband's successful amputation of a young miner's leg. She uses the opportunity to focus on the suffering miner and the proximity of death to those in the camps rather than putting the emphasis on the surgical success of her young and inexperienced physician husband.

Upon leaving the mines, Fayette went to Hawaii where he was hired by the king in the treatment of smallpox and vaccinations. He returned in ill health to Massachusetts in 1854, and in 1856, the Clappes divorced. She was thirty-eight years old. What ended their relationship can only be surmised. When Clappe alluded to marriage in a letter to Alexander Hill Everett, he questioned whether the marriage was "one of sentiment or of convenience" (February 2, 1847, *Shirley Papers*). If it was initially a love match, perhaps Clappe's new self that was fashioned in the mines contributed to their marital problems. She had a taste of life in a more uninhibited and self-directing society, and it could be assumed that she valued her independence more than the social respectability she would lose as a divorced woman.[25]

Clearly the freer life in the mining camps threatened the domestic sphere. Although the statistics for this period are unreliable, they show that the divorce rates for states that were part of the mining frontier were higher than for the United States as a whole, except for some areas in the South. As mentioned in chapter 2, California's permissive divorce law contributed to these statistics. However, living in a new environment with less rigid sexual mores would make even the ideal home less attractive and help in part to explain these higher rates. And the scarcity of women was another contributor. For an unsatisfied wife, there was plenty of opportunity for her to find another husband. It is interesting to note that given this inflated marriage market in California, Clappe never remarried.

After her divorce, Louise remained in San Francisco where she met Ferdinand Ewer, the fiancé of a woman who boarded with Clappe's sister Henrietta. Ewer was the editor of the *Pioneer*, San Francisco's first literary magazine. As a result of Ewer's friendship, Clappe submitted for publication her letters from the mines and essays on sexual equality and superstition. After two years, the *Pioneer* folded, and Clappe, who needed to support herself, got a teaching position at Denman School where she taught for twenty-four years. After her retirement, she lived first in New York City and then in Morristown, New Jersey, where she remained until her death on February 9, 1906.

※　※　※　※

At the beginning of her trip to the mines, she commented that she could never understand why anyone would want to make one's wrists ache by knocking to bits "gloomy pieces of stones" (25). However, in her letter of November 25, 1851, Clappe claims that she herself has become a "mineress": "I wet my feet, tore my dress, spoilt a pair of new gloves, nearly froze my fingers, got an awful headache, took cold and lost a valuable breastpin, in this my labor of love" (74). For her efforts, she received three dollars and twenty-five cents—and, most important, new knowledge.

> Having fathomed the depths of "shafts," the mazes of "Coyote holes," I intend to astonish the weak nerves of stay-at-homes if I ever return to New England—by talking learnedly on such subjects, as "one having authority." (161)

Significantly, it is her knowledge of the land that gives her authority. Authorized by the woman who has "fathomed the depths," Clappe's text evidences her assimilation. Note the inwardness of her language here— the process of her change is not to be viewed as linear. And her transformation did not require that she explore a vast territory. She investigated the subtle layers of race, gender, and culture in a limited pocket of space along the upper Feather River. Having revised her literary notions about the West by firsthand experience, she now is able to assume the position of "insider." To anticipate the title of Farnham's narrative, Clappe is now at home both "indoors and out." In her letters, her cabin has served as both a correlative for the state of her interior being as well as a metaphor for the text itself. She no longer needs the house because she has integrated what it represents.

By the fall of 1852, Clappe notes that most companies of Rich Bar had failed and that there were fewer than twenty men remaining on Indian Bar, which was "thickly peppered with empty bottles, oyster cans, sardine boxes, and brandied fruit jars" (195). As she and her husband prepare to depart, she admits that she likes "this wild and barbarous life" and leaves it "with regret" (198). Recognizing that her stay in the mines has provided her with a chance to break out of "proper" social structures of entrapment governing female behavior, she wonders how she will ever be content to live once again in "a decent, proper, well-behaved house."

Among the most popular gold rush postcards is a drawing of a miner looking amazed at the large elephant looming before him. Not introduced to the East Coast until 1796, the elephant was an exotic animal that astounded those fortunate enough to see it. To boast that you had seen the elephant was to suggest that you had seen everything. The gold miners' application of the term meant that you had been initiated into the mining life and had come away with no illusions. When Clappe boasts that she has "seen the elephant," she is using the miners' trope to suggest the enormous changes she is undergoing. Actual residence in the West has not only given Clappe strength, resourcefulness, and a new language that includes Spanish, mining terms, and slang, but it has transformed her into a realist. She got a good long look at the California elephant; nothing about the beast escaped her probing eye.

Clappe concludes her text by distinguishing between her former invalid self and her new strong and healthy person. Again, she draws attention to her change by associating it with nature.

> Here, at least, I have been contented. The "thistle seed," as you
> called me, sent abroad its roots right lovingly into this barren soil,
> and gained an unwonted strength in what seemed to you such
> unfavorable surroundings. You would hardly recognize the feeble
> and half-dying invalid, who drooped languidly out of sight, as
> night shut down between your straining gaze and the good ship
> *Manilla*, as she wafted her far away from her Atlantic home, in the
> person of your now perfectly healthy sister. (198)

It is the soil that has allowed her to take root and has nourished her metamorphosis. Driven by an insatiable curiosity and blessed with superb powers of observation, Clappe provides us with the human side of the mining frontier and a glimpse of the personal lives of the miners that is available in few other sources. Whereas many of the accounts of the California Gold Rush romanticize it as a place and time when men were self-sufficient and women were unnecessary, Clappe's revisionist account details its tensions and emphasizes the possibilities it afforded women. She offers her transformed self as evidence of its potential.

Unlike her first letter, Clappe no longer identifies herself as the wife of Fayette, lost in the wilderness on the way to Rich Bar. Having dismantled the hierarchical assumptions that privilege masculine experience over feminine, she is able to conclude her epistle in a statement that could almost stand as her manifesto: "You would hardly recognize me . . . in the person of your *now* perfectly healthy sister." Linking her recovery to her association with the feminine, she is marked by her new status. She is no longer the "shrinking, timid, frail thistle" that she was. Louise Smith Clappe has seen the elephant. And as she writes in her nineteenth letter, not just his tail, but "the entire 'Animal' has been exhibited to [her] view" (157).

> *It must not be forgotten that life in California is altogether anomalous, and that it is no more extraordinary for a woman to plough, dig, and hoe with her own hands, . . . than for men to do all their household labor for months.*

ELIZA BURHANS FARNHAM
At Home in the California Wilderness

Historians rarely mention that single and widowed women traveled west and lived in the settlements established by gold miners and pioneers. These women were frequently responsible for all the chores necessary to run a homestead. For them, "women's work" was a misnomer—they did whatever work needed to be done. When Eliza Burhans Farnham went to California in 1849 and started a rancho in Santa Cruz County, she was responsible for all the chores both inside and outside her house. She plowed, washed clothes, herded cattle, cared for children, mended the clothes, and planted vegetable gardens.

Published in 1856, Farnham's narrative of frontier experiences, *California, In-doors and Out*, is the first book about California to be written by a woman. Farnham rejects the monomyth of western expansion and uses individual authority to appropriate the frontier—this is *her*story. She writes for and about women, encouraging them to enter the wilderness with eyes wide open to the challenges they will face. Like the other women in this study, Farnham disrupts the fixity of separate spheres, the ideology that holds that there is a public sphere inhabited by men and a private sphere reserved for women. As her narrative emphasizes, the role of frontier women is both recuperative and subversive: it implies a maturity and an awareness that contradict the stereotype of the reluctant and shrinking wife, submissively following her husband into the wilderness.

Farnham casts herself as the mother of not only two sons but of all of those at her ranch. But Farnham's family configuration does not obscure her attentiveness to the significance of the land itself. Working her fields, she makes the terrain her own. In the process, she loses her emigrant status and becomes rooted in California soil. As she describes the landscape in her narrative and finds the imagery to designate her relation to it, she makes the terrain symbolically her own. This grounding, both literal and textual, contradicts the wild, chaotic frontier conditions created by transients with their lust for quick riches. Her persona suggests the possibility of harmonious intimacy between human beings and nature. However, this is not an eroticized nature designed to fulfill the desires of a white male hunter or an isolated Adamic adventurer. Farnham's imaginative play instead focuses on the maternal characteristics of nature. Moreover, although Farnham was a rancher and dependent upon the land economically, her initial and primary attachment was to the inherent beauty of the place.

The fourth of five children, Eliza Wood Burhans was born in the village of Potter Hollow, near Rensselaerville, New York, on November 17, 1815.[1] After her Quaker mother, Mary Wood Burhans, died in 1820, Eliza and her siblings were separated. Eliza was sent to live with an aunt and an alcoholic uncle on a small farm in Maple Springs, New York. Later retitled *Eliza Woodson* (1864), *My Early Days* (1859) is a semiautobiographical account of her childhood and her developing appreciation of nature. In 1831 Farnham was reunited with her brothers and sisters in Palmyra, New York. One of her brothers supported her study at a Quaker boarding school. For a while she worked as a teacher, and then, again with the help of her brother, she enrolled in the Albany Female Academy. In 1835, exhausted from her first-year examinations, she went to live with her married sister Mary near Groveland in Tazewell County, Illinois.

On July 12, 1836, after only a little more than a year in Illinois, Eliza married Thomas Jefferson Farnham, a young lawyer from Vermont.[2] The couple resided for three years in the village of Tremont. Eliza's sister Mary died of consumption at age twenty-five in July 1838, and two weeks later, Eliza's infant son died in the yellow fever epidemic. While her husband was away on an exploratory trip to Oregon in 1839 and 1840, Eliza most likely lived with one of her brothers. *Life in Prairie Land* (1846) is her autobiographical depiction of frontier Illinois. Not only is it an interesting account of the changing frontier, but it is also a revealing self-portrait of a woman's relationship with the environment. In her narrative, the land fulfills the familial connections she had been deprived of in childhood: Farnham sees herself as a child welcomed by "a strong and generous parent, whose arms are spread to extend protection, happiness, and life" (xxxiii). The trees represent "elder brothers" and the "idea of home." The new prairie West, she boasted, was to be preferred over all other portions of the globe.

When Farnham's husband returned in 1840, the couple moved to New York and settled at Washington Hollow near Poughkeepsie. While her husband worked on his *Travels in the Great Western Prairies* (1843), Eliza became involved in prison reform, phrenology, and the role of women. In 1844 she won appointment as the matron of the women's section of Sing Sing Prison.[3] Despite the improvements she made, her liberal views regarding rehabilitation instead of repression brought her into conflict with other staff members, and she was forced to resign in 1848. She then worked briefly at the Perkins Institute for the Blind in Boston where she assisted Dr. Samuel Gridley Howe with his student Laura Bridgman, the first known deaf and blind person to be successfully educated in the United States.

In September 1848, Farnham's husband contracted "intermittent fever" and died in San Francisco. The following spring, after a period of ill health, she began to make plans for herself and her two sons to leave for California to settle his estate. Believing that women's presence would provide positive moral and social influence in the West, she attempted to organize a party of 130 "intelligent, virtuous, and efficient" women to immigrate to California with her.

> There is no country in the world where the highest attributes of the
> female character are more indispensable to the social weal than in
> California; for nowhere else have indomitable energies, the quick
> desires, and the wide-reaching purposes of the Saxon nature been
> submitted to so severe a test of their self-regulating power. (295)

These women were to be twenty-five years of age or older. They were to have a letter from their clergyman testifying to their education and character, and they were to contribute $250 to defray the expense of the voyage and to make possible their stay in San Francisco until they could find a job.

Farnham ran an advertisement in the paper that included signatures of supporters such as William Cullen Bryant, Henry Ward Beecher, Catherine Sedgwick, Caroline Kirkland, and Horace Greeley.[4] A two-month illness following the publication of this ad prevented her from following through with her female emigration plan, and only three of the more than two hundred women who had expressed interest made the journey with her. Two of these women returned to the East "with the means of living comfortably the rest of their days and with unstained reputations" (27). The third, Lucy Sampson (Miss S.), became a member of Farnham's family.

Eliza Farnham

portrait, ca. 1864. Courtesy of the New-York Historical Society, New York City, PR 011, negative number 16951.

On May 19, 1849, at the age of thirty-four, Eliza Farnham sailed to California. After settling her husband's estate, she decided to stay. She started a farm, or as she called it, a rancho. El Rancho la Libertad was located in Santa Cruz County, about seventy miles south of San Francisco and twenty miles north of Monterey.[5] For more than five years, she farmed two hundred acres there with her children and Miss Sampson. Sometime during that period, her former assistant matron at Sing Sing, Georgiana Bruce Kirby (Geordie), joined her.[6] In 1856, Farnham wrote and published *California, In-doors and Out,* an autobiographical account of her life in Santa Cruz County with an emphasis on the importance of women to California's frontier society.

Instead of traveling overland, Farnham took the more expensive route around Cape Horn to California.[7] In her narrative she represents her ocean voyage in terms of erratic motion. She views the shipboard challenges as a kind of necessary seasoning for the rigors that await her in California. Central to this initial experience is the cruel captain of the *Angelique* who mistreats his female passengers. According to Farnham, "he never named women but to deprecate them in the coarsest terms" (7). When he refused to stop for fresh water at St. Catharine's, Brazil, the passengers signed a protest that was drawn up by Farnham. As a consequence, Farnham became the target of the captain's wrath, and he attempted revenge by encouraging Farnham's nurse to desert her and marry one of his stewards. The marriage took place at Valparaiso, Chile, and Farnham went ashore to engage a Chilean woman to finish the voyage with her as a nurse to her two sons. While she was off the ship procuring the proper papers for the woman, the captain set sail. She returned to the dock just in time to witness the vessel disappearing into the horizon.

Abandoned in a foreign country, without family, friends, luggage, or money, Farnham is able to comment on the outcast situation of the female traveler and on the journey's disruption, not only of home life but also of domestic ideology. She has been cast out of the web of social relationships and familiar spaces. The features of her stable world are redefined as fluxional, introducing the theme of transience, which finds expression in all aspects of Farnham's narrative. As a consequence of the captain's machinations, she has become altogether stripped of things familiar. Anticipating her outsider position during the first year in Santa Cruz County, Farnham dramatizes her dependence on the hospitality of the residents of Valparaiso and their "local knowledge" to live for a month in their town while she waits for another ship bound for San Francisco.

Farnham's report of the captain's mistreatment of the female passengers and especially herself certainly records aspects of her literal journey, but it also critiques gender and class hierarchies and underscores the egalitarian assumptions that she will attempt to realize in California as well. Doubly marginalized, she is both a woman and a member of the passenger class that is under the command of the captain. Additionally, the surreal experience of being left at the dock while the ship with her children sails on to California serves as metaphoric commentary on the confusing psychological reorientation necessary to her survival in California's new social space. Arriving in San Francisco, she locates her children and friends, but the reintegration of Farnham into her former domestic and social relations is on new terms. Assuming a position of authority, she attempts to get legal retribution for the inconveniences she suffered and the captain's encroachment upon her rights.

During the first months of 1850, Clappe, Royce, and Farnham all lodged in San Francisco. We can easily imagine them passing each other as they walked along the city's main streets, roads that would have been turned into mud mires by the winter rains. Perhaps they exchanged glances as they pushed their way through the heterogeneous throng that filled the city of hastily built temporary dwellings of sheet metal, cardboard, and canvas. As women, newly arrived and undoubtedly overwhelmed by the unreality of the place—the mingled aromas of filth and exotic foods and the torrent of different languages that accosted their ears—they would have looked at each other for some semblance of normalcy. If they had seen each other in New York City or St. Louis, they might not have taken the slightest notice. But here in the West, the situation is changed. Because of who they are and where they are, they now have so much in common that they are metaphoric sisters. Certainly, they would have acknowledged each other, had they crossed paths in the dirty streets of San Francisco.

In order to settle her husband's estate, Farnham and her family had to stay in San Francisco for two months. Although she would return later and offer a more positive perspective of the new metropolis, her first impression was not positive. According to Farnham, women especially suffered indignities. They were such rarities that when they ventured out onto the city's streets they "felt themselves uncomfortably stared at." Farnham wrote, "Doorways filled instantly, and little islands in the streets were thronged with men who seemed to gather in a moment, and who remained immovable till the spectacle passed from their incredulous gaze" (22–23). She concludes her passage on San Francisco by stating that she felt grateful that her attempts to bring eastern women to a place as morally and socially impoverished as California failed. She confides that now that she has seen the place, "it would be a painful responsibility, which I could never throw off, if I had to reflect that there were persons here through my instrumentality who were less happy or good than they might have been remaining at home" (24).

Farnham, her two sons, and Miss Sampson reached Santa Cruz on February 22, 1850, landing "like bales of goods through the surf, partly in boats and partly in the arms of the seamen" (42).[8] Her boxes of personal belongings have broken open, and many of the articles are afloat or scattered about the beach: "Boxes had been burst, baskets, bags, and other articles slyly set afloat by the [surf], with intent to their felonious removal to deep water; and all these accidents had raised questions of jurisdiction which only the most exceeding vigilance could settle in favor of the little disputant, who ran nimbly about, dodging the great broadsides of his antagonist" (51). Whether consciously intended or not, this passage enunciates Farnham's sense of radical displacement and the hardships she has endured on her journey west. It also prepares readers for what is about to happen to her now that she is in California. The water and beach are quite literally marked by her formerly protected and organized boxed goods—tokens of her prior home and prior self—and that marking suggests how the landscape transforms its inhabitants and reshapes them without regard to personal desires.

In contrast to Louise Clappe who becomes comfortable with the physical freedom provided by her Indian Bar cabin before she moves outdoors to explore her surroundings, Farnham does a quick survey of her husband's "forlorn *rancho*" and moves quickly outside. She finds herself in such beautiful surroundings that she is totally unprepared "for the sort of impression it produced" (44). And it is not the cultivated garden that catches her eye, but unspoiled nature. She describes the area as exceedingly quiet and lovely. The sound of the surf "rather aids than breaks the silence," she writes (44). For one hour, she completely forgot "that life subjects the spirit to jar or discord, and [was] only conscious of the harmony that flows from the generous breast of nature into our own." Forgetting the "hateful stir of the world in which [she] had been lately stirred up," she is conscious only of peace and harmony. Her romantic appreciation of the benevolence of the natural world unites her with Emerson. She gazes at the sparkling waters of the bay and the surrounding coastal hills, and she deems it a "fairy scene, rather than a portion of the real, peopled earth."

> So bright is it, in its newness and unrevealed deformities, so tender in its solitude and purity, so holy in its beauty, overhung by a sky whose pure blue seems made only to veil the heaven we imagine above from that we gaze upon beneath, I wonder, while beholding it, that religious and devout thankfulness to God does not continually ascend from the hearts of those who dwell in so fair a portion of his creation. (46)

Farnham acknowledges her belief that unspoiled nature's influence on the human spirit is purifying. When she is awakened from her meditation by her sons' shouts, it is with great reluctance that she detaches herself. They enter the house where she gives them some bread, and then she returns hurriedly to the brook of beauty. It is too late: "the charm was broken; there was no return to the world from which they had recalled me," she writes (47).

Farnham's survey of the "inside" world is "less delightful." Her husband's dwelling is made of slabs. It doesn't have "a foot of floor, nor a pane of glass, nor a brick, nor anything in the shape of a stove." It is in such a wretched state that she fantasizes about how her new home will be as she begins her housekeeping. In terms of symbolic displacement, Farnham emphasizes her preparation to take over the old and become the shaper of her own world. By virtue of her gender—emphasized by her housekeeping fantasies—she radically alters the chains of inheritance and claims a place for women in the frontier. In her imaginings, Farnham "inverted the black walls, turned them inside out" (48). To make a home of this place, she needs to wash away the filth of years of neglect, lay a floor, erect a closet, and "set apart a corner for a bedroom." The contrast between the imagined future house and her husband's homestead is striking. Insofar as men allow their houses to fall into such a slovenly condition, the woman stands as the appropriate heir as her influence is needed to elevate the cultural regression on the frontier. As a result of her inheritance, however, Farnham is forced into a new relationship with the wilderness. No longer can she be content to simply appreciate its beauty—now she must depend on its cultivation for her survival.

The title of her narrative, *California, In-doors and Out*, emphasizes Farnham's liminal position on the threshold of two dominant ideologies: an interior, home-centered domesticity and an exterior, frontier individualism. According to Ann Romines in *The Home Plot: Women, Writing, and Domestic Ritual*, for many American woman writers, housekeeping operates as "the center and vehicle of a culture invented by women, a complex and continuing process of female, domestic art" (14). Similarly, Farnham's homemaking asserts the value of female enterprise, albeit through a radical insistence on alternative values in place of traditional domestic arts. Declaring that "life in California is altogether anomalous, and that it is no more extraordinary for a woman to plough, dig, and hoe with her own hands, if she have the will and strength to do so" (28), Farnham fashions her own house and fields. She is housekeeper, carpenter, and farmer. Building her own house (both interior and exterior) and working her two hundred acres, she is putting her stamp on frontier spaces otherwise appropriated by men. This connection between home and environment is significant. Like later writers such as Mary Austin, Helen Hoover, and Ann Zwinger who cherish wildness, Farnham seeks a way to make herself as comfortable in "this strangest of all countries" (41) as she is in her house. But she is not blind to the beauties of nature, and she wants to be as enthusiastic about her "forlorn habitation" as she is about the wilderness places of California. Using the metaphor of nature as home, she looks forward to being at home in California both "indoors and out."

Exploring Farnham's contradictory attitude toward domesticity involves first looking at the California "homes" she inhabits. Her deceased husband's house, El Rancho la Libertad, was "not a cheerful specimen even of California habitations," so she slept on the ground in a white tent until she could "re-erect" a new home on the foundation of the old one. By July 4, she had the lines for the new foundation sketched on the ground. "It seemed to me a great step taken, actually to see my future house defined on the very ground it was to cover" (104). This "ground design" reflects Farnham's vision to build a space for herself where she is in command of her life, a space dedicated to the expression of her own *libertad*, both physical and spiritual. The significance of the beginning of her text, where she describes her trip around the Horn and the captain's dictatorial and brutal treatment of his virtually enslaved passengers, is to set the contrast to the freedom she is endeavoring to make for herself in Santa Cruz County.

Similar to Louise Smith Clappe's cabin in Indian Bar, Farnham's rancho can be seen as a governing metaphor for her narrative. In contrast to Clappe, however, Farnham did all the carpenter work for her elaborate two-story house herself. The value of her house-building lies in the possibilities it offers as a representation of her female self. "Let not ladies lift their hands in horror," she admonished. "I laughed whenever I paused for a few minutes to rest, at the idea of promising to pay a man fourteen or sixteen dollars per day for doing what I found my own hands so dexterous in" (107). One morning she was on the roof shingling, and a stranger passed by and began to talk to her about the philosophy of Swedenborg. Interested, she laid down her hammer, took off her nail pocket, and "descended the ladder with the help of [her] visitor's hand" (144). She boasts to her reader that she needed his help only because this was early in her experience as a roofer. With practice, she writes, she was able to "go up and down alone with perfect freedom and ease."

Farnham began her house-building attired in a long dress, but she soon wore the suit she used for "gymnastic exercises," an outfit that became "famous as the Bloomer, though then the name had not been heard of" (108). Whereas at the start she kept an eye out for visitors so that they would not catch her in her masculine attire, later she grew so accustomed to her comfortable "working costume" that the chance of being seen no longer bothers her. "If I saw a man coming, I did not stroll away to the shanty, to keep out of sight till he was gone, or to change my dress. This was a great victory" (133). Her victory here is her refusal to be confined to female attire. Her decision to wear pants, as well as the open design of her house, can be seen as her attempt to escape from repressive patriarchal confines into the liberated space of her own authority.

Months later, when she is attempting to apprehend a cow, she also dresses in men's clothing. Attired in a suit and hat "*a la monsieur,*" she leaves off her glasses in order to avoid being recognized by her neighbors (189). But without her glasses, her vision is altered: she "could not tell, at twenty rods, whether it was an ox or a man approaching." Having established for her readers the connection between the freedom to cross-dress, to play outside the borders of stereotypical gender definition and the resulting change in perspective, she then emphasizes her engagement with the chase. She becomes so totally involved in the excitement of apprehending the cow that she completely forgets the fact that she doesn't want to be seen in masculine attire by her neighbors (191).

In her narrative, Farnham catalogues the chores that she attempts, reinforcing for her reader her ability to perform tasks that include, but are not limited to, domestic activities. Not only can she "keep" house, she can literally construct a house. Clearly, she is proud of her attempt to do work that is considered masculine. Her humorous descriptions of her neighbors' responses to her "unladylike" behavior only serve to reinforce her sense of strength and ingenuity.

After she erects her house, Farnham's thoughts turn seriously to farming (58). She boasts that her text won't be about mining, as so many others are devoted to it. Instead she will describe farming in order to prove that there is life worth considering in California besides that which is associated with prospecting. "It is the land of vine and olive," she writes (30). If half of the "stout hearts and strong hands" that leave for the mining regions would direct their efforts toward California's "teeming vales and plains and hills, for here all are fertile," there would be "an annual saving of wealth, health, life, and virtue," she informs her readers.

J. Hector St. John de Crèvecoeur's *Letters from an American Farmer* is considered by many scholars of American literature to be the foundation of the American national myth. Published in 1782 and following the American Revolution, the "What is an American?" section of Crèvecoeur's text articulates the central cultural myth that constituted America as a new nation—the myth that associates the development of the national character with a close and symbiotic relation to the American land. Under the adopted persona of Farmer James, Crèvecoeur defines the farming of the fertile and maternal American terrain as the activity that defines the essence of this new American man and American egalitarianism. Although the author did not conclude his letters with the same opinion of the land's potential, at this point in the text, Crèvecoeur's discourse is a combination of systematizing and articulating identity and travel narrative. Similarly, Farnham presents herself as the innocent farmer and traveler. As she draws the lines of her future house on the ground, cultivates her land, and wanders through the surrounding coastal hills, she is literally and figuratively staking a claim to the land and delineating its borders.

In *Imperial Eyes: Travel Writing and Transculturation*, Mary Louise Pratt compares the "generalizing voice" of ethnography to the landscape narrator of the travelogue: one scans the indigenous inhabitants as bodyscapes and the other focuses on land as landscape, with an eye out for prospects. The combined rhetoric of ethnography and travel writing shapes and authorizes Farnham's narrative. The idealized depiction of Santa Cruz County and her increasing symbiotic relationship between herself and the maternal landscape lead her to a new definition of self. The tilling of the soil represents not only new independence but also a keener understanding of the valley and its inhabitants. She learns, for example, that most men were not willing to work for two dollars a day when they might earn a hundred dollars a day in the mines. The only men willing to hire on as farm laborers were "invalids or drunken sailors," she writes. In addition to the scarcity of competent hired help, she learns about agricultural operations. She loses one crop to grasshoppers and another to cattle. Wild mustard grew in her wheat field, and one season the ground wouldn't yield a single crop even though it was planted four times.

Not infrequently, Farnham was called away from her digging and planting when sick neighbors needed her homeopathic skills. These professional visits allowed her to become better acquainted with the terrain and many of the features of life on the ranches. Perhaps even more important was the opportunity these outings gave her to reconnect with her home after each absence. When her neighbor Captain Graham falls ill, she and a friend travel to his house five miles away. On their return home, they get lost and stop at several houses for directions, but the occupants can only speak Spanish. Finally, after getting directions from a Canadian, they reach the rancho, "glad enough to see its cheerful interior."

> The black walls clothed, as they now were, with clean, light cloth;
> the stove open, with a blazing fire inside it; and a neat hearth and
> the clean-swept floor suggesting an idea of comfort and home I
> had not felt at sight of any other house I had seen. (65)

The impression evoked by these lines is of a woman delighted in her home in the wilderness. Her phrasings remind the reader that her husband's crude casa has been transformed into a comfortable establishment. For Farnham, a house needed to have floors, windows, and a hearth. The casa's transformation is a result of her own labor—"the black walls clothed, as they now were." And the change is profound. Farnham focuses here on the class markers of domestic comfort: light and clean walls, the neat, warm hearth, and the swept floor. The cumulative effect of these details is twofold. First, it emphasizes a woman's ability to create civilized, orderly conditions amid the disruptions of the frontier. "Only in the presence of women is to be found the efficient remedy for these great evils," she writes of the "martyr women of California" who come to the frontier, regardless of the trials that await them (294). And second, it emphasizes that frontierswomen could survive in the West without relinquishing their gentility.

Later on a return trip from San Francisco, Farnham stops for the night at Isidro Castro's Spanish rancho. Hungry and tired, she goes into the kitchen, hoping to find a warm fire and place to sit until dinner. She addresses her Yankee housewife reader, reminding her that Yankee kitchens and California frontier kitchens can be two different things. Farnham is mortified at the filth of the place. A "dirty" Indian girl with "suspicious-looking arms" and a filthy apron was making tortillas, dumping lumps of dough into an "ill-favored basin of water, into which she occasionally thrust her hands" (125). The dinner of tortillas, *caldo* (soup), and frijoles was delicious, but when she returns to the kitchen and observes the dishwashing process, she is again disgusted. The Indian girl dashed a "handful or two of water over the plate, tilted on the edge of the kettle, and, shocking to tell, wiping them on the very apron!" Before she leaves the kitchen that evening, Farnham decides not to breakfast the next morning but to return as rapidly as possible to the "neat table-service, and wholesome cleanliness of La Libertad."

Farnham's bedchamber at Castro's rancho also served as "a clothes closet, storeroom and granary." She objected to the door because it had no latches and to the bed because it was not fresh enough. Her final image of the Spanish rancho is of the Indian girl the following day. Farnham saw her washing an iron pot with the handkerchief she had worn on her head the night before. As Farnham rode off, she "offered a silent thanksgiving that home was so near."

Using herself and the rancho she has built as the ideal, Farnham demonstrates that it is possible with great effort to maintain "Yankee" standards of neat, wholesome cleanliness in California. The contrast between La Libertad and Castro's rancho is pronounced and demonstrates Farnham's belief that while women were needed to elevate frontier conditions, they could also degenerate as a result of the harsh conditions surrounding them. According to Farnham, California was a moral wilderness, and a woman will "feel, in the moral atmosphere which surrounds her, such taint, such infection, that she will scarcely hope to find the integrity and purity that would inspire trust" (156). Consequently, she believed, only certain women should emigrate: women with "fortitude, indomitable resolution, dauntless courage, and a clear self-respect" who were willing to take up the physical necessities of washing linen, cleansing houses, cooking, and nursing. A woman in California is in "an enemy's country," as Farnham phrased it, and must remain constantly on the alert. "None but the pure and strong-hearted of my sex should come alone to this land," she warned (156–57).

Women who emigrated west across the plains underwent such a physical and psychological ordeal that they began to degenerate even before they arrived in California, according to Farnham. And although emigration around the Horn required much less exertion than the overland route, the thoughts of the passengers were so occupied with gold that it produced a "stultification of the better powers" (257). Obsessed with the idea of gold before leaving his former home, once in the goldfields, the miner allowed his obsession to sever all connection with friends and relations. Gold caused "forgetfulness of old ties, purposes, motives, restraints," Farnham lamented. Once emigrants were a part of the "harum-scarum life" in California, she feared that most of them would never be able to recover their "old standard" again.

Similar to Sarah Royce, Farnham admitted that there were as yet relatively few severe difficulties arising out of the "disorderly state of affairs." However, she was worried about California's future because the desperate class of miners was rapidly increasing in numbers. As witnessed by Royce and Clappe, Farnham observed that the miners were so interested in selfish purposes that they took no stake in social welfare or in California affairs in general. She pitied the religious teacher in California where "vice carries so unblushing a front" and "the pursuit of wealth is so absorbing" (139).

> Even Puritanism, tough and tenacious though it was, would have been shorter lived had the *Mayflower* landed her inflexibles on this laughing coast. The rock-bound shores and inhospitable soil, the wintry skies overhanging the sterile mountains and stony vales of New England, were far more favorable to earnestness in the religious as well as the working life of man than ours will ever be. (139)

Indeed, Farnham comes close to condemning the Edenic characteristics of the terrain, suggesting that the land's bounty encourages the self-centered, riotous lifestyle of its inhabitants. The degenerating effects of the area touch her as well. Admitting that even she herself is much more engrossed with her own private interests and concerns than with any of a public character, she concludes this section of her narrative by moving to a dramatic discussion of enemies to her peace and prosperity: grasshoppers and cattle.

Her problems at the ranch began to weigh on her, and consequently she was no longer able to appreciate the "nobler relations" of nature:

> A few acres of potatoes, a few thousands of brick and shingles, and the four walls of a house that could separate us from the winds and clouds, could shut her out of my soul for the time; could so weary and subdue my spirit, that it settled down in abject bondage to them, and almost forgot that it had ever nobler relations, greater freedom, more joyous life. (151–52)

Estranged from the "loving mother," she writes that her "eye was dimmed to her pure glories." Her "dimmed eye" or "I" is directly related to the Emersonian transparent eyeball through which circulate the currents of the universe. "Shut up in [her] narrow house," she is disconnected from the healing and rejuvenating relation with nature. The house that she had earlier viewed as commodious is confining when it is cut off from the energies of nature. She is also circumscribed because her actions are confined to the limited sphere of those in her family circle. In this confined, narrow space, she feels "sadly out of place" (155). Heightening her sense of dislocation is the lack of a female friend. She considered her isolation from the companionship of other women to be the "keenest" of her trials (158).

The unbalanced gender ratio during the California Gold Rush not only influenced sexuality but social relations overall. However, although Farnham lacked female camaraderie because there was a scarcity of women nearby, she also was unable to make friends easily. Unlike Clappe and Royce, Farnham's attitude toward the frontier inhabitants was frequently one of superiority, and her remarks were often condescending. She thought that many of her neighbors were rude and uneducated and often belittled their dress and lack of refinement. For example, at a Methodist church meeting, she characterized the young girls' lack of taste:

> Hideous bonnets of all fashions, which their grandmothers might have worn, deformed their heads and concealed their fine faces; gowns pinned at the waist in front; monstrous shoes, or maybe none at all, showed the want of supplies in the country, if it also argued some lack of taste in its inhabitants. (136)

Her exclusiveness and superior attitude contributed to her loneliness, a condition not broken until the arrival of her friend Georgiana Bruce Kirby, an educated Englishwoman who had worked with Farnham at Sing Sing Prison's women's division (164).[9] A friend of Margaret Fuller, Geordie had lived three years at Brook Farm, the transcendentalist community near Boston. She and Farnham shared eastern acquaintances and intellectual interests. "There was nothing to check that free interchange of thought and sentiment to which [our] natural state of frankness inclines," Farnham confides to her readers (73). Women's rights and their opportunity for self-fulfillment were constant topics of their talks.

As the two women begin to farm together, Farnham once again feels the connectedness to the land that she had felt when she first arrived in Santa Cruz. Referring to the fields they worked as paradise, she writes that they "grew large" in their calm state.

> Could it be possible that hurry and confusion were still anywhere on the earth that was so full of repose about us; possible that people were anywhere swallowing hurried, leaden meals, and rushing off to narrow counting-rooms or noisy manufactories, with no blessed earth to stretch their weary limbs upon, nor blue heaven to pour serenity into their souls, nor birds, nor sighing winds, nor chime of sea to drive the din of the stirring world from their ears? (179–80)

In protest against the excision of women from the American frontier, Farnham exchanges the classic American male-bonding-in-nature story for a feminist version. She provides the reader with the image of two female farmers working together in their shared fields. They are removed from the exploitation of the counting houses and factories of the East. Exploding the traditional familial configuration that gives women responsibility only within the confines of their houses and under the auspices of their husbands, Farnham describes Geordie and herself as working together in their fertile fields as daughters of the land, finding only delight in each other and in their duties. Setting her revised familial community in nature against images of industrialization and urbanization, Farnham portrays the western frontier as the site in which women can find self-fulfillment and where an idealized society might be realized.

In the spring, Farnham and Geordie, accompanied by two "gentlemanly neighbors, Messrs. G. and K.," take a forty-mile trip up the coast to the strawberry region. Farnham uses this section of her text to combine travel narrative, meditation, poetry, and cultural critique to develop her conception of an idealized society. Writing to an audience of easterners, she depicts the terrain they travel through in vivid detail for readers who have never set foot in the American West. She portrays the landscape with active voice—describing the hills "flecked with golden, purple, scarlet, and pink flowers," the sound of the surf beating against the coastal rocks, and the feel of the wind fresh in their faces. Furthermore, she shifts the subject from "we" to "you," deliberately closing the gaps between herself and her reader. I want to suggest that Farnham's purpose here is multileveled and is, in fact, more concerned with the issue of freedom than the local flora of the coastal region. Emphasizing a unique mixture of outside and inside spaces, she creates a congenial landscape upon which her vision of social harmony can be brought out.

The expansive landscape includes the enclosed, bounded landscape. Their first evening's campsite becomes a meeting ground for opposites: a landscape of wildness and cultivation and a potential sanctuary for the foursome. Significantly, Farnham moves the domestic hearth outdoors, but its symbolic place markers remain the same—the fire is lit and the blankets spread out. The enclosed space becomes the center of relaxation with books, good conversation, cakes, and brandied peaches: "we felt much of the cozy comfort of a snug home" (220). By presenting a protected area of wilderness with a set of domestic images designed to help women readers forge comfortable anticipatory relationships with unfamiliar terrain, Farnham redefines the term "frontier" for her eastern readers.

Farnham's outward journey to the strawberry fields is central to her personal enlightenment. After her companions are asleep, her spirit "unfolded," and she fell into a reverie of her childhood: "all rose as vividly before me as if they were not memories but passing realities" (222). Identifying the land metaphorically not only as feminine but again as mother, Farnham acknowledges nature as the provider of the life food to her earlier self: "Childhood is so inestimably blest where nature is its nursing mother. My early hopes had been inspired by her; my victories gained at her bidding"(223). The phrasing here is pointed. These lines suggest the adult Farnham's recognition of the interpenetrative powers of nature on human beings, reminiscent of Emerson's vision of the promise of the individual's mystical relation to nature. Her reverie affirms the concept of the environment as one of the preeminently formative influences in her early life and her continuing dependence on nature as her emotional center. As Annis Pratt and Barbara White put it, the adult Farnham can "look back to moments of naturistic epiphany as touchstones in a quest for her lost selfhood" (17). For Farnham, nature is a corrective: it is able to restore right relation to self and to community.

On the day before their return, the four companions shared the "deep precious sense of the rare freedom of coming and going at will, of lounging, sitting, reading, eating, riding or walking, at the bidding purely of our pleasure" (234–35). They listen to Geordie read John Sterling's "Sexton's Daughter," and Farnham notes that their heightened sensitivity to nature has given them a "keener sympathy" to the poem: "We listened, at whiles, with glistening eyes, and a keener sympathy, with all the variety of hopeful, anxious, tender, and religious emotion, than we should have felt elsewhere, and were silent after its close" (235). Their receptivity enhanced by their wilderness setting, they enter into an extended discussion of liberty and the intersection of community and individual rights. Instead of placing this discussion solely in her own words, Farnham has the four companions engage in an intimate and heartfelt conversation that allows them (and the reader/eavesdropper) to listen to and support each other's ideas.

First, Farnham puts readers in close contact with unspoiled nature and lulls them into an idyllic mood. Then she broaches the more controversial critique of lack of freedom and the solution needed to preserve freedom and intimacy with nature in the midst of the complexities of an increasingly technological life. Actively engaging readers in the group's conversation, Farnham brings them into their wilderness setting and thus encourages them to share in their "keener sympathy" as they consider the issue of personal freedom. Through the group conversation, Farnham envisions for the reader a society that works for the land and societal relationships based on an intimate knowledge of the natural world.

While her words often convey simple observations about her surroundings in California, Farnham's linking together of the natural world and the establishment of a conception of the proper human relationships forms the underlying motif in her text. Echoing Emerson, Farnham considers the individual's receptivity to nature as essential to independence. This influence of unspoiled nature on the individual is "purifying, ennobling, and elevating" (*Life in Prairie Land*, xxxiii) and safeguards the individual's physical freedom, a freedom never realized in the actual frontier. For Farnham, ideal freedom is absolute—all social distinctions leveled and all fields open to both men and women. The name of her ranch, El Rancho la Libertad, testifies to her dedication to this ideal.

Farnham uses her trips into San Francisco as opportunities to reinforce her ontological sense of home. Her housekeeping, farm duties, and exploration of unspoiled nature provide her with opportunities to experience both physical and mental freedom. Farnham's narrative tone in these sections is most frequently serious and at times sentimental. In contrast, the comic mode she uses in much of her description of San Francisco highlights the disagreeableness of the place. The harmony and order of her rancho is set in opposition to the rowdy lawlessness of the city. Unlike the geography and climate of Santa Cruz that Farnham extols, San Francisco has "the most disagreeable climate and locality of any city on the globe" (77). She praises the natural environment surrounding her ranch, claiming that it leads its inhabitants toward self-reliance and self-transcendence.

Similarly, Farnham uses the geographic features of the city's area to anticipate the mean habits and crude living arrangements of its inhabitants: "There is scarcely anything deserving the name of society in San Francisco," she laments (286). Although it now boasted storekeepers, teachers, and lawyers and was no longer the city of tents as depicted by Royce the year earlier, Farnham describes it as still inhabited by gold seekers. The city has no moral cohesion, Farnham complained, and she details the residents' "scheming, gaming, profanity, licentiousness, and intemperance." She pokes fun at their pretensions. One gentleman, for example, when asked if he had read *The Last of the Mohicans*, replied that he had not, but that he had been very pleased with the first (289).

Although San Francisco had several churches as early as 1849, Farnham wrote that so few people attended services that it was the responsibility of the newspapers to influence morality. She contrasts her brief description of the churches with an elaborately detailed description of one of the many gaming houses in the city. "It was not merely the gaming that gave character to these pestilent places," she writes, but their bars and the people that haunted them (273).

Before the gold rush, California was a contented country. It was "the world's nursery of freedom," according to Farnham (327). "Broad, genial, maternal," California "nursed" her residents "to the noblest ends of self-development and fraternal helpfulness" (329). All that changed with the gold rush. The impact of gold turned California into a "theatre of unrest, of reckless, hazard, and unscrupulous speculation," Farnham complained (330). Its growth from a city of twenty thousand inhabitants by the end of 1849 to fifty-five thousand in 1855 was "more like fable than reality," she wrote (270). And this rising number of residents was changing the spirit of the place:

> Nature still is fair and liberal, as she was wont to be; but her broad acres, instead of reposing in the peace of past ages, are vexed with all the toil of modern husbandry. The solitude of the plains, where only the low and tramp of herds broke the silence, is replaced by the noise of vehicles and of groups of footmen and horsemen, moving in various directions so earnestly. (325)

A constant critic of San Francisco society, Farnham contends that the gold rush attracted a vibrant mix of aggressive, energetic people from all parts of the globe. Amid the chaos and confusion, one could see Spanish or Mexican women playing monte and smoking *cigaritas*, Chinese tailors, Parisian artists, and Swiss watchmakers. According to Farnham, Malays, Chinese, Swedes, Yankees, and Britons swarmed the wharves. Miners came down from the hills to the bustling metropolis in order to enjoy whiskey, fights, gambling rooms, and fandangos. And waiting for them were merchant profiteers who attempted to separate the prospectors from their gold. The strains on family and spousal relationships and the failure of many miners to realize their dreams of wealth added to the tensions of the city.

Despite Farnham's depiction of the kaleidoscopic nature of the place, between the lines of her text one discovers the beginnings of a cultural maturity. Farnham is a defender of lynch laws and the vigilance committee's attempts to give stability to the confusion. Although seeming to contradict the concept of order and justice, these measures were "purely self-defensive on the part of the people," she observes, and operated for the well-being of the city (319). She describes the rapid increase of permanent structures, commercial businesses, schools, newspapers, and dramatic and musical entertainment. According to Farnham, the Metropolitan on Montgomery Street was the "principal theatre of the state." Catherine Sinclair "has served the public in her managerial capacity with a generosity and industry rarely equaled," Farnham writes, and as a consequence of Sinclair's work, she revised her earlier opinion that California's entertainment was only decently mediocre (283).

At the beginning of her narrative, Farnham promises that she will not discuss mining because so many of her predecessors did. But after she has lived in California a while, she realizes that the consequences of the gold rush are so vast and far-reaching that no book about the state would be complete without a description of the mining operations. The impact of the gold rush touched the lives of men and women everywhere in California. It altered the very geography of the place. Farnham devotes chapters 36 through 39 to her observations of mining practices and the consequential impact on nature and society. Similar to Clappe in her account of Rich and Indian Bars, Farnham witnesses the ways in which the miners have changed the landscape of California:

> It is curious to see, in these regions, how nature is forced out of her
> lawful ways. Some of the largest mountain streams of California
> are now lifted from their beds for miles, and the earth, over which
> they have rolled since the edict "Thus far and no farther" was spo-
> ken to them is being searched and researched, washed and
> rewashed, one year after another. (343)

As previously discussed, Farnham associates nature with freedom, and a distinguishing characteristic of her narrative is that she claims this physical freedom for women as well as for men. The miners are guilty of breaking statutory boundaries by lifting streams "from their beds" and forcing them into controlled waterways. Although women and nature manifest male dominance in different ways, both are left bereft of their rights. In response to the growing number of miners working in increasingly confined spaces, mining itself became more complex, more collective, and, as Farnham notes, more destructive as men began to alter streams, rivers, and landforms.[10]

Like Royce and Clappe, Farnham tried her luck in washing a panful of dirt, and for her efforts, she was rewarded with a particle of gold, "which did not in the least excite the desire to continue the search" (353). Her experience illustrates her cynical attitude toward the tens of thousands of miners who participated in the mad, speculative gamble.

Miners were so obsessed with gold that even obligations to children were forgotten. In Farnham's opinion, one of the saddest features of the mines was the condition of the children (357).[11] Mining camps provided the worst conditions for children, more deplorable than even the large urban areas. Even "the Sabbath was a day of dissipation," she asserts (357). As capable of being seduced by the gold fever as their male counterparts, women neglected their children and spent their time mining next to their husbands. Instead of keeping their children clean or preventing them from swearing or behaving badly, they sat by their husbands' rockers "in the bared bed of the river" (346).

Farnham helps her readers explicitly see the consequences on the children. She sets us on a horse and takes us through a dusty street to "a garden spot, wherein a few cabbages, laden with dust, plead silently for water, and half a dozen rows of choked potatoes remonstrate against their hard lot" (345). At the door of a miner's shanty, readers see "a child who looks much like the plants" because its parents are involved in the search for gold. This picture of neglect emphasizes the child as a victim of a debilitating freedom while simultaneously addressing the need for maternal control associated with children's education. Significantly, Farnham links the child to the landscape as if it were part of it instead of the offspring of the miner and his wife.

Farnham's representations of negligent frontierswomen need to be seen in relation to her own self-representation. Their neglect establishes her own authority and reinforces her self-image as independent, capable, and resourceful. However, her special focus on personal freedom does not mean that she is opposed to marriage. Unlike Louise Smith Clappe, who believed marriage settled women into a state of nothingness, marriage for Farnham is a social contract where husband and wife "promise to study each other's happiness, and endeavor to promote it" (*Life in Prairie Land,* 20). Although Clappe never remarried after her divorce, Farnham did. Interestingly, despite her desire for independence, her friend Georgiana Bruce Kirby's disapproval, and her philosophical views on equality in a marital relationship, Farnham entered into a brief and unhappy marriage with William Alexander Fitzpatrick on March 23, 1852.[12]

On June 25, 1853, Farnham gave birth to a daughter, Mary. Two years later, Eliza's youngest son, Edward, died, and shortly after so did two-year-old Mary. Farnham's grief was complicated by financial problems, her failed farming venture, and her husband's abuse. In 1856, Farnham got a divorce, one of the first in Santa Cruz County.[13] In that same year she returned to New York City and published *California, In-doors and Out* and began work on *Woman and Her Era* (1864), in which she asserts the superiority of women. On May 13, 1858, she spoke at the National Women's Rights Convention in New York City. Farnham returned to California in 1859. While she was there, she delivered a number of public lectures, organized several parties of destitute women seeking homes in the West, and from 1861 to 1862 worked as the matron of the female department of the Insane Asylum in Stockton.

In 1862, Farnham returned to New York City, and in July, she volunteered for service as a field nurse at Gettysburg where she contracted tuberculosis. She died of the disease in New York City on December 15, 1864, and is buried in the Quaker cemetery at Milton-on-Hudson.[14]

Dedicated to "WOMAN, whose gifts and responsibilities it seeks to set forth," *Woman and Her Era* was published by A. J. Davis and Company in 1864. It propounds the superiority of women and Farnham's belief that women are the chief agents of human improvement. Her fictional explanation of her views on gender differences, *The Ideal Attained*, was also published posthumously in 1865. It is a story about a beautiful young widow who sails to California and marries a man of good character.

✳   ✳   ✳   ✳

Farnham concludes *California, In-doors and Out* by saying that she did not attempt to conceal either the positive or the negative features of the place. For her, California is by definition full of contradictions: "To-day is black, tomorrow white" (367). The only constant is the people's lack of mutual sympathies. However, Farnham ends her narrative on an encouraging note—with the belief that after life becomes more settled and the population has lost its "emigrant mixed character," and "society has struck its roots into Californian soil," then the country will be able to return to its earlier contentment.

As Euro-Americans moved west, they needed to "find a way of claiming a pedigree, a line of descent, a status of legitimacy," historian

Patricia Nelson Limerick observes. "In a society that rested on a foundation of invasion and conquest, the matter of legitimacy was up for grabs" (*Something in the Soil*, 295, 261). Farnham's powerful final chapter details the Donner party's 1846 journey from Springfield, Illinois, to California and the courage and sacrifice of these emigrants. She focuses on the hardships of the women, who triumphed over nature. This epic event in western history is significantly pre-1849: it displaces the gold rush as California's official founding myth.[15]

While Susan Shelby Magoffin was making her way down the Santa Fe Trail behind Kearny's troops, the Donner party traveled leisurely across the plains. At Fort Bridger, the group made the disastrous decision to take the cutoff promoted by Lansford Hastings. By the time they reached the Truckee River and began the climb up the Sierra Nevada, it was mid-October. Although they tried to cross the pass above Donner Lake, the snow drove them back. Marooned in makeshift huts by the lake, they soon ran out of provisions. Twice some of them tried to walk out but failed. In the middle of December twelve men, including two Indians, and five women attempted to make it out, but they ran out of rations. The starving whites killed the Indians and ate their remains. Two men and five women finally made it to a ranch. In February, March, and April, four rescue efforts were made to retrieve the members of the party still at the lake. Rescuers found that these overlanders, too, had resorted to cannibalism.

As Farnham examines the Donner tragedy, she is particularly impressed about the differences in mortality between men and women—female mortality was comparatively low. She suggests that the women survived the ordeal because they had a greater psychological stamina than the men.

> Thus have many delicate women, who at home were invalids, exhibited on these dreadful journeys such powers, such miraculous endurance, such indifference to personal suffering, such fertility of resource, in serving others, as have seemed incredible when related. (455)

In Farnham's opinion, the women's sympathy and "better nature," which encourage them to make sacrifices for the sake of the family, gave them the adaptability and perseverance that contributed to their survival.

Attempting to promote western emigration to her women readers, Farnham introduces and concludes her narrative with stories of emigration: first her own and later the Donner party's. This framing device bestows a textual sense of unity to her work, reminding readers of the trials of the journey west and the hardships awaiting them once they arrive.

Simultaneously it provides her readers with a literary sense of California's growing stability and permanence by giving them a glimpse of strong pioneer women. The women in the Donner party and Farnham's narrator-traveler exemplify the community spirit and self-sacrifice not exhibited by the miners. They are the kind of women needed to shape California's political and social institutions and form the California character.

The introductory and concluding travel narratives enclose Farnham's settlement narrative. In these center chapters she traces her transformation from outsider to resident. This metamorphosis is in large part a result of the liberating environment of the West. Although Farnham appropriates domestic chores, she also engages in work typically consigned to men. Conversely, she is involved in the public sphere, but she does not omit women's private concerns. Although she presents herself as a civilizer, she does not confine her influence to the hearth. She is ambiguously positioned both out of doors and in. And whereas at the beginning of her narrative, Farnham is an outsider looking in, by the conclusion of her narrative, she is writing from the insider's perspective. Rooted now in California, she is at home—both indoors and out.

> *I had "gone for a soldier," and a soldier*
> *I determined to be.*

LYDIA SPENCER LANE

The Tender Recollections of an Old Soldier

Lydia Spencer married Lieutenant William Bartlett Lane on May 18, 1854, in Carlisle, Pennsylvania. Immediately afterward, her husband joined his regiment in Texas and she elected to go along. Like Susan Shelby Magoffin, Lane traveled to the Southwest as a young bride: she was only nineteen years old. Also similar to Magoffin, Lane welcomed adventure, suffered deprivation with humor, and remained open to change. She was not reluctant to leave civilization. But whereas Magoffin begins to hunger for the lush green vegetation of her homeland when she is on the trail from Santa Fe to Chihuahua, Lane grows increasingly fond of the landscape of the Southwest and doesn't want to return to the East.

Since the 1850s, officers' wives have been accompanying their husbands to military garrisons. Moreover, many of these women wrote about their westering experiences.[1] Until recently, however, they have lurked in the background of literary scholarship. According to Sandra L. Myres, over thirty books and articles by frontier army wives appeared in print prior to 1920, and an almost equal number have been discovered and published since that time.[2] However, there are not many accounts by officers' wives that deal with life in the frontier army in the trans-Mississippi West prior to the Civil War. Lydia Spencer Lane, Mary Henderson Eastman, Eliza Griffin Johnston, Teresa Griffin Viele, and Marian Sloan Russell are among this small group.[3] Their memoirs are especially valuable because they provide readers with a rare glimpse of the nineteenth-century southwestern military frontier—which includes the antebellum period—from a woman's perspective. Men's accounts of the army, usually taken to be normative, become visible as male constructions and merely one understanding of camp life when read in tandem with the narratives of these women.

In her personal narrative, Lane details her transient experiences as an officer's wife. Her life intersects many of the most interesting personalities and events in the Southwest between the years 1854 and 1870. She observes an increase in Indian tensions and is an eyewitness to the Southwest's divided response to the Civil War. At one point she travels in a caravan with Major Isaac Lynde and the troops that surrendered to Colonel John R. Baylor.[4] She meets the legendary frontiersman Kit Carson, whom she describes as a "quiet, reticent man" (148). At Fort Bliss, Texas, she visits the home of the brother-in-law of Susan Magoffin, trader James Magoffin.[5] Moreover, the actors in Lane's text are not all white male rugged individuals. Her cast of characters attests to the diversities of race, ethnicity, class, and gender in the American Southwest.

To a great extent, the landscape shapes Lane's narrative. She uses her text not only to remember the Southwest as it was between 1854 and 1870, but also to articulate the alterations that modernization has brought to the Indians and Hispanics who live in the territory at the time of her writing over thirty years later. After five journeys across the plains in an ambulance (a two-wheeled light carriage pulled by two or four mules), she is able to make the trip partway by train in 1867 and 1869, and her narrative sheds light on the changes accompanied by the coming of the railroad. The new geographical space she inhabits has its parallel in new interior space, and Lane's memoir is valuable not only for what it tells us about the changing nineteenth-century Southwest and its inhabitants, but also for what it tells us about how her life was irrevocably affected by the frontier experience. Her narrative is a way of distilling this change for her reader.

According to Michele J. Nacy, "Army officers' wives have little in common with frontier women or Western farmwomen except for their environmental surroundings—and that is a limited likeness" (3). The institutional environment of the army and the geographical isolation of the frontier forts contributed to the uniqueness of their experience. In addition, few places have been more identified with maleness than the military outposts of the nineteenth-century American West. An officer's wife who lived within the walls of the army garrison resided in a masculine preserve, and as a result, she frequently suffered from her dependency role. Lane, however, makes the officer's wife's liminality central to her narrative. Significantly, then, her reconstruction of military life helps

Lydia Spencer Lane.
Photo by John N. Choate,
Carlisle, Pennsylvania.
Courtesy of the Cumberland
County Historical Society.

create a more inclusive and, consequently, less distorted conception of the social reality of the frontier garrison.

As Michele Nacy has noted, particularly problematic to officers' wives was "the challenge of developing some notion of their proper role within an institution that was dominated by masculine protocols and regulations" (41). These women did not want to be thought of merely as camp follow-ers. Lane's memoir gives the officers' wives both the recognition and the visibility they deserve. As her narrative shows, Lane considers herself to be a vital part of her husband's regiment. When contemplating the yellow fever epidemic and a long march from one frontier outpost to the next, she writes, "I had 'gone for a soldier,' and a soldier I determined to be" (22). However, although she sees herself as part of the army's enterprise, as a soldier's wife, she acknowledges that she is marginalized within it. She observes that "the wives were not taken into consideration, nor even remembered, when their husbands were assigned for duty at a post" (140). Constructing a self that negotiates and adapts to the gendered dynamics of the army, Lane is able to turn her limitations to her advantage. Her reminis-cences of military life underscore her transformation from young civilian bride from the East to "soldier" of the Southwest, a person whose growth is achieved through ingenuity, control, and discipline. At the end of her narrative, Lane is able to boast, "When brought face to face with danger, as I have been on more than one occasion, I flatter myself I behaved pretty well, being outwardly at least, very cool and quiet" (170).

Focusing on women's issues, Lane gives officers' wives a place in the garrison. She rescues them from the margins by putting the focus of her narrative on herself, not on men and not, for the most part, on military affairs. She is after a sense of what daily life was like for the ladies of the army. Her persona is of importance not as an extraordinary individual but as a representative member of a community of officers' wives stretched out over two decades. These women, she attests, influenced the army community in particular and the Southwest frontier in general. They established a role and a place for themselves, and according to Lane, as a partial result of their efforts, the frontier has vanished. In her preface, Lane tells her readers that now "the wilderness blossoms as a rose; our old deadly enemy, the Indian, is educated and clothed" (13). Even the dreaded Jornada del Muerto that so daunted Magoffin has changed: there is now an abundance of water and a ranch stockade for traveler protection. She describes its present state as "an oasis in the desert" (178).[6] This is a purposeful ploy.

In writing her memoir, Lane has two distinct goals. First, she is attempting to re-create the old army way of life on the frontier. The U.S. Census Bureau announced the disappearance of a contiguous frontier line in 1890. Three years later Frederick Jackson Turner delivered his essay, "The Significance of the Frontier in American History," to a meeting of the American Historical Association at Chicago's World Fair. Turner took the closing of the frontier as an opportunity to reflect upon the influence it had exercised.[7] Significantly, in that same year, 1893, Lane does something similar. Acknowledging herself as a source for firsthand experiences from a bygone era, she writes to take her readers back to a vanished frontier and the old way of army life. For Lane, as for Turner, the frontier is essential to the development of the American character. It cultivates strength, acuteness, a restless energy, and an inventive turn of mind.

Lane's second goal is to write about the positive changes that have occurred since the closing of the frontier, improvements that have made the Southwest safe for women and children. Emphasizing scenes and places that will evoke in her readers a sense of "now" (1893) and "then" (1854 to 1870), she is writing as a promotionalist for young women, encouraging them to follow her own example and accompany their husbands to frontier army outposts. To achieve this goal, she constitutes the army community as an extended family and the southwestern landscape

Towns and military forts in Texas and New Mexico. Map by Tom Jonas.

as exotic but unthreatening and as an appropriate backdrop for domestic relations. She establishes herself as a kind of protoparent, addressing her narrative to her daughters and sisters, an audience of young officers' wives with "no knowledge of ante-bellum days" (192).

Similar to Sarah Royce, Lane wants her narrative to serve as a model of active forbearance. But whereas Royce's intended reader was her son, Lane is writing primarily to young women who did not themselves choose to relocate to the Southwest but were obliged to follow their husbands. In a voice of motherly concern, Lane assumes a didactic role in telling her story, an act that reflects her sense of authority in relation to her readers. As the "old campaigner," she presents the details designed to remove any romantic notions her young readers might harbor. She describes her own harrowing experiences of frontier travel, the deplorable and temporary garrison homes, and the challenges of raising children in a wilderness setting. The disappearance of the wilderness has improved army life, she contends, and "the army woman of to-day has no idea of the hardships so patiently endured by her mother (in the army, also)" (134).

One hardship Lane recognizes is the fragility of the female-centered community on the frontier. She realizes that an army wife's sense of psychological isolation is directly related to her physical isolation. Some remote outposts, like Fort Stanton, New Mexico, Lane writes, seemed so isolated to her that "it was like being buried alive to stay there" (64).[8] In order to give her readers a sense of Fort Stanton's remoteness, she describes the expectancy with which she and the other fort's inhabitants awaited the mail: "There was but one mail a month, and on the day it was expected we dropped all work and fixed our eyes on a certain hill, round which the man with the mail, carried on a mule, was bound to appear, after a while, if the Indians had not caught him" (64–65). Things are not so bad today, Lane assures her readers. While they can still feel isolated, young officers' wives can now "talk to their husbands, then at the seat of war, through the telephone" (191). The railroad has minimized the rigors of travel, the Southwest has become Anglo-Americanized, and army garrisons are not as crude as they were in earlier days.

According to Lane, women who are discontent with the difficulties and limitations of life at the outpost should not grumble at their situation; instead, they should consider the advantages they have over their mothers. "Compare your lot with your mother's, and see how much more comfortable you are than she was," Lane writes (135). She also encourages her young readers to set the past in context before they judge her: "You will think I was a dreadful coward; but put yourself in my place, you woman, and would you have felt any braver than I did?" (170). Lane's narrative attempts to convey that context.

Lane articulates the frontier as it was, with all its complexity. An optimistic, well-educated woman of middle-class sensibility, she narrates both her enchantment and disenchantment with the Southwest. The conflicts between individual autonomy and institutional authority and fantasy versus reality are exposed in the opening pages of her story. Creating the gestalt for the Cinderella paradigm that implies that they "lived happily ever after," Lane opens her narrative with "And so they were married" (15). However, immediately following the ceremony in Carlisle, Pennsylvania, Lydia and Lieutenant William Bartlett Lane, U.S. Mounted Rifles, are ordered to Jefferson Barracks in Missouri. The young married couple arrives in the midst of a cholera epidemic. Before they can settle in, they are sent to Texas. When they reach Corpus Christi, the "people were dying on every side from yellow fever" (21).

What follows continues in the same key, and Lane's progress from bad to worse insinuates doubts about her future happiness as an officer's wife. However, as outside developments threaten her self-sufficiency, she begins to respond with competence and self-reliance. Lane's responsiveness to the environment and her capacity to change allow her to retain a portion of her premarital individuality. The garrisons she lives in and the things that she sees on the frontier are not the detached objects of her thought. They correspond to Lane's growth, her increase in strength and resilience. As such they mark stages in the formation of her character.

Lane animates her scenes by evoking the sights, sounds, smells, and activities from perspectives of up close and farther away. She writes, "My eyes, from long practice, were as keen as a frontiersman's and nothing escaped them" (153). By identifying in her present with aspects of her former frontier life, although she is removed from it, she is able to return to the past in memory. Now, years later, living in comfort somewhere "civilized," she can still smell, hear, and taste the frontier. She recalls, "I never get a whiff of burning cedar, even now, that the whole panorama does not rise up before me, and it is with a thrill of pleasure I recall the past, scents and all" (93). The composition of her narrative allows her to live again in the old army and keep the frontier Southwest alive. Despite her losses and sufferings, she cannot bear to sever these ties to the past.

Our understanding of women's history has been greatly expanded during the past two decades. Historians, among others, now recognize that female experiences varied as much as men's did. Nevertheless, as an upper-middle-class woman from the East, Lane had most certainly been inculcated with the virtues of "true womanhood" which decreed that a woman should be pious, submissive, and domestic—providing her family with a proper, safe, and stable home.[9] Additionally, this ideology included the notion that men and women had separate spheres of activity. Lane brought these values with her to the highly regulated military society of the garrison with its own systems of conduct appropriate to her rank and that of her husband. However, the rugged life on the frontier and the garrison world in which she lived challenged and modified these well-defined conceptions of womanhood. Lane's writing reveals the flexibility of her self-conception and the changes she makes as she attempts to create a sense of home amid her successive moves from post to post.

Lane's journal is most concerned with the problems of housekeeping and raising a family under new, unstable, and challenging conditions. Composed of insecure walls and crumbling ceilings, her permeable frontier structures are symbolic. Unlike the ideal nineteenth-century middle-class home where the domestic space was private and separate from the public world, an officer's wife's domestic quarters are somewhere in that indistinct liminal space between public and private. Lane's existence is determined by the military, and her home is mobile. Houses are traditionally domestic sanctuaries and at least limitedly under the control of the wife. However, as a military wife on the frontier, Lane does not have the ability to make the most fundamental decisions regarding her personal environment. Her succession of homes is temporary and provisional. Blurring the boundaries between inside and outside, they are also isolated and primitive. She encounters toads on her doorstep, tarantulas in her kitchen, snakes in her bedroom, and bats in her bed.

Although the movement of her narrative is chronologically sequential, Lane structures her account not so much according to temporal days but by the succession of moves she makes from one isolated outpost to the next. Her shift in emphasis from when to where allows her to foreground the significance of her change, both physical and mental. At the time of writing her memoir, Lane is living a comfortable and settled life in the East. However, the defining activity of her narrative is motion. The initial movement is from Pennsylvania to Missouri and then on to Texas. She sets out from "the States" into the Southwest, from the known and civilized into the unknown and uncivilized. Although in reality she wanders at the margins of another culture through most of her narrative, Lane doesn't present herself as the outsider. Instead, the frontier landscape, the Hispanics, and the Indians are presented as the Other.[10] She sees them through a single lens: the departure from normative white, Protestant, and middle-class America.

Lane's narrative suggests that one can be at home in foreign places by reconstructing "home" as ideological and physical structures and by transforming her own sense of self. Her urge to domesticate is in part an attempt to create a self-confirming and safe place from which she can begin to understand the foreign. She enjoys structuring, ordering, and civilizing her army quarters because she is demonstrating at least some sense of autonomy. The very telling and fashioning of her narrative is a remembering, a projecting of herself outside the boundaries of her eastern home. Lane is not so much pleased with the persona she plays at any one moment of her narrative as she is impressed with her role-changing itself, with the fluidity of identity she has achieved through movement.

Lane's emphasis on movement allows for a revision of gender expectations because her travels are constantly forcing her to dismantle and remake her home. Never staying more than six months at any one place, she is most often on the road and outside the domestic sphere. As soon as she sets up housekeeping at one post, she and her husband get their marching orders to travel to a different fort. In fact, at one point she acknowledges that she has homesickness for sleeping in tents and refers to her group as "all shabby together" and resembling "a band of gypsies" (126). At times she confesses to losing narrative control of her rambling fragments of story, and significantly, as she struggles to return to her thesis, she employs the language of travel. After one digression, she writes, "But I am loitering and digressing when I should be many miles on the road" (84). On another occasion, finding herself distanced from her main point, she apologizes: "While making speeches I have left the Santa Fé trail far behind, and I must hurry to the crossing of the Arkansas River" (135). The force of travel is digressive and expansive. Even her decision to segment her story into successive removals to new homes in remote areas of the Southwest is an emblem of the nomadic lifestyle of the officer's wife. Lane's life is not ordered by eastern civilian clock time, but in relocations that are marked by army bugles. Crossing the hot summer prairies, she wakes to "reveille" as early as two A.M. When "boots and saddles" rings out, she falls into line along with the troops and she marches until the bugle calls a halt. Her good night to her husband is accompanied by "taps."

In spite of the fact that she travels at the whim of the army, however, it is evident that she relishes the constant change and that this delight contradicts the stereotype of women as desirous of stasis and stability. She confides to the reader that the "roving life" suits her. The deployment of motion and stasis in her narrative deconstructs conventional values of masculine travel and feminine stasis. In fact, by structuring her text around her moves, Lane suggests a way out of a stereotyped and confining Victorian gender role that had identified women's proper place as in the home.

✳   ✳   ✳   ✳

Lydia Lane was born about 1834. She was the youngest daughter of Major George Blaney, U.S. Engineer Corps, and Mary Elizabeth Biddle Blaney, who came from a wealthy Carlisle family. Her brother lived in St. Louis and her sister, Valeria Elliott, the wife of Captain Washington L. Elliott, was also an officer's wife stationed in the Southwest. Lane and her husband had three children: Minnie, born at Fort Clark, Texas, in 1855, Susan born at Fort Bliss in 1859, and a son born back east in 1866. However, like Sarah Bayliss Royce, Lane does not use her text to focus on her husband or her children. Through most of the narrative, she refers to her husband as "the Lieutenant." Although she mentions her three children, she only gives her reader the name of her oldest daughter.

Lane relegates her family members to the margins of her story and instead focuses on herself. She writes to tell her readers how she adapted to particular situations and lived her life within limiting social conditions. She does not portray herself as exceptional, but as representative of the many women who accompanied their husbands in the frontier army. She writes, "My experience was that of hundreds of other women, many of whom are far more capable than I of telling the story" (192). Strategically, playing down the individuality of her family members, Lane dramatizes the hardships and compensations officers' wives faced and the negotiations they needed to make in order for them to make homes on the frontier.

The first chapters detail Lane's attempts to adjust to the frontier conditions as she begins her housekeeping. This enterprise she describes as a very "uphill business." She records her efforts to turn jacals, tents, and poor quality adobe army quarters into havens of domesticity. In her jacal at Fort Clark, she cheerfully writes that since the kitchen floor was "nothing but the ground," she wouldn't have to scrub it.[11] Their houseguests included the rats and mice who "came and went without ceremony" and "a tremendous snake" she discovered on the mantelpiece (38). In Kansas a wild storm of wind and rain collapsed her tent and completely soaked all of their belongings. A cloudburst in the Organ Mountains of southern New Mexico caused a river of water to rush through her quarters at Fort Fillmore. Wading in water up to her knees, Lane hurried to retrieve furniture and carpets. Although the Lanes were able to take possession of the dry rooms next door, a poisonous snake in the bedroom and a bat in her bed thwarted her comfort there as well.

With a happy faculty of seeing the humor in a situation, she describes entertaining seventeen people one evening. An ominous crack over her head precipitated the ceiling's caving in on her back and on the table, covering everything with plaster. After cleaning up the debris, she prepared a second dinner for her guests. Lane does not use the scene to illustrate her resentment of or discouragement by her disorderly conditions. Indeed, implicit and explicit in the entry is her usual strong sense of self and her ability to establish order in the chaos. With her habitual good humor, she confesses, "You will see, from the foregoing, house-keeping on the frontier had its drawbacks" (146).

In the performance-oriented frontier, a woman's talents rather than her image mattered. As a young bride, Lane had little experience with domestic chores, and she struggled to learn the particulars of housekeeping. She relied on hired help to assist with the household tasks. However, female servants were in short supply on the frontier and were notoriously unreliable. Lane writes: "We were obliged to overlook many vagaries and eccentricities of deportment, if we hoped to keep a maid on the frontier at the time. A woman of any kind was thought better than none" (173). Even with assistance, Lane had numerous housekeeping responsibilities. She details her struggles to teach herself to cook, make butter, can fruit, and raise chickens. "I succeeded remarkably well, considering all things," she boasts (171). However, she was not always successful. At Camp Stockton, she was unable to hire a laundress so she borrowed a tub and board, rolled up her sleeves, and attempted to wash clothes herself.[12] The cleaned clothes, she relates, looked worse when she had finished than before they had passed through her "unskillful hands." Not least of all, she was obliged to take care of her children, an arduous task given the primitive conditions at the frontier outposts. She writes of her anxieties at the birth of her first child and her concerns of caring for her newborn. "If the poor child had known of how many comforts she was deprived by coming into the world on the Western frontier, she would have been much aggrieved," Lane confides (39).

Isolated post conditions required army wives to use ingenuity and self-reliance. Lane's image of domesticity is one in which women play very important roles. Not only is her seasoning paired with a change in her responsibilities, but also her duties as an officer's wife often transcend the traditional women's sphere. When her husband was away from home, Lane made family decisions and acted as the head of the house. While stationed at Fort Fillmore, her husband is called away to Dog Canyon.[13] Lane takes his place as commander of the post. She is left in charge of the sergeant and ten men who remained at the fort. Responsible for the fort's money as well, she writes that if she lost her life in protecting it, she "would have done [her] whole duty" (101). Similar to Magoffin who assumes the role of "traderess" during her husband's absence, Lane enters the masculine realm—and not for the first time.

Officers' wives like Lane have to endure many of the same hardships that the soldiers endure. She shares the inadequate pay, the primitive living conditions at the posts, and the frequent moves to new stations. At bugle's call, Lane marches with the command, sick or well. She treks through dangerous Indian territory. With very little protection from the weather, she travels through dust, heat, rain, and wind. Lane describes how one night a windstorm was so severe it gathered up a tent in which a child slept. Although the baby was rescued, the tent and cot were not. One night when Lane was traveling without her husband, her ambulance driver climbed into her wagon. Terrified, she lay in her bed until morning, awake and clutching a butcher knife. She tells her reader that she was prepared to kill the intruder if he attempted to molest her.

Frequent moves require Lane to constantly dismantle and remake her new living quarters for her family. Because she traveled in an ambulance, a crude mule-driven army wagon, her baggage was restricted. Her emphasis on the wagon becomes a symbolic element in the development of the theme of the terrain and travel as obstacles to household and personal paraphernalia—items that are needed for the establishment of the home at the journey's end. As she becomes used to her transient lifestyle, she begins to reassess her priorities. Fewer and less expensive items provide the advantage, she quips, of not having to worry about robbers, "having nothing anybody would carry off" (182). It is noteworthy that her resistance to acquisition is not only practical, it is symbolic. Lane's treatment of furnishings and material objects suggests how profoundly they can shape and limit. The accumulation of material things encumbers rather than enhances her life. The shabby houses that in the beginning of her narrative corresponded to the destitute and desolate scenery slowly begin to look more familiar and inviting.

Clothing considered appropriate in the East is also a burden on the frontier. Lane writes, "To show you how little use a bonnet was to any of us, . . . Mrs. Lawrence Baker . . . found [hers] occupied by a hen, setting on a number of eggs" (65). Lane associates her change of clothing with her transition from the innocent army bride to the seasoned traveler. Fancy garments, which defined eastern genteel female status, distinguish the newcomer. When, for example, Lane is on her fifth "march" to New Mexico, she travels in a party with six brides. The uninitiated women's "dainty costumes," she writes, were "more suitable for Fifth Avenue" than for crossing the plains (131). Referring to herself as "an old campaigner," she describes her traveling outfit: a calico frock, no hoops, and a sunbonnet. Lane's garments are both practical and symbolic: they suggest that her body is now more durable and resilient as well. Although she realizes that to the fashionable brides she must have looked "outlandish," she comments with pride that "there was not a husband who did not commend my common-sense dress, urging their wives to adopt it" (132).

Lane's comfortable and practical dress reaffirms her contention that women who journey west must adapt and change rather than conform to the values of the home they have left. Just as Clappe, in her eighteenth letter, observes the fashionable newcomers to the upper Feather River and compares their fancy clothes with her old unstylish outfit, Lane is using the comparison to display her new seasoned self to its advantage. Traveling through Kansas, Lane loses her belongings in a prairie fire, and she dons a blue flannel blouse like the soldiers wore. She says that on the frontier "no one had much inclination to watch his neighbor nor care about his appearance; he had enough on hand to keep alive" (86).

Lane's narrative suggests that travel on the army frontier demanded that women deviate from feminine standards of dress and behavior. Travel also encouraged them to reassess their preconceived notions regarding Indians as a consequence of their contact with them.[14] Whereas many journals by nineteenth-century officers' wives reveal a change in their ingrained preconceptions, Lane's does not. Although she is curious about their culture, like Sarah Royce she maintains her mostly anti-Indian perceptions that she brought with her from the East.

Through most of the nineteenth century, the army's principal mission in the West was directly related to the Indians, so it's not surprising that officers' wives wrote about them. Lane's text is filled with her tensions and worries regarding the Indians. Stories of massacres and captivity narratives were widely circulated in the nineteenth century, and the white woman as victim characterized her culture's image of the female on the frontier.[15] Lane observes the Indians she encounters within the context of the well-defined preconceptions and prejudices she brought with her. For example, with fearful fascination, she observes the yearly distribution of annuities at Fort Stanton. She records how when the butcher knives were brought out, "deep guttural sounds from the men and screams of delight from the women were heard on all sides. I felt as if we were going to be scalped" (67). Her genteel eastern cultural attitudes clearly determined her pejorative interpretation of the scene.

On a journey from New Mexico to Texas in 1859, Lane is terrified of the Kiowa, Comanche, and Apache raiders. The language she uses to depict her fears seems directly attributable to sensationalized accounts:

> Woe to the hapless party that fell into the devilish hands of a band of Indians! Men were generally put to death by slow torture, but they were allowed to live long enough to witness the atrocities practiced on their wives and children, such things as only fiends could devise. (73)

According to Lane, after "dashing out the babies' brains," the Indians do something even worse to the women, a violation she can't mention to her genteel readers. The danger the women faced, that Lane must leave unspoken, is inextricably bound up with their sexuality.

Capture was a fearful prospect for all army wives. Army wives Elizabeth Custer, Frances Roe, and Martha Summerhayes were told by their husbands to take their own lives rather than allow themselves to be captured by Indians. Not surprisingly then, another danger that Lane particularly feared was that her fair-haired, blue-eyed children would be seized and carried off by Indian captors. "I tried to keep her [her daughter Minnie] out of sight," she writes, "but she never was one easy to suppress, and kept me in . . . agony by evidently enjoying the admiration she excited" (57). Although Lane's fears are never realized, she cannot dismiss her anxiety. She tells her reader that whenever she travels, she is constantly searching the countryside for evidence of Indians.

Lane's portraits of Indians exaggerate her fears and the Indians' undesirable qualities instead of demonstrating the contradictions between her fearful expectations and the fact that they never come about. Clearly, for Lane, years of being steeped in anti-Indian prejudice hold more sway than eyewitness evidence to the contrary. Significantly, in the retrospective moment of writing, Lane does not feel the anxiety, and yet, in her attempt to portray herself and her situation with psychological accuracy, she retroactively creates a sense of her vulnerability and weaves her earlier feelings of fear into the text.

Despite her fears, however, Lane is curious. She is especially interested in the Indians' lack of dress. Her recurrent descriptions of Indian men's scarcity of clothing cannot be overlooked. On one occasion, Lane is appalled to discover that her uninvited Indian guests are wearing nothing but heavy blankets, which they remove as soon as it gets hot (178). Unable to attain control of the situation, she must wait until the rain comes and her naked guests decide to leave. On another occasion, she wryly comments that one Indian was elaborately attired from the waist up—"a regular dandy," dressed in an officer's jacket, sword, and hat. He was, however, without pants. His naked limbs troubled her feminine modesty, reaffirming the stereotype of the sexually threatening Indian man that is an integral component of the captivity literary tradition. Interestingly, in her preface, Lane has told her reader that the Indian is no longer without clothes (13). Her emphasis on the dressing, and implicit de-sexing, of the native man can be seen as Lane's attempt to promote the Southwest as a place now fit for genteel ladies.

The comments Lane makes about Indian women serve as vehicles through which the reader can observe her reflecting upon herself and even engaging in debate about women's proper role in society, the value of physical activity, and the nineteenth-century middle-class methods of childbirth. Similar to Susan Shelby Magoffin in her entry at Bent's Fort, Lane remembers her astonishment at the ease with which Indian women experience childbirth. Finding an Apache woman sitting by her house, she records that although it was a cold winter's day, the mother had her baby strapped to a board. The baby was two hours old. After Lane gave her food, the mother picked up her baby and walked three miles back to her camp (66). Lane concludes her vignette by noting that earlier the Indian had treated her newborn to an ice-cold bath. Like Magoffin, Lane is unable to express open admiration for the vitality or fortitude of the mother and baby. Instead, her sole comment is that "it must have been disagreeable" (67). However, the spare details remembered so many years after the fact attest to the impact this experience must have had on her.

Although Lane is curious about the Indians, she is also the object of their curiosity. This voyeurism reversal dramatizes the permeability of her domestic haven, the space that she is entitled to claim as veiled from public vision. Lane describes the habit of the Mescalero Apaches to peer in at her through the windows of her army quarters when she is sewing or reading. Like Peeping Toms, they watch her with "wondering eyes," violating her private space (66). She finds herself powerless under their gaze: "Often while sitting beside [the window] a shadow would come between me and the light, and on looking up I would find two or three hideous creatures, with noses painted every color flattened against the glass. I could not endure to be watched so curiously" (66). The Mescaleros infringe upon Lane's right to privacy. A home by definition is a secluded, protective sphere, the domain of private family and intimacy. As an upper-middle-class woman, Lane derives her very raison d'être from this space, and the Mescaleros' gaze represents an invasion.

Sometimes Lane looks up from an activity to find the Indians in the room with her. Upset at their encroachment, she chases them out of her house, "locking the door behind them." Anxious to separate herself from them, she writes, "I could not endure to be watched so curiously." Although Lane attempts to lock them out, their repeated intrusions break down the distinction between public and private spheres.

Lane presents the frontier as a culturally contested terrain. She never questions the presence of the army in the Southwest, and she never expresses doubts about the moral legitimacy of a military mission that supports an invasion of Indian lands by white people. Lane rarely comments on the power relations between the U.S. Army and the Indians, and even more interesting, she never comments on the reasons for her husband's frequent relocations. For Lane, the army is the avant-garde of white settlement, and the right to invade is the prerogative of the privileged white people. When the Mescaleros invade the privacy of her personal space, they disturb and reverse the relationship between property and privilege.

Although she views the Indians as intrusive and troublesome, Lane's observations of the Hispanic Americans and their settlements are more positive. Given the anti-Mexican tone of much of the nineteenth-century literature written by Americans, this viewpoint is surprising. Lane comments extensively on the Hispanic culture, which she finds so different from her own. She gives a detailed description of the Mexican adobes along the Rio Grande, and she is especially impressed by their cleanliness. The interior white walls of the adobes were done by the women, "and they used the same material for beautifying their complexions," she adds (95).

However, the invasion of the domestic space is clearly an important pattern of her narrative, and when she is a guest in a Mexican house, Lane again presents herself as the object of cross-cultural voyeurism. She says that the Mexicans "did not appear to be at all curious about us, but I think it probable we were watched by many a pair of soft, dark eyes when utterly unconscious of it" (96). In contrast to the Mescaleros' staring through her windows, in her Hispanic home away from home, she can't see the Mexicans gazing at her—she can only *feel* their eyes. She is, nevertheless, uncomfortable because she experiences herself as the object of their controlling gaze.

Traditionally, the idea of the "home" is built on a pattern of select inclusions and exclusions. Similarly the term *home-country* expresses the notion of having a place of one's own and having the ability to limit access. Lane is challenged to reconfigure her definition of *home* as a result of the insufficiency of her provisional frontier quarters to provide privacy and security. She has no control over her domestic space because army outposts were not in the "home-country," and also because her home was controlled by an institution that was dominated by masculine protocols and regulations. For example, army etiquette dictated that as an officer's wife Lane had to entertain visitors and newcomers to the post. From the day she "began housekeeping," she complained, she had to entertain travelers (31): "We are told to take in the stranger, as by doing so we 'may entertain an angel unawares.' I do not think that class of guests often travelled in Texas and New Mexico . . . if they did . . . their disguise was complete" (146). Lane reports that she became "very weary" of entertaining people of whom she knew nothing.

Lane faced the challenge of coping with army protocol in all phases of her life. A soldier's rank and seniority conferred his wife's status in the post, and his wife was obliged to observe codes of conduct appropriate to her rank. This hierarchical system affected the domestic sphere. Officers' wives did not consider the wives of noncommissioned officers and enlisted soldiers as "members of the regiment." According to Michele J. Nacy, when officers' wives wrote in their diaries that there were "no other women" at the post, in reality there were usually at least a few other females present—they just weren't officers' wives (56). Indeed, in the rare instance when a white woman who is not an officer's wife enters Lane's text, it is usually as unreliable domestic help.

Lane did not enjoy all aspects of the army's social class system. For instance, each time the Lanes arrived at a new post, their quarters hinged on rank. After they had moved in, whenever an officer with higher rank or seniority arrived on post, the procedure of "ranking" out began, because the new arrival had the choice of all the units occupied by his junior officers. Often the occupants were given only a few hours to vacate. Lane remembers being driven out of her home at Fort Fillmore by a senior officer and feeling grateful that they had so little furniture that the move was quite easily made.

Another effect of the ranking system that bothered Lane was the army's traveling order. Lane writes, "Each ambulance was given its position in line according to the rank of the officer whose family occupied it; consequently, the wives and children of the lieutenants suffered much from the dust made by a long line of vehicles ahead of theirs" (83). She says that a number of the wives complained that they had to "swallow more than their allotted 'peck.'" In fairness, she suggests, the ambulances should be able to take turns so that the position at the head of the column would rotate, but, she continues, "those in command did not look on it that way" (83).

As Darlis Miller has noted, army wives generally present an attractive picture of military life in their narratives, and despite some of her complaints, Lane is no exception.[16] She sympathizes with the soldiers' hard life, and she frequently acknowledges the favors and small kindnesses the men extended to her family. At one point, she notes that, with only one or two exceptions, she "had always found them polite and respectful." She especially enjoyed the attention from the officers, and now that she is in the East and back in civilian society, she admits that it is hard for her to join the "wall flowers" again.

Lane tells her readers that "the less a woman knew of military affairs, and what went on in the garrison, the better for all" (162). However, occasionally she lapses and provides them with comments on military policies. When she does, she supports her observations with authoritative comments from military professionals. Her portrayal of Major Lynde is an example. Seemingly sympathetic to the Confederates, Lynde put the troops at Fort Fillmore at risk. According to Lane, "there could not have been a better man in command to help the Southern cause, nor a worse for the government, than Major Lynde" (106). In order to underscore and substantiate her opinion, she quotes Dr. J. C. McKee, one of two physicians in charge of the hospital at Fort Fillmore. She has McKee describe in detail Lynde's surrender to the Texans on July 25, 1861. By having her military opinions confirmed and expanded upon by a male voice of authority, she is able to validate not only her comments but also her right to comment on military policies.

When Lane's husband is retired from active service in 1870, Lane leaves the army with regret. Like Louise Smith Clappe, she had enjoyed the peripatetic lifestyle: "I had become so accustomed to change station every few months, I liked it, and was always ready and glad to go when an order came to move" (84). She writes that she developed the habit of using very few tacks in her curtains and carpets so that it was easier to pull them up when it came time to move. Times have changed, she says, and today's army wives can dismantle their homes slowly and with the help of professional packers. Lane has feelings of homesickness for her crude army houses. She confides, "There was certainly something fascinating in the roving life we led that exactly suited me" (137).

*　*　*　*

The nostalgia and yearning for the early army days mark Lane's writing. Her narrative ends with a summation of the theme of remembrance and with her imaginative connection to the past.

> The relics of our "old army" days are few now; but occasionally in unpacking our chests and trunks, stowed away in a garret, I find something that brings years vividly before me; it may be a tarnished shoulder-strap, a spur, or a big knife in its leather sheath; each has its history, and I dream while holding them in my hand; the lapse of time is forgotten. I am young again, wandering through the old familiar scenes. (192)

Memory is powerful. In the chest, Lane discovers an old battered tin box that carried their lunch when they traveled from camp to camp. She raises the lid, and the odor brings back memories of the former happy traveling days. Her engagement is sensory. The faint odor that seems to rise from the depths of the box carries her back to the past. Sighing, she closes the lid and puts the box aside as worthless, to be thrown away. But then, on second thought, she realizes it is worth saving, not just for itself, but for the stories behind it. Lane recognizes here that the artifact not only inspires the recollections, but that the significance of the artifact is retained by the discourse that supports it. She puts the "worn-out box" in a chest, "retiring it, like an old soldier, from active service forever!" (193). It is not just a "worthless" object, but an "old friend" who inspires "tender recollections."

The artifacts—the old tin lunch box, the tarnished shoulder strap, the spur, and the knife—provide a key to a transformed understanding of self, of cultural encounter, of frontier, and of old army life. By opening the box or holding the knife in its leather sheath, Lane is carried back to the past. The material aids stimulate her memory and give her an imaginative empathy. Like these relics of the old army days, Lane's memoir transports readers into a landscape that is a rich blend of history, culture, and memory.

For too long army outposts in the Southwest have been identified with maleness. Lane's text illuminates female participation on the military frontier. Not only does her writing sharpen our perception about the reality of the West and women's lives on the frontier, but it also records the customs and attitudes of the old army and "the days of small things"—less money, fewer people, but greater hardship. Lane's "tender recollections" are a superb evocation of an important dimension of frontier military experience—from the woman's perspective.

Lydia Spencer Lane died on June 27, 1914, at the age of seventy-nine. Her memoir, *I Married a Soldier*, was first published by Lippincott in 1893. It received a favorable review by Charles King in the February 1, 1893, issue of the *Dial*. In 1910, a second edition was published, and in 1964, the Albuquerque firm of Horn and Wallace made a reprint with a new foreword written by Mamie Doud Eisenhower. The 1987 edition, which includes an introduction by Darlis A. Miller, was published by the University of New Mexico Press.

Conclusion

To travel is to change. The women in this study are not the same people they were before they traveled. Magoffin, Royce, Clappe, Farnham, and Lane grappled with words and techniques within which to apprehend their new surroundings, the transformation they underwent as they attempted to make a place for themselves and their families on the frontier, and the process by which they grew attached to the land.

For each of these women the landscape is integral, not incidental, to their stories. They unfold their dramas on a frontier landscape that is indispensable to their narratives. The frontier supplies the motivation and the shape for their plots. Each text juxtaposes a linear narrative with moments of contact with the land. Royce's visionary moment in the desert, for example, links her internal condition to her external condition. And by recreating the event years later for her readers, Royce preserves the site as a continuing source of epiphanic experience. In each of the five narratives, the westering experience is presented as initially disorienting for the traveler; however, it also inspires her textual response, either immediately or as a recollection. Plagued by inexpressible uncertainties, these five women have to explain who they are in relation to where they are.

The similarities among my chosen authors run deep: all traveled from the East to the frontier, and each used the frontier as a means of moving beyond her eastern self. As a consequence of their dislocation, they had to redefine themselves. Their journeys give them an ambidexterity that their stay-at-home counterparts did not have. They were still able to partake of the culture they had left, but their frontier travels gave them new characteristics. All of them developed a distinct frontier survivor psychology. Without exception, they became more self-reliant, more confident, more creative, and more open to change. For Farnham, living in California meant affirming independence and assuming responsibility for cultivating a farm, and for Clappe it meant breaking away from the conventions of marriage into a vocation. Whereas Clappe and Farnham credit the West for empowering them with unbounded vigor, Royce and Magoffin claim spiritual health. Clappe's and Farnham's self-fashionings include the ability to use a kind of hybrid speech that reflects their attempts to depict the multiculturality of the frontier through language. Despite Lane's nostalgic rhetoric, many of her vignettes portray both her tension about and her accommodations to her daily activities. With the exception of Magoffin, the longer these women are on the frontier, the more their voices become distinct and engaged. They are constantly expecting the unexpected. As they become more comfortable and consequently less disengaged from the experiences, their perceptions and responses become integral to the journey itself. This personal involvement is facilitated by the journal format.

Critics such as Margo Culley and Penelope Franklin have suggested that personal writing is crucial to a sense of self-construction. As bell hooks argues, "the art of expressing one's feeling on the written page" is associated with self-identity and "the effort to be fully self-actualized" (72). For the five women in this study, writing provided a conduit for self-assertion in the midst of change. Either retrospectively or in the midst of transforming circumstances, they constructed their own identities both for themselves and for their intended readers. Though it is tempting to think of personal narratives as immediate textual responses, they are not. Even Magoffin's diary evidences a thoughtful arrangement of imagistic and thematic repetition. Examining the stylistic choices in Magoffin's, Royce's, Clappe's, Farnham's, and Lane's narratives leads to an additional appreciation of how they have used their writing not only to sustain their identity but also to help them adjust to the foreign landscapes and empty spaces through which they are traveling.

The entity called "frontier" was fashioned not only from native inhabitants but also by those who were outsiders traveling through it. As a consequence, outsiders' travel narratives are significant because they reflect the way the journey transforms the greenhorn traveler into the seasoned narrator. In the cases of the five women I have discussed here, each place they visit becomes an emblem of their new stage of development. At first, they find the unfamiliar landscape physically, aesthetically, and linguistically disorienting. Unsettled, they slowly begin to yield to the demands of the environment. Among the unique and valuable contributions of these women is their ability to convey a sense not only of wilderness scenery but also of daily life on the road, in the mining camp, or at the army outpost. In addition, their writing illuminates their approach to the contradictory demands of travel and domesticity. Although each one of them attempts to create homes on the frontier, their roles are to some extent subversive. Travel has given them a new awareness that contradicts the limits imposed by the ideology of domesticity or the idea of separate spheres for men and women. Questioning traditional gender roles, they find that their relationships to home are increasingly complicated. The legacy conferred by their narratives is an appreciation of the range of their authors' complexity.

Each of the writers in this study promotes western exceptionalism, a mythology that characterizes life in the West as fundamentally different from life in the East. And yet, paradoxically, their texts affirm Richard Slotkin's belief that life on the frontier becomes a synecdoche for the whole of American experience (35). In contrast to the Old World of Europe and the eastern United States, gold rush California provided women with new options. Clappe, Royce, and Farnham portray the choices available to women because they are a numerical minority. The unbalanced sex ratios increased demand for domestic skills, profoundly shaping women's opportunities for autonomy and independence. They also portray the myth of the frontier as a nurturing ground for a truly democratic society by dramatizing the increase in multicultural and racial tensions. All five women agree that the frontier is both isolating and arduous for women who shoulder multiple demands. Not only are frontier women responsible for making homes and raising a family under new and difficult conditions, but they frequently are required to do "men's work" as well. However, despite the challenges and perhaps in part because of them, Royce, Clappe, Farnham, and Lane convey a nostalgic image when they think back to their life in the West.

The longer they are in the territory, the more it becomes less alien—not always comfortable, as shown by Magoffin's experience, but more familiar. Their narratives portray a metamorphosing world that alters their sense of self. They have been led astray from the well-ordered ideological paths of the East toward change and, in some cases, unorthodoxy. Although they all negotiate the unfamiliar territory, meeting the trials and challenges and facing the unpredictable, their conclusions are varied. Magoffin ends her diary exhausted and literally and psychologically sick of being on the road. Clappe and Lane realize how sad they are to leave the frontier, and Farnham and Royce have made homes for themselves in the West.

These women are all the central figures of their own accounts. While they travel and become adjusted to the frontier, they are between places: they have left their homes in the East, and they are not as yet at home in the West. For Royce and Farnham who settle, their homes mediate the foreign and the familiar. The word *liminality*, which is derived from the Latin word *limen*, meaning "threshold," aptly describes the position of these five westering women. They are neither who they used to be nor who they are becoming. Their liminal position gives them a vulnerability, which is accompanied by a receptivity to change. All five of these women are multifaceted. They are able to shift clothing and identities as needed. Although they comply with basic gender norms, these women cross boundaries of nineteenth-century gender roles when their situations demand it. As a cultural phenomenon, dress signals personal identity. It connects an individual to a specific community. Royce, Clappe, and Lane link their frontier condition to their new attire. They contrast the well-dressed, fashionable but inexperienced newcomers with their poorly attired but seasoned selves. Farnham challenges local customs by pulling on a pair of trousers. Thus costumed, she moves beyond a gender identity defined by custom as she performs masculine tasks on her rancho, jobs that express her creative ingenuity as well as her physical strength.

Despite these similarities, however, there are key differences among the writers in this study. Magoffin wrote for her family and friends, and Royce, Clappe, Farnham, and Lane wrote with publication in mind. Whereas Clappe, Farnham, and Lane spent a good deal of time in the West, Royce made her permanent home there. In contrast, after Magoffin's trip down the Santa Fe Trail, she is exhausted and sick and leaves the Southwest with gladness.

Westering women's writing provides insight into their effort to negotiate between cultures. A common theme in these women's travel narratives is the configuration of the landscape as a rich medley of races and cultures. Frequently they are perplexed by their multicultural encounters. With American Indians, they were often anxiety-ridden. The images and stories they brought with them from the East exerted a powerful influence. Some women, Lane and Royce included, never surrendered their prejudices toward the Indians even when their fears never manifested. They continued to interpret their new experiences through the filter they had brought from home. More often, however, we see their attitudes change when they encounter new facts that conflict with old beliefs. And their narratives are records of their changing ideas about themselves and the spaces they inhabit.

The diaries, journals, and letters by westering women offer a framework for the domestic novel of frontier relocation.[1] Although the literary establishment may not yet appreciate these narratives, the development of western fiction cannot be explained apart from them. The westering women writers in this study are the literary foremothers of authors like Mary Austin, Helen Hunt Jackson, Josephine Clifford McCrackin,[2] Mary Hallock Foote, and Willa Cather. These women's writings encompass customary western themes of open country and isolation, but at the same time, they address assimilation to a new environment, shifting stances toward issues of power, authority, and ideology, and the making of homes under challenging wilderness conditions. The texts of these women demonstrate the subversive strength of travel writing as a narrative strategy.

The American literary West has been identified with white masculinity for too long. For students in American literature, the history, myths, and notions of the West are defined by Daniel Boone, Cooper's Leatherstocking, Kit Carson, Wild Bill Hickok, and Buffalo Bill. It is time that we in literary studies turn our attention to the narratives of nineteenth-century westering women. We cannot dismiss them. In order to appreciate the evolution of the western regions, the history of the frontier must involve multiple points of view. Perspective makes all the difference. We must address the ways that the frontier has been nonfictionally constructed—from the woman's perspective. This approach involves analyzing both how the frontier has functioned in the diaries, journals, and letters of frontier women and a revised critical analysis of western literature that is a more complete and truer reconstruction of the past.

Notes

Introduction

1. Nancy Cott examines the sources of this ideology in *The Bonds of Womanhood: "Woman's Sphere" in New England, 1780–1835.* See also Elizabeth Fox-Genovese, *Within the Plantation Household: Black and White Women of the Old South*; Mary P. Ryan, *Cradle of the Middle Class: The Family in Oneida County, New York, 1790–1865*; Monika M. Elbert, ed., *Separate Spheres No More: Gender Convergence in American Literature, 1830–1930.*

2. For an interesting discussion of the invisibility of frontier women as portrayed in early western studies, see Joan Jensen and Darlis Miller, "'Gentle Tamers' Revisited: New Approaches to the History of Women in the American West," in *Women and Gender in the American West*, 9–36.

3. Published over twenty years ago, Dee Brown's *The Gentle Tamers: Women of the Old Wild West* was one of the earliest books to provide an analysis of the roles of frontier women. Brown's depiction of white women as harbingers of civilization continues to dominate literature and classroom.

4. According to Susan Armitage, women were overlooked in western history because they were engrossed in domestic duties. For an interesting discussion of the omission of women from early western history and the consequences the female perspective will have on future historical research, see her article "Women and Men in Western History: A Stereoptical Vision." As T. A. Larson observed in "Women's Role in the American West," women "did not lead expeditions, command troops, build railroads, drive cattle or ride Pony Express." See also Sandra L. Myres's essay "Women in the West" for a discussion of T. A. Larson and earlier historians.

5. For an examination of women's private writing, see Helen M. Buss, "'The Dear Domestic Circle': Frameworks for the Literary Study of Women's Personal Narratives in Archival Collections," and Personal Narratives Group, *Interpreting Women's Lives: Feminist Theory and Personal Narratives.*

6. As Margo Culley observes in "Women's Vernacular Literature": "In releasing the word 'literature' from a capital 'L' and giving it the broadest possible construction—texts fashioned of letters—we may include women's diaries and journals, letters, memoirs, autobiographies, essays, speeches, stories, oral narratives, and songs. Texts are everywhere, and the limits to the sources for study are only the limits of our imagination" (*Women's Personal Narratives: Essays in Criticism and Pedagogy,* 13). For a few representative works of new western women's

history, see Elizabeth Jameson and Susan Armitage, *Writing the Range: Race, Class, and Culture in the Women's West*; Julie Roy Jeffrey, *Frontier Women*; Vera Norwood and Janice Monk, *The Desert Is No Lady: Southwestern Landscape in Women's Writing and Art*; Glenda Riley, *The Female Frontier: A Comparative View of Women on the Prairie and the Plains* and *Confronting Race: Women and Indians on the Frontier, 1815–1915*; Mary Ann Irwin and James F. Brooks, *Women and Gender in the American West*.

7. For an examination of how several authors work through their grief by extending themselves into the natural world, see Mark Allister, *Refiguring the Map of Sorrow: Nature Writing and Autobiography*.

8. In "Letting Go Our Grand Obsessions: Notes toward a New Literary History of the American Frontiers," Annette Kolodny describes *la frontera*, or the borderlands, as a "liminal landscape of changing meanings on which distinct human cultures first encounter one another's 'otherness' and appropriate, accommodate, or domesticate it through language" (9).

1. Susan Shelby Magoffin

1. See Marc Simmons, "Women on the Santa Fe Trail: Diaries, Journals, Memoirs. An Annotated Bibliography," 233–43.

2. For a detailed description of the character and hazards of the Santa Fe Trail at the same time as Magoffin but from a trader's perspective, see James Josiah Webb, *Adventures in the Santa Fe Trade, 1844–1847*. Seventeen-year-old Lewis Hector Garrard also traveled the Santa Fe Trail the same year as Magoffin. For his observations of the route, see *Wah-To-Yah and the Taos Trail; or, Prairie Travel and Scalp Dances, with a Look at Los Rancheros from Muleback and the Rocky Mountain Campfire*. Research on the Santa Fe Trail should begin with Jack D. Rittenhouse, *The Santa Fe Trail: A Historical Bibliography*. See also Stanley Vestal, *The Old Santa Fe Trail*, and David Dary, *The Santa Fe Trail: Legends and Lore*.

3. See Patricia Jean Manion, *Beyond the Adobe Wall: The Sisters of Loretto in New Mexico, 1852–1894*. In 1852 a small group of sisters left the Loretto motherhouse in Kentucky for the Southwest. Led by Bishop Jean Baptiste Lamy, they traveled the Santa Fe Trail in Dearborn wagons. Manion traces the history of the early years of the Sisters of Loretto in Santa Fe.

4. For an interesting discussion of Stella M. Drumm's editing of *Down the Santa Fe Trail and into Mexico*, see Virginia Scharff, *Twenty Thousand Roads: Women, Movement, and the West*. According to Scharff, Drumm used her annotations to commemorate not Magoffin's story, but rather the "march of American conquest" (39).

5. As many trail historians have noted, women diarists tend to be formulaic at the beginnings of their journey, overcome with the anxieties of leaving family and friends behind. Two exceptions are Magoffin and Helen Carpenter. With enthusiastic anticipation and a vivacious spirit similar to Magoffin's, Carpenter begins her five-month trek to California in 1857. She, too, is an eighteen-year-old bride. Her diary's opening entry, "Ho for California," is telling of her naiveté. Like Magoffin, Carpenter matures into the seasoned westering traveler, keen to the dangers of the journey.

6. For a discussion of the preconceptions and prejudices women carried with them into the West, see Glenda Riley, *Confronting Race: Women and Indians on the Frontier, 1815–1915*. Riley contends that although westering white women tended to change their attitudes toward Indians, they remained colonist in outlook toward all other groups they encountered on the frontier. See also Sandra L. Myres's *Westering Women and the Frontier Experience, 1800–1915*.

7. Frequently mentioned in diaries, Pawnee Rock was a famous Santa Fe Trail landmark. Although it was one of the most dangerous points on the trail because the Plains Indians used it as an observation point, many travelers took the risk and the time to carve their names in the soft Dakota sandstone. It was here in 1826 that while standing guard one night seventeen-year-old Kit Carson shot his own mule, mistaking it for an Indian.

8. Bent's Fort was erected by the Bent brothers, Willam and Charles, and Ceran St. Vrain on the upper Arkansas River in present southeastern Colorado. A symbol of western expansion, the fort served as a trading post on the Santa Fe Trail. Magoffin's diary is one of the most complete descriptions of the 1846 fort. As her diary indicates, it was also the rendezvous point for Kearny's march on Santa Fe. For a good history of the fort and related activities along the trail, see *Bent's Fort* by David S. Lavender.

One of the Mexican women Magoffin describes in this scene is the wife of George Bent, the brother of William and Charles.

9. The room used by Susan Magoffin during her ten-day stay has been re-created for tourists at the Bent's Old Fort national historic site.

10. See Mary Louise Pratt, *Imperial Eyes: Travel Writing and Transculturation*. Her idea of "contact zones" illuminates Magoffin's Las Vegas anxieties. For Pratt, contact zones are "social spaces where disparate cultures meet, clash, and grapple with each other, often in highly asymmetrical relations of domination and subordination-like colonialism, slavery, or their aftermaths as they are lived out across the globe today" (4). In her study, Pratt examines not only the ways that the colonizers represent the other culture but also the ways that imperial writers frequently try to maintain differentiation between themselves and the colonized. According to Pratt, "While the imperial metropolis tends to understand itself as determining the periphery . . . it habitually blinds itself to the ways in which the periphery determines the metropolis" (6).

11. See Sandra L. Myres, "Women on the Santa Fe Trail." For the Anglo-American man's views of Mexicans along the Santa Fe Trail, see Janet Lecompte, *Pueblo, Hardscrabble, Greenhorn: The Upper Arkansas, 1832–1856*.

12. Magoffin's depiction of the Hispanic women was a source of inspiration for writers of early novels set on the Santa Fe Trail. Some examples of characters influenced by Magoffin include Gertrudis Barceló in *The Wind Leaves No Shadow* by Ruth Laughlin, Josefina Maria del Carmen Torres in *The Spanish Bride* by Walter O'Meara, and Santa Fe Cameron in *The Turquoise* by Anya Seton.

13. See Shirley Seifert, *The Turquoise Trail*, and Jean M. Burroughs, *Bride of the Santa Fe Trail*.

14. According to the 1836 property list (Deed Records, Santa Fe County Courthouse, Book P-1, 461), house number 3, owned by Don Juan Rafael Ortiz, was the property rented by the Magoffins for the thirty-two days they were in

Santa Fe. Eugene A. Fiske bought the house in 1818, and photographs of the house after the Fiskes remodeled it in the 1890s were labeled "Magoffin House" (Museum of New Mexico Archives). This is the current site of the La Fonda Carriage House.

15. In *Commerce of the Prairies*, Josiah Gregg describes La Tules as a "female of very loose habits" (168) and the "expert 'monte dealer' in all Santa Fe" (169). For an excellent analysis of the creation of the legend of La Tules, see Deena F. Gonzalez, "La Tules of Image and Reality."

16. For an examination of the Santa Fe–Chihuahua trade, see Max Moorhead, *New Mexico's Royal Road: Trade and Travel on the Chihuahua Trail*. In chapter 7, Moorhead discusses the precariousness of the Magoffin caravan during the wartime conditions of 1846. See also Mark L. Gardner, ed., *Brothers on the Santa Fe and Chihuahua Trails: Edward James Glasgow and William Henry Glasgow, 1846–1848*. Like Samuel Magoffin, the Glasgows are traders who were forced to follow Kearny's Army of the West as it occupied New Mexico and Chihuahua. According to Marc Simmons, New Mexico's historian laureate, studies of Santa Fe–Chihuahua merchants are one of the largest untapped areas for Santa Fe Trail research.

17. A major player in the story of American western nineteenth-century expansion, Colonel Alexander Doniphan was a politician turned soldier. On September 25, 1846, Kearny left Santa Fe, leaving Doniphan in charge of military forces. In mid-December, Doniphan began his march to Chihuahua to reinforce Zachary Taylor's army. He defeated the Mexicans at El Brazito and Sacramento before joining forces with Taylor at Saltillo.

18. The Taos Revolt broke out on January 19, 1847, when a group of Spanish descendants, Indians, and Mexicans murdered Governor Charles Bent and others sympathetic to the American occupation of their territory. When the news of the rebellion reached Santa Fe, Colonel Sterling Price led a force toward Taos where they defeated the rebels in the final battle at the Taos Pueblo Church. Lewis Hector Garrard, who traveled the Santa Fe Trail the same year as Magoffin, witnessed the hanging of the instigators. See Garrard, *Wah-To-Yah and the Taos Trail*.

19. For an informative analysis of Rowlandson's rendering of biblical doctrine and her mourning practices, see Mitchell R. Breitwieser, *American Puritanism and the Defense of Mourning*.

20. A broad, flat valley with no water, grazing, or firewood for ninety miles, the Jornada del Muerto, or Journey of the Dead, was the roughest and most desolate stretch of the trail from Santa Fe to Mexico City.

21. Jane Magoffin married George Taylor of Ohio. She survived and was responsible for preserving her mother's diary.

2. Sarah Bayliss Royce

1. For overland trail statistics, see John D. Unruh, *The Plains Across: The Overland Emigrants and the Trans-Mississippi West, 1840–1860*, and Merrill J. Mattes, *Platte River Road Narratives: A Descriptive Bibliography of Travel over the Great Central Overland Route to Oregon, California, Utah, Colorado, Montana, and Other Western States and Territories, 1812–1866*.

2. For biographical information on Royce, I am indebted to Paul Rodman, "Sarah Eleanor Bayliss Royce," and Robert V. Hine, *Josiah Royce: From Grass Valley to Harvard*, 3–16.

3. For an interesting discussion of Mary Rowlandson as the archetypal female captive, see Rebecca Blevins Faery, *Cartographies of Desire: Captivity, Race, and Sex in the Shaping of an American Nation*. Also see Kathryn Zabelle Derounian-Stodola's fascinating introduction to the history and influence of the genre in *Women's Indian Captivity Narratives*.

4. Many towns along the Missouri River, such as Kanesville, Independence, and St. Joseph, served as jumping-off points for the westbound emigrants. See Unruh, *The Plains Across*, for a good description of these trailheads.

5. For an overview of wagon descriptions and how the interior space was utilized, see Sharon Brown, "What the Covered Wagon Covered," and Sandra L. Myres, *Westering Women and the Frontier Experience, 1800–1915*.

6. Despite the fact that children participated in the westward movement, they remain one of the most neglected subjects of frontier scholarship. Recent efforts to address this oversight include Elliott West, *Growing Up with the Country: Childhood on the Far Western Frontier;* Linda Peavy and Ursula Smith, *Frontier Children*; Emmy E. Werner, *Pioneer Children on the Journey West*; and Mary Barmeyer O'Brien, *Into the Western Winds: Pioneer Boys Traveling the Overland Trails* and *Toward the Setting Sun: Pioneer Girls Traveling the Overland Trails.*

7. See Ray A. Billington, "Books That Won the West: The Guidebooks of the Forty-Niners and Fifty-Niners," 25. Trail guides had their genesis in diary accounts of the journey west. Of the few guidebooks published before 1848, two popular ones were John Charles Frémont's and Lansford Hastings's. Frémont's *Report of the Exploring Expedition to the Rocky Mountains in the Year 1842, and to Oregon and North California in the Years 1843–44* was more widely read than any other account of the West prior to the gold rush. The 1846 edition sold over 21,000 copies by 1849. Hastings's *Emigrants' Guide to Oregon and California*, published in 1845, was a widely circulated book, as was Edwin Bryant's *What I Saw in California*, published in 1846.

8. See *Covered Wagon Women: Diaries and Letters from the Western Trails, 1840–1849*, vol. 1, edited by Kenneth L. Holmes. These thirteen women's personal writings provide insight into the roles of women on the trail during the time of Royce. Also see Lillian Schlissel, *Women's Diaries of the Westward Journey*, 19–75. For an examination of the ways trail duties were determined by gender, see John Mack Faragher, *Women and Men on the Overland Trail*.

9. See Charles Rosenberg, *The Cholera Years: The United States in 1832, 1849, and 1866*. See also Robert W. Carter, "'Sometimes When I Hear the Winds Sigh': Mortality on the Overland Trail."

10. See Glenda Riley, *Confronting Race: Women and Indians on the Frontier, 1815–1915*. Riley argues that women didn't represent Indians in the same way as male migrants and that women discarded stereotypes about them more easily than men. Royce, however, fails to change her attitude and finds the Indians' constant begging for food bothersome.

11. Referring to the newly arrived westering women, Louise Smith Clappe observed that "the poor women arrive, looking as haggard as so many Endorean

witches; burnt to the color of a hazel-nut, with their hair cut short, and its gloss entirely destroyed by the alkali" (181).

12. The ill-fated Donner party left the Great Salt Lake Valley on August 25, 1846. Arriving in Salt Lake City on August 18 and staying in town eleven days, the Royces are now lagging behind the Donners in terms of lateness in the season. As a consequence, they have to face the ordeal of a Sierra winter.

The Mormons arrived in the Great Salt Lake Valley in July 1847. Their way through the Wasatch Mountains was made easy by the Donners' roadwork the year before. By the end of 1848, the town boasted five thousand residents. During the 1849–1850 rush to the California goldfields, the Mormon settlement continued to prosper as Salt Lake City residents traded with the trail travelers, supplying them with fresh livestock and crops.

13. Extending for over a hundred miles in some directions, the Great Salt Lake Desert is almost completely white and level. Edwin Bryant's 1846 trail account describes the salt flats as dry and dusty until the desert center, where a shallow lake had turned the alkali into mush.

The Royces came upon the Humboldt River at what is now Moleen, Nevada. They intended to follow it until it vanishes into its sink. Trail travelers grazed their cattle here before they began their hike across the Forty-Mile Desert to reach either the Truckee or the Carson River, depending on which route the party had decided to take. Unfortunately, the Royces bypassed the sink and entered the desert unprepared. Learning of their mistake, they had no choice but to turn back. For Carson River route travelers like the Royces, the Forty-Mile Desert extends from the Humboldt Sink at present-day Ragtown to the current town of Fallon, Nevada.

14. The relief company that rescues the Royces is sent by the U.S. government. For information on the U.S. Army's efforts to rescue newly arrived overlanders during the fall of 1849, see J. S. Holliday, *The World Rushed In: The California Gold Rush Experience,* chapter 9.

15. See Patricia Caldwell, *The Puritan Conversion Narrative: The Beginnings of American Expression.* Conversion narratives flourished in seventeenth-century Puritan New England, for reasons Caldwell associates with the Puritan migration and the Puritans' attempt to work out and define its membership in the wilderness of the New World. The conversion requirements usually involved members giving an oral recollection of their experience in front of the church congregation. During the oratory process, the members gained a new identity in both the eyes of God and the community. The written narrative usually began with a disclaimer about the author's verbal inadequacy, but it had to necessarily be followed by a verbal performance strong enough to convince the reader of the speaker's sincerity.

16. For an excellent overview of the California gold rush, see Holliday, *The World Rushed In.* Also see Malcolm J. Rohrbough, *Days of Gold: The California Gold Rush and the American Nation.* Particularly pertinent to my examination of Royce's experience in California is Jo Ann Levy, *They Saw the Elephant: Women in the California Gold Rush.*

17. The Royces experienced Sacramento's first devastating flood. Water covered the city for a mile east of the normal banks of the Sacramento River. For a detailed description of the flood, see Holliday, *The World Rushed In,* 324–26, and

Rush for Riches: Gold Fever and the Making of California, 146; for a good description of early Sacramento, see *Rush for Riches*, 188–94.

18. For an examination of the volatile California frontier, see Albert L. Hurtado, *Intimate Frontiers: Sex, Gender, and Culture in Old California*. See also David Wyatt, *Five Fires: Race, Catastrophe, and the Shaping of California*.

19. For an examination of the freedom for women during the California Gold Rush, see Levy, *They Saw the Elephant*, 108–25. For an interesting discussion of divorce and the American West, see Glenda Riley, *Building and Breaking Families in the American West*, 113–44. Hurtado provides an interesting discussion of gold-rush California's moral climate and divorce practices in *Intimate Frontiers*, 75–113.

20. An issue just emerging in feminist scholarship is the significance of women's household activities in the early stages of frontier settlement. Relevant to this discussion is Susan Armitage, "Women and Men in Western History: A Stereoptical Vision."

21. For an excellent biography of philosopher Josiah Royce Jr., which includes a section on Sarah Royce's influence on her son, see Hine, *Josiah Royce*.

3. Louise Smith Clappe

1. See note 15, chapter 2.

2. See Malcolm J. Rohrbough, *Days of Gold: The California Gold Rush and the American Nation*, 37–38.

3. The quotes from Clappe in this study are from the Peregrine Smith edition of Clappe's letters. See also the introduction by Marlene Smith-Baranzini in Heyday Books' 1998 edition.

4. For a collection of essays, poems, and stories by women in gold rush California, see Ida Rae Egli, ed., *No Rooms of Their Own: Women Writers of Early California, 1849–1869*. See also Frances Fuller Victor, *Women of the Gold Rush: "The New Penelope" and Other Stories*, and Michael Kowalewski, ed., *Gold Rush: A Literary Exploration*.

5. See Mary Louise Pratt, *Imperial Eyes: Travel Writing and Transculturation*.

6. For biographical information on Clappe, see Rodman W. Paul, "In Search of Dame Shirley," and Sandra Lockhart, "Louise Amelia Knapp Smith Clappe."

7. For Everett's initial impressions of Louise, see Alexander Hill Everett to Louise, January 26, 1842, in the Louise A. K. S. Clappe Manuscript Collection, California State Library. All letters to Louise Smith are found in this collection unless otherwise noted.

8. The Clappes' ocean voyage on the *Manilla* is recorded in the ship file, San Francisco Maritime Museum. The forty-niners had three main routes to the California goldfields: the land route across the plains and desert and over the Sierra Nevada, the land-sea route across the Isthmus of Panama, or the route across the tip of South America to San Francisco. For information on seafaring gold seekers, see Rohrbough, *Days of Gold*, 55–71, and Jo Ann Levy, *They Saw the Elephant: Women in the California Gold Rush*, 30–52. Also see Oscar Lewis, *Sea Routes to the Gold Fields: The Migration by Water to California in 1849–1852*, and James P. Delgado, *To California by Sea: A Maritime History of the California Gold Rush*.

9. Clappe, *The Shirley Letters from the California Mines, 1851–1852*, 183, n 32. Clappe and Sarah Royce are in San Francisco at the same time. They are both witnesses to the city's spectacular fires. Clappe claimed that San Francisco was "built one day and burnt the next" ("Letter from Plumas," April 8, 1851, *Marysville (CA) Herald*).

10. See Massett's autobiographical *The First California Troubadour*. A songwriter, poet, monologue entertainer, and writer, Massett also wrote a comic novel, "*Drifting About*"; or, What "Jeems Pipes, of Pipesville," Saw-and-Did.

11. The earliest California magazine, the *Pioneer* was devoted primarily to historical articles and travel accounts. It was founded and edited by Ferdinand C. Ewer. Clappe's letters appeared in every issue of the *Pioneer* from January 1854 through December 1855, when the literary monthly ceased publication.

12. Lake Oroville now covers the site of Bidwell's Bar, a mining camp forty miles north of Marysville on the middle fork of the Feather River. It was named for John Bidwell, a member of the first overland wagon train to California in 1841. A friend of John Sutter, Bidwell began prospecting in early 1848, and on July 4 at Bidwell's Bar, he made one of the richest strikes in the gold rush.

13. Rohrbough, *Days of Gold*, 109–10, and Levy, *They Saw the Elephant*, 95–103, 211–12.

14. For a good description of seasonal fluctuations in the California mining camps, see Rohrbough, *Days of Gold*, 144–45, and Susan Lee Johnson, *Roaring Camp: The Social World of the California Gold Rush*.

15. Some historians estimate that from 1851 to 1853, one out of every five persons died within six months of their arrival in California. See Mitchel Roth, "Cholera, Community, and Public Health in Gold Rush Sacramento and San Francisco."

16. Albert L. Hurtado, *Indian Survival on the California Frontier*, and Kevin Starr and Richard J. Orsi, *Rooted in Barbarous Soil: People, Culture, and Community in Gold Rush California*. See also Glenda Riley, *Confronting Race: Women and Indians on the Frontier, 1815–1915*.

17. For an interesting discussion of the environmental effects of the gold rush on California, see John McPhee, *Assembling California*. Also see Raymond F. Dasmann, "Environmental Changes before and after the Gold Rush."

18. Dear friend of Eliza Burhans Farnham, Georgiana Bruce Kirby was an early advocate of women's rights. She founded the first Santa Cruz Society of Suffragists in 1869 and wrote articles for the *Santa Cruz Sentinel*, *Old and New*, and *Overland Monthly*. For her early California experiences, see "Journal, 1852–1860."

19. For an examination of women who worked in both conventional and unconventional jobs during the California Gold Rush, see Levy, *They Saw the Elephant*, 91–125. Levy's working women include a French woman barber, a woman bullfighter, and a Mexican woman who had a string of mules and brought flour to the mining camps. See also Johnson, *Roaring Camp*.

20. For a firsthand account of a working woman in the San Francisco gold rush, see Mary Jane Megquier, *Apron Full of Gold: The Letters of Mary Jane Megquier from San Francisco, 1849–1856*. Promising to "come trudging home with an apron full" of gold, Megquier and her physician husband left Maine for California in 1849. Her letters document their journeys across the Isthmus of

Panama and her growing delight in gold-rush California and the economic freedoms it offered women. Megquier ran a San Francisco boardinghouse and commented that "if I had not the constitution of six horses, I should have been dead long ago." For a letter that gives readers a detailed description of her work, see June 30, 1850.

21. Levy, *They Saw the Elephant*, 94.

22. For an overview of the ethnic and cultural diversity in gold-rush California, see Johnson, *Roaring Camp*; J. S. Holliday, *The World Rushed In: The California Gold Rush Experience*, and *Rush for Riches: Gold Fever and the Making of California*, 88–92; and Sucheng Chan, "A People of Exceptional Character: Ethnic Diversity, Nativism, and Racism in the California Gold Rush." A few examples of the vast body of work in this area include Rudolph M. Lapp, *Blacks in Gold Rush California*; Hurtado, *Indian Survival on the California Frontier*; Edwin A. Beilharz and Carlos U. López, *We Were 49ers! Chilean Accounts of the California Gold Rush*; Jay Monaghan, *Chile, Peru, and the California Gold-Rush of 1849*; Rosaline Levenson, "Jews in the Gold Rush: Thirty-Seven Years of Jewish Shopkeepers and Postmasters in Butte County, California"; Claudine Chalmers, "Francois, Lucienne, Rosalie: French Women-Adventurers in the Early Days of the California Gold Rush"; Jo Ann Levy, "Chinese in the Gold Rush."

23. See C. W. Harper, "Committee of Vigilance and Vigilante Justice," and Martin Ridge, "Disorder, Crime, and Punishment in the California Gold Rush."

24. Nina Baym, "Melodramas of Beset Manhood: How Theories of American Fiction Exclude Women Authors."

25. For an excellent discussion of the freedoms for the women in gold rush California, see Jo Ann Levy's chapter "Free to Be" in *They Saw the Elephant*, 108–25. For an insightful examination of why the American West had the highest divorce rate in the world, see Glenda Riley, *Building and Breaking Families in the American West*.

4. Eliza Burhans Farnham

1. For information about Eliza Farnham's life, see W. David Lewis, "Eliza Wood Burhans Farnham"; Madeline B. Stern, introduction to *California, Indoors and Out*; Pamela Herr, "Reformer"; John E. Hallwas, "Eliza Farnham's Life in Prairie Land"; and Jo Ann Levy, *Unsettling the West: Eliza Farnham and Georgiana Bruce Kirby in Frontier California*.

2. The works of Thomas Jefferson Farnham include *Travels in the Great Western Prairies: The Anahuac and Rocky Mountains, and in the Oregon Territory* (1843), *Mexico: Its Geography, Its People, and Its Institutions* (1846), and *Life, Adventures and Travels in California* (1849). In California, he practiced law and had a freighting business on the Sacramento River and on San Francisco Bay. He died in San Francisco on September 13, 1848.

3. Many of Farnham's methods of prison reform were based on phrenological concepts. In 1846, she published *Rationale of Crime: Marmaduke B. Sampson's "Treatise on Criminal Jurisprudence Considered in Relation to Cerebral Organization,"* an American edition of a treatise by English phrenologist Marmaduke Blake Sampson.

4. For an examination of Farnham's plan to bring the civilizing influence of women to California, see Georgiana Bruce Kirby, *Georgiana: Feminist Reformer of the West,* 18–20.

5. Isaac Graham helped Thomas Jefferson Farnham secure about two hundred acres of land in the Santa Cruz Valley as compensation for engineering his release after Graham was arrested as a dangerous foreigner and sent to Mexico. Deeds show that Farnham obtained title in August 1847.

6. For the journal of Georgiana Bruce Kirby with a biography based on the research of Carolyn Swift, Helen Giffen, and Judith Steen, see *Georgiana;* see also Levy, *Unsettling the West.*

7. For research on the sea routes to California at midcentury, see chapter 3, note 8.

8. Formerly Branciforte County, Santa Cruz County was formed in 1850 shortly before Farnham's arrival.

9. For a discussion on Farnham and Bruce's California relationship, see Levy, *Unsettling the West.* See also Madeline B. Stern, "Two Letters from the Sophisticates of Santa Cruz," and "A Feminist Association."

10. See note 17, chapter 3.

11. Anyone interested in the history of children on the frontier should begin with Elliott West, *Growing Up with the Country: Childhood on the Far Western Frontier.*

12. Both Farnham and Georgiana Bruce were married on March 23, 1852. Bruce wed Richard C. Kirby, the owner of a Santa Cruz tannery.

13. For the local paper's recording of the divorce, see *Santa Cruz Sentinel,* July 5, 1856, p. 2.

14. For information on Farnham's later life and death, see the *New York Times,* May 14, 1858, p. 5, and December 18, 1864, p. 3. For a tribute to Farnham and description of the Santa Cruz rancho by Helen Hunt Jackson, see *Bits of Travel at Home.*

15. For an excellent source on the Donner party's ordeal, see Kristin Johnson, *"Unfortunate Emigrants": Narratives of the Donner Party.* Johnson's book contains reprints of out-of-print accounts of the ordeal, including Eliza Burhans Farnham's 1856 article based on interviews with some of the Donner party survivors. For a fairly accurate chronicle of events, see Frank Mullen, *The Donner Party Chronicles: A Day-by-Day Account of a Doomed Wagon Train, 1846–1847.*

5. Lydia Spencer Lane

1. With the recent interest in the role played by women, more accounts of individual wives of the frontier army are being reprinted. For an overall picture of the role played by the wives and dependents of the frontier army, see Patricia Y. Stallard, *Glittering Misery: Dependents of the Indian Fighting Army,* and Michele J. Nacy, *Members of the Regiment: Army Officers' Wives on the Western Frontier, 1865–1890.*

2. See Sandra L. Myres, "Army Women's Narratives as Documents of Social History: Some Examples from the Western Frontier, 1840–1900," 177.

3. Accounts by officers' wives that deal with life in the frontier army prior to the Civil War include Mary Henderson Eastman, *Dahcotah; or, Life and Legends*

of the Sioux around Fort Snelling; Eliza Griffin Johnston, "The Diary of Eliza Johnston (Mrs. Albert Sidney)"; Teresa Griffin Viele, *"Following the Drum": A Glimpse of Frontier Life*; and Marian Russell, *Land of Enchantment: Memoirs of Marian Russell along the Santa Fe Trail, as Dictated to Mrs. Hal Russell*. For an excellent stylistic comparison of the memoirs of Eliza Griffin Johnston, Teresa Griffin Viele, and Lydia Spencer Lane, see Sandra L. Myres's foreword to the 1984 edition of *Following the Drum*.

4. On July 25, 1861, Fort Fillmore's commander, Major Isaac Lynde, surrendered his 492-man force to Confederate Colonel John R. Baylor despite objections from many of his officers. Baylor declared Arizona Territory as part of the Confederate States of America in Mesilla on August 1 and proclaimed himself governor. See James Cooper McKee, *Narrative of the Surrender of a Command of U.S. Forces at Fort Fillmore, New Mexico*.

5. See Wilbert H. Timmons, *James Wiley Magoffin: Don Santiago—El Paso Pioneer*.

6. The Jornado del Muerto, or Journey of Death, is in southwestern New Mexico between Doña Ana and Radium Springs in the south and Socorro in the north. Early travelers feared this ninety-mile stretch of flat desert for its Apaches and its lack of water. Although it no longer takes two or three days to cross the Jornada, as it did the Magoffins with their heavy wagons, the modern-day traveler is still impressed by the austere landscape in this area.

7. See Frederick Jackson Turner, *The Frontier in American History*. See also John Mack Faragher, *Rereading Frederick Jackson Turner: The Significance of the Frontier in American History, and Other Essays*.

8. Established in 1855 for the purpose of controlling the Apaches in the area, Fort Stanton is located on the banks of the Rio Bonito. It is bounded on the west by the towering Sierra Blancas and on the north by the Capitan Mountains. Complaining of the fort's remoteness, Lane wrote, "Nothing ever passed that way, and it was seldom a stranger came among us" (64). The fort was commanded at one time by Kit Carson, and Black Jack Pershing was stationed there on two occasions.

9. Recent scholarship has reexamined the ideology of separate spheres and notions such as "the cult of true womanhood" and has provided great contributions to our understanding of the diversity of female experience. See, for example, Monika M. Elbert, *Separate Spheres No More: Gender Convergence in American Literature, 1830–1930*. For an examination of the ways in which the "separate spheres" paradigm distorted western women's experiences, see Robert Griswold, "Anglo Women and Domestic Ideology in the American West in the Nineteenth and Early Twentieth Centuries."

10. In *Discourses of Difference: An Analysis of Women's Travel Writing and Colonialism*, Sara Mills examines travelers' "othering" practices. For an examination of the ways Anglos have perceived and documented Native Americans and Hispanics in the Southwest, see Audrey Goodman, *Translating Southwestern Landscapes: The Making of an Anglo Literary Region*. For a discussion of the way officers' wives viewed enlisted men, blacks, and Mexicans on the frontier, see Nacy, *Members of the Regiment*, 55–64. For a discussion of white women's encounters with Indians on the frontier, see Glenda Riley, *Confronting Race: Women and Indians on the Frontier, 1815–1915*. For army officers' wives' percep-

tions of Indians, see Nacy, *Members of the Regiment*, 23–38. See also Sherry L. Smith, *The View from Officers' Row: Army Perceptions of Western Indians*, "A Window on Themselves: Perceptions of Indians by Military Officers and Their Wives," and "Officers' Wives, Indians, and Indian Wars."

11. Established June 20, 1852, Fort Clark is at Moras Springs. The fort's purpose was to guard the Mexican border, defend against Indians along the Rio Grande, and protect the military road to El Paso. It was the home for the Seminole-Negro Indian Scouts as well as the headquarters for Colonel Ronald S. Mackenzie's raiders.

12. Camp Stockton was established in March 1858 at Comanche Springs. It was renamed Fort Stockton in 1867. Troops stationed here protected the San Antonio–San Diego mail line and protected travelers and traders from Indians.

13. Established in 1851, Fort Fillmore is located on the left bank of the Rio Grande, six miles south of Mesilla, New Mexico. For ten years, it provided safety to troops and travelers. As Lane details in her narrative, Union troops abandoned the fort on July 26, 1861, and it was seized by Confederate forces who invaded New Mexico from El Paso.

14. See chapter 2, note 10.

15. For a discussion of the role that the captivity narratives and the dime novels had in defining Indians for Anglo women, see Riley, *Confronting Race*, 32–48.

16. See Darlis Miller, "Foragers, Army Women, and Prostitutes."

Conclusion

1. See Michael Olsen, "Depictions of Women in Santa Fe Trail Novels."

2. Josephine Clifford McCrackin married an army officer and followed him to his Southwest assignment. She traveled in the same column with Lydia Spencer Lane.

Bibliography

Allen, Martha Mitten. *Traveling West: Nineteenth-Century Women on the Over-land Routes*. El Paso: Texas Western Press, 1987.

Allister, Mark. *Refiguring the Map of Sorrow: Nature Writing and Autobiography*. Charlottesville: University Press of Virginia, 2001.

Armitage, Susan. "Women and Men in Western History: A Stereoptical Vision." *Western Historical Quarterly* 16 (1985): 381–95.

Bachelard, Gaston. *The Poetics of Space*. Boston: Beacon Press, 1969.

Baym, Nina. "Melodramas of Beset Manhood: How Theories of American Fiction Exclude Women Authors." *American Quarterly* 33 (1981): 123–39.

Beilharz, Edwin A., and Carlos U. López, eds. *We Were 49ers! Chilean Accounts of the California Gold Rush*. Pasadena, CA: Ward Ritchie Press, 1976.

Bender, Barbara, ed. *Landscapes: Politics and Perspectives*. London: Berg Publishers, 1993.

Benstock, Shari, ed. *The Private Self: Theory and Practice of Women's Autobiographical Writings*. Chapel Hill: University of North Carolina Press, 1988.

Billington, Ray A. "Books That Won the West: The Guidebooks of the Forty-Niners and Fifty-Niners." *American West* 4 (August 1967): 25.

Bradstreet, Anne. *The Works of Anne Bradstreet*. Ed. Jeannine Hensley. Cambridge, MA: Belknap Press of Harvard University Press, 1967.

Breitwieser, Mitchell R. *American Puritanism and the Defense of Mourning*. Madison: University of Wisconsin Press, 1990.

Bryant, Edwin. *What I Saw in California*. Minneapolis: Ross and Haines, 1967.

Brooks, James F. "'This Evil Extends Especially to the Feminine Sex': Captivity and Identity in New Mexico, 1800–1846." In *Writing the Range: Race, Class, and Culture in the Women's West*. Ed. Elizabeth Jameson and Susan Armitage. Norman: University of Oklahoma Press, 1997.

Brown, Dee. *The Gentle Tamers: Women of the Old Wild West*. 1958. Rpt. Lincoln: University of Nebraska Press, 1981.

Brown, Gillian. *Domestic Individualism: Imagining Self in Nineteenth-Century America*. Berkeley: University of California Press, 1990.

Brown, Sharon. "What the Covered Wagon Covered." *Overland Journal* 4 (Summer 1986): 32–39.

Brown, William. Letters, 1849–51. Manuscript Collection. Huntington Library, San Marino, California.

Bunkers, Suzanne L., and Cynthia A. Huff, eds. *Inscribing the Daily: Critical Essays on Women's Diaries*. Amherst: University of Massachusetts Press, 1996.

Burroughs, Jean M. *Bride of the Santa Fe Trail*. Santa Fe, NM: Sunstone Press, 1984.

Buss, Helen M. "'The Dear Domestic Circle': Frameworks for the Literary Study of Women's Personal Narratives in Archival Collections." *Studies in Canadian Literature* 14 (1989): 1–17.

———, and Marlene Kadar, eds. *Working in Women's Archives: Researching Women's Private Literature and Archival Documents*. Waterloo, Ontario: Wilfrid Laurier University Press, 2001.

Caldwell, Patricia. *The Puritan Conversion Narrative: The Beginnings of American Expression*. Cambridge, MA: Cambridge University Press, 1983.

Caples, Mrs. Mary Jane. Reminiscence. California State Library, Sacramento.

Carpenter, Helen. "A Trip across the Plains in an Ox Wagon, 1857." In *Ho for California! Women's Overland Diaries from the Huntington Library*, edited by Sandra Myres. San Marino, CA: Huntington Library, 1980.

Carter, Robert W. "'Sometimes When I Hear the Winds Sigh': Mortality on the Overland Trail." *California History* 74 (1995): 146–217.

Chalmers, Claudine. "Francois, Lucienne, Rosalie: French Women-Adventurers in the Early Days of the California Gold Rush." *California History* 78 (1999): 38–153, 213–14.

Chan, Sucheng. "A People of Exceptional Character: Ethnic Diversity, Nativism, and Racism in the California Gold Rush." *California History* 79 (2000): 44–85.

Clappe, Louise A. K. S. Manuscript Collection. California State Library, Sacramento.

Clappe, Shirley. "Letter from Plumas." April 8, 1851, *Marysville* (California) *Herald*.

———. *The Shirley Letters: Being Letters Written in 1851–1852 from the California Mines*, introduction by Richard Oglesby. Salt Lake City: Peregrine Smith Books, 1995.

———. *The Shirley Letters from the California Mines, 1851–1852*, edited by Marlene Smith-Baranzini. Berkeley: Heyday Books, 1998.

Coffman, Edward M. *The Old Army: A Portrait of the American Army in Peacetime, 1784–1898*. New York: Oxford University Press, 1986.

Comer, Krista. *Landscapes of the New West: Gender and Geography in Contemporary American Women's Writing*. Chapel Hill: University of North Carolina Press, 1999.

Cott, Nancy. *The Bonds of Womanhood: "Woman's Sphere" in New England, 1780–1835*. 2d ed. New Haven, CT: Yale University Press, 1997.

Crackbon, Joseph. Diary, 1849–50. California State Library, Sacramento.

Crèvecoeur, J. Hector St. John de. *Letters from an American Farmer*. 1782. New York: Penguin, 1986.

Culley, Margo, ed. *A Day at a Time: The Diary Literature of American Women from 1764 to the Present*. New York: Feminist Press, 1985.

———, and Lenore Hoffman, eds. *Women's Personal Narratives: Essays in Criticism and Pedagogy*. New York: MLA, 1985.

Dary, David. *The Santa Fe Trail: Legends and Lore*. New York: Alfred A. Knopf, 2000.

Dasmann, Raymond F. "Environmental Changes before and after the Gold Rush." *California History* 77 (1998–1999): 105–22.

Davis, Gayle. "Women's Frontier Diaries: Writing for Good Reason." *Women's Studies* 14 (1987): 5–14.

Delgado, James P. *To California by Sea: A Maritime History of the California Gold Rush.* Columbia: University of South Carolina Press, 1990.

Derounian-Stodola, Kathryn Zabelle, ed. *Women's Indian Captivity Narratives.* New York: Penguin, 1998.

Deutsch, Sarah. *No Separate Refuge: Culture, Class, and Gender on the Anglo-Hispanic Frontier in the American Southwest, 1880–1940.* New York: Oxford University Press, 1987.

Eastman, Mary Henderson. *Dahcotah; or, Life and Legends of the Sioux around Fort Snelling.* 1849. Rpt. New York: Arno Press, 1975.

Egli, Ida Rae, ed. *No Rooms of Their Own: Women Writers of Early California, 1849–1869.* Berkeley, CA: Heyday Books, 1997.

Elbert, Monika M., ed. *Separate Spheres No More: Gender Convergence in American Literature, 1830–1930.* Tuscaloosa: University of Alabama Press, 2000.

Everett, Alexander Hill. Letters. The Shirley Papers. California State Library, Sacramento.

Faery, Rebecca Blevins. *Cartographies of Desire: Captivity, Race, and Sex in the Shaping of an American Nation.* Norman: University of Oklahoma Press, 1999.

Faragher, John Mack. *Rereading Frederick Jackson Turner: The Significance of the Frontier in American History, and Other Essays.* New York: Henry Holt, 1994.

———. *Women and Men on the Overland Trail.* New Haven, CT: Yale University Press, 1979.

Farnham, Eliza Burhans. *California, In-doors and Out; or, How We Farm, Mine, and Live Generally in the Golden State.* 1856. Rpt. Nieuwkoop, Netherlands: B. DeGraaf, 1972.

———. *Eliza Woodson; or, the Early Days of One of the World's Workers,* 2d ed. New York: A. J. Davis, 1864.

———. *The Ideal Attained.* New York: C. M. Plumb, 1865.

———. *Life in Prairie Land.* 1846. Rpt. New York: Arno Press, 1972.

———. *Woman and Her Era.* 2 vols. New York: A. J. Davis, 1864.

———, ed. *Rationale of Crime: Marmaduke B. Sampson's "Treatise on Criminal Jurisprudence Considered in Relation to Cerebral Organization."* 1846. Rpt. Montclair, NJ: Patterson Smith, 1973.

Farnham, Thomas J. *Life, Adventures and Travels in California.* 1849. Rpt. as *Travels in California.* Oakland, CA: Biobooks, 1947.

———. *Mexico: Its Geography, Its People, and Its Institutions.* New York: H. Long and Brother, 1846.

———. *Travels in the Great Western Prairies: The Anahuac and Rocky Mountains, and in the Oregon Territory.* 1843. Rpt. Monroe, OR: Northwest Interpretive Association, 1983.

Fender, Stephen. *Plotting the Golden West: American Literature and the Rhetoric of the California Trail.* Cambridge, MA: Cambridge University Press, 1981.

Fox-Genovese, Elizabeth. *Within the Plantation Household: Black and White Women of the Old South*. Chapel Hill: University of North Carolina Press, 1988.

Franklin, Penelope, ed. *Private Pages: Diaries of American Women, 1830s–1970s*. New York: Ballantine Books, 1986.

Frémont, John Charles. *Report of the Exploring Expedition to the Rocky Mountains in the Year 1842, and to Oregon and North California in the Years 1843–44*. Rpt. Santa Barbara, CA: Narrative Press, 2002.

Fryer, Judith. *The Faces of Eve: Women in the Nineteenth-Century American Novel*. New York: Oxford University Press, 1976.

Gardner, Mark L. *Brothers on the Santa Fe and Chihuahua Trails: Edward James Glasgow and William Henry Glasgow, 1846–1848*. Niwot: University Press of Colorado, 1993.

Garrard, Lewis Hector. *Wah-To-Yah and the Taos Trail; or, Prairie Travel and Scalp Dances, with a Look at Los Rancheros from Muleback and the Rocky Mountain Campfire*. 1850. Rpt. Norman: University of Oklahoma Press, 1955.

Georgi-Findlay, Brigitte. *The Frontiers of Women's Writing*. Tucson: University of Arizona Press, 1996.

Gonzalez, Deena F. "La Tules of Image and Reality." In *Unequal Sisters: A Multicultural Reader in U.S. Women's History*. Ed. Vicki Ruiz and Ellen DuBois. New York: Routledge Press, 1994.

Goodman, Audrey. *Translating Southwestern Landscapes: The Making of an Anglo Literary Region*. Tucson: University of Arizona Press, 2002.

Greenfield, Bruce. *Narrating Discovery: The Romantic Explorer in American Literature, 1790–1855*. New York: Columbia University Press, 1992.

Gregg, Josiah. *Commerce of the Prairies*. 1844. Ed. Max L. Moorhead. Norman: University of Oklahoma Press, 1954.

Griswold, Robert. "Anglo Women and Domestic Ideology in the American West in the Nineteenth and Early Twentieth Centuries." In *Western Women: Their Land, Their Lives*, edited by Lillian Schlissel, Vicki Ruiz, and Janice Monk. Albuquerque: University of New Mexico Press, 1988.

Hallwas, John E. "Eliza Farnham's *Life in Prairie Land*." In *Old Northwest* 7 (1981–1982): 295–324.

Hampsten, Elizabeth. *Read This Only to Yourself: The Private Writings of Midwestern Women, 1880–1910*. Bloomington: Indiana University Press, 1982.

Harper, C. W. "Committee of Vigilance and Vigilante Justice." *Journal of the West* 17 (January 1978): 2–7.

Hastings, Lansford. *Emigrants' Guide to Oregon and California*. 1845. Rpt. Bedford, MA: Applewood Books, 1994.

Herr, Pamela. "Reformer." In *The Women Who Made the West*, edited by the Western Writers of America. Garden City, NJ: Doubleday, 1980.

Hine, Robert V. *Josiah Royce: From Grass Valley to Harvard*. Norman: University of Oklahoma Press, 1992.

Holliday, J. S. *Rush for Riches: Gold Fever and the Making of California*. Berkeley: University of California Press, 1999.

———. *The World Rushed In: The California Gold Rush Experience*. New York: Simon and Schuster, 1981.

Holmes, Kenneth L., ed. *Covered Wagon Women: Diaries and Letters from the Western Trails.* 11 vols. Lincoln: University of Nebraska Press, 1996.

hooks, bell. "Writing from the Darkness." *Triquarterly* 75 (1989): 71–77.

Hurtado, Albert L. *Indian Survival on the California Frontier.* New Haven, CT: Yale University Press, 1988.

———. *Intimate Frontiers: Sex, Gender, and Culture in Old California.* Albuquerque: University of New Mexico Press, 1999.

Irwin, Mary Ann, and James F. Brooks, eds. *Women and Gender in the American West.* Albuquerque: University of New Mexico Press, 2004.

Jackson, Helen Hunt. *Bits of Travel at Home.* Boston: Roberts Brothers, 1880.

Jameson, Elizabeth, and Susan Armitage, eds. *Writing the Range: Race, Class, and Culture in the Women's West.* Norman: University of Oklahoma Press, 1997.

Jeffrey, Julie Roy. *Frontier Women.* New York: Hill and Wang, 1979.

Jensen, Joan, and Darlis A. Miller. "'Gentle Tamers' Revisited: New Approaches to the History of Women in the American West." In *Women and Gender in the American West,* edited by Mary Ann Irwin and James F. Brooks. Albuquerque: University of New Mexico Press, 2004.

Johnson, Kristin, ed. *"Unfortunate Emigrants": Narratives of the Donner Party.* Logan: Utah State University Press, 1996.

Johnson, Susan Lee. "Bulls, Bears, and Dancing Boys: Race, Gender, and Leisure in the California Gold Rush." *Radical History Review* 60 (1994): 4–37.

———. "'A Memory Sweet to Soldiers': The Signficance of Gender in the History of the 'American West.'" *Western Historical Quarterly* 24 (November 1993): 495–517.

———. *Roaring Camp: The Social World of the California Gold Rush.* New York: W. W. Norton, 2000.

Johnston, Eliza Griffin. "The Diary of Eliza Johnston (Mrs. Albert Sidney)." Ed. Charles P. Roland and Richard C. Robbins. *Southwestern Historical Quarterly* 60 (April 1957): 463–500.

Kirby, Georgiana Bruce. "Journal, 1852–1860." In *Georgiana: Feminist Reformer of the West,* edited by Carolyn Swift, Helen Giffen, and Judith Steen. Santa Cruz, CA: Santa Cruz Historical Trust, 1987.

Knight, Oliver. *Life and Manners in the Frontier Army.* Norman: University of Oklahoma Press, 1993.

Kolodny, Annette. *The Land Before Her.* Chapel Hill: University of North Carolina Press, 1984.

———. *The Lay of the Land: Metaphor as Experience and History in American Life and Letters.* Chapel Hill: University of North Carolina Press, 1975.

———. "Letting Go Our Grand Obsessions: Notes toward a New Literary History of the American Frontiers." *American Literature* 64 (March 1992): 1–18.

Kowalewski, Michael, ed. *Gold Rush: A Literary Exploration.* Berkeley, CA: Heyday Books, 1997.

Lane, Lydia Spencer Blaney. *I Married a Soldier; or, Old Days in the Army.* 1893. Rpt. Albuquerque: University of New Mexico Press, 1987.

Lapp, Rudolph M. *Blacks in Gold Rush California.* New Haven, CT: Yale University Press, 1977.

Larson, T. A. "Women's Role in the American West." *Montana: The Magazine of Western History* 24 (Summer 1974): 2–11.

Laughlin, Ruth. *The Wind Leaves No Shadow*. New York: McGraw Hill, 1948.

Lavender, David S. *Bent's Fort*. Lincoln: University of Nebraska Press, 1972.

Lecompte, Janet. *Pueblo, Hardscrabble, Greenhorn: The Upper Arkansas, 1832–1856*. Norman: University of Oklahoma Press, 1978.

Leed, Eric J. *The Mind of the Traveler*. New York: HarperCollins, 1991.

Levenson, Rosaline. "Jews in the Gold Rush: Thirty-Seven Years of Jewish Shopkeepers and Postmasters in Butte County, California." *Western States Jewish History* 25 (April 01 1993): 227.

Levy, Jo Ann. "Chinese in the Gold Rush." *Dogtown Territorial Quarterly* 39 (1999): 16–22.

———. *They Saw the Elephant: Women in the California Gold Rush*. Norman: University of Oklahoma Press, 1990.

———. *Unsettling the West: Eliza Farnham and Georgiana Bruce Kirby in Frontier California*. Berkeley: Heyday Books, 2004.

———. "We Were Forty-Niners, Too! Women in the California Gold Rush." *Overland Journal: The Official Journal of the Oregon-California Trails Association* 6 (1988): 29.

Lewis, Oscar. *Sea Routes to the Gold Fields: The Migration by Water to California in 1849–1852*. New York: Alfred A. Knopf, 1949.

Lewis, W. David. "Eliza Wood Burhans Farnham." In *Notable American Women, 1607–1950*, edited by Edward T. James, et al. 3 vols. Cambridge, MA: Harvard University Press, 1971.

Limerick, Patricia Nelson. *The Legacy of Conquest: The Unbroken Past of the American West*. New York: Norton, 1987.

———. *Something in the Soil: Legacies and Reckonings in the New West*. New York: Norton, 2000.

Lockhart, Sandra. "Louise Amelia Knapp Smith Clappe." *Legacy* 8 (1991): 141–48.

Magoffin, Susan. *Down the Santa Fe Trail and into Mexico*. Ed. Stella M. Drumm. Lincoln: University of Nebraska Press, 1982.

Manion, Patricia Jean. *Beyond the Adobe Wall: The Sisters of Loretto in New Mexico, 1852–1894*. Independence, MO: Two Trails Publishing, 2001.

Marks, Paula Mitchell. *Precious Dust: The American Gold Rush Era, 1848–1900*. New York: William Morrow, 1994.

Massett, Stephen C. *"Drifting About"; or What "Jeems Pipes, of Pipesville," Saw-and-Did*. New York: Carleton Publisher, 1863.

———. *The First California Troubadour*. Oakland: Biobooks, 1954.

Massey, Doreen. *Space, Place and Gender*. Minneapolis: University of Minnesota Press, 1994.

Mattes, Merrill J. *Platt River Road Narratives: A Descriptive Bibliography of Travel over the Great Central Overland Route to Oregon, California, Utah, Colorado, Montana, and Other Western States and Territories, 1812–1866*. Urbana: University of Illinois Press, 1988.

McDowell, Linda. *Gender, Identity, and Place: Understanding Feminist Geographies*. Minneapolis: University of Minnesota Press, 1999.

————, and Joanne P. Sharp. *A Feminist Glossary of Human Geography*. New York: Oxford University Press, 1999.

McKee, James Cooper. *Narrative of the Surrender of a Command of U.S. Forces at Fort Fillmore, New Mexico*. Houston, TX: Stagecoach, 1960.

McPhee, John. *Assembling California*. New York: Farrar, Strauss, Giroux, 1993.

Megquier, Mary Jane. *Apron Full of Gold: The Letters of Mary Jane Megquier from San Francisco, 1849–1856*. Ed. Polly Welts Kaufman. Albuquerque: University of New Mexico Press, 1994.

Meyer, Marian. *Mary Donoho: New First Lady of the Santa Fe Trail*. Santa Fe, NM: Ancient City Press, 1991.

Miller, Darlis. "Foragers, Army Women, and Prostitutes." In *New Mexico Women: Intercultural Perspectives*, edited by Joan Jensen and Darlis A. Miller. Albuquerque: University of New Mexico Press, 1986.

Mills, Sara. *Discourses of Difference: An Analysis of Women's Travel Writing and Colonialism*. London: Routledge, 1991.

Monaghan, Jay. *Chile, Peru, and the California Gold-Rush of 1849*. Berkeley: University of California Press, 1973.

Moorhead, Max. *New Mexico's Royal Road: Trade and Travel on the Chihuahua Trail*. 1958. Norman: University of Oklahoma Press, 1994.

Mullen, Frank. *The Donner Party Chronicles: A Day-by-Day Account of a Doomed Wagon Train, 1846–1847*. Reno: Nevada Humanities Committee, 1997.

Myres, Sandra L. "Army Wives in the Trans-Mississippi West: A Bibliography." In *Following the Drum: A Glimpse of Frontier Life*, edited by Teresa Griffin Viele. Lincoln: University of Nebraska Press, 1984.

————. "Army Women's Narratives as Documents of Social History: Some Examples from the Western Frontier, 1840–1900." *New Mexico Historical Review* 65 (April 1990): 174–98.

————. "Romance and Reality on the American Frontier: Views of Army Wives." *Western Historical Quarterly* 13 (October 1982): 409–27.

————. *Westering Women and the Frontier Experience, 1800–1915*. Albuquerque: University of New Mexico Press, 1982.

————. "Women in the West." In *Historians and the American West*, edited by Michael Malone. Lincoln: University of Nebraska Press, 1983.

————. "Women on the Santa Fe Trail." In *The Santa Fe Trail: New Perspectives*. Niwot: University Press of Colorado, 1992.

Nacy, Michele J. *Members of the Regiment: Army Officers' Wives on the Western Frontier, 1865–1890*. Westport, CT: Greenwood Press, 2000.

Nasatir, Abraham. *The French in the California Gold Rush*. New York: American Society of the French Legion of Honor, 1934.

Neisser, Ulrich. *Cognition and Reality: Principles and Implications of Cognitive Psychology*. San Francisco: W. H. Freeman, 1976.

Norwood, Vera, and Janice Monk, eds. *The Desert Is No Lady: Southwestern Landscape in Women's Writing and Art*. New Haven, CT: Yale University Press, 1987.

O'Brien, Mary Barmeyer. *Into the Western Winds: Pioneer Boys Traveling the Overland Trails*. Guilford, CT: Falcon, 2002.

———. *Toward the Setting Sun: Pioneer Girls Traveling the Overland Trails.* Guilford, CT: Falcon, 1999.

Olsen, Michael. "Depictions of Women in Santa Fe Trail Novels." *Wagon Tracks* 14 (May 2000): 10–14.

O'Meara, Walter. *The Spanish Bride.* 1954. Rpt. Santa Fe, NM: Friends of the Palace Press, 1990.

Paul, Rodman W. "In Search of Dame Shirley." *Pacific Historical Review* 33 (May 1964): 127–46.

———. "Sarah Eleanor Bayliss Royce." In *Notable American Women, 1607–1950,* edited by Edward T. James et al. 3 vols. Cambridge, MA: Harvard University Press, 1971.

Peavy, Linda, and Ursula Smith. *Frontier Children.* Norman: University of Oklahoma Press, 1999.

Personal Narratives Group, ed. *Interpreting Women's Lives: Feminist Theory and Personal Narratives.* Bloomington: Indiana University Press, 1989.

Porteous, J. Douglas. *Landscapes of the Mind: Worlds of Sense and Metaphor.* Toronto: University of Toronto Press, 1990.

Pratt, Annis, with Barbara White et al. *Archetypal Patterns of Women's Fiction.* Sussex: Harvester, 1981.

Pratt, Mary Louise. "Arts of the Contact Zone." *Profession* 91 (1991): 33–40.

———. *Imperial Eyes: Travel Writing and Transculturation.* New York: Routledge, 1992.

Reaves, Gerri. *Mapping the Private Geography: Autobiography, Identity, and America.* Jefferson, NC: McFarland, 2001.

Ridge, Martin. "Disorder, Crime, and Punishment in the California Gold Rush." *Montana* 49 (1999): 12–27.

Riley, Glenda. *Building and Breaking Families in the American West.* Albuquerque: University of New Mexico Press, 1996.

———. *Confronting Race: Women and Indians on the Frontier, 1815–1915.* Albuquerque: University of New Mexico Press, 2004.

———. *The Female Frontier: A Comparative View of Women on the Prairie and the Plains.* Lawrence: University Press of Kansas, 1988.

Rittenhouse, Jack D. *The Santa Fe Trail: A Historical Bibliography.* Albuquerque: University of New Mexico Press, 1971.

Rohrbough, Malcolm J. *Days of Gold: The California Gold Rush and the American Nation.* Berkeley: University of California Press, 1997.

Romines, Ann. *The Home Plot: Women, Writing, and Domestic Ritual.* Amherst: University of Massachusetts Press, 1992.

Rosenberg, Charles. *The Cholera Years: The United States in 1832, 1849 and 1866.* Chicago: University of Chicago Press, 1962.

Roth, Mitchel. "Cholera, Community, and Public Health in Gold Rush Sacramento and San Francisco." *Pacific Historical Review* 66 (1997): 527–51.

Rowlandson, Mary. "A True History of the Captivity and Restoration of Mrs. Mary Rowlandson." In *Colonial American Travel Narratives,* edited by Wendy Martin. New York: Penguin, 1994.

Royce, Sarah. *A Frontier Lady: Recollections of the Gold Rush and Early California.* Ed. Ralph Henry Gabriel. 1932. Rpt. Lincoln: University of Nebraska Press, 1977.

Russell, Marian. *Land of Enchantment: Memoirs of Marian Russell along the Santa Fe Trail, as Dictated to Mrs. Hal Russell.* Albuquerque: University of New Mexico Press, 1993.

Ryan, Mary P. *Cradle of the Middle Class: The Family in Oneida County, New York, 1790–1865.* Cambridge: Cambridge University Press, 1981.

Sampson, Marmaduke B. *Rationale of Crime, and Its Appropriate Treatment; Being a Treatise on Criminal Jurisprudence Considered in Relation to Cerebral Organization; . . . with Notes and Illustrations by E. W. Farnham.* New York: D. Appleton, 1846.

Sanders, Scott Russell. *Staying Put.* Boston: Beacon, 1993.

Scharff, Virginia. *Twenty Thousand Roads: Women, Movement, and the West.* Berkeley: University of California Press, 2003.

Schlissel, Lillian. *Women's Diaries of the Westward Journey.* New York: Schocken, 1982.

Schriber, Mary Suzanne. *Writing Home: American Women Abroad, 1830–1920.* Charlottesvillle: University Press of Virginia, 1997.

Seifert, Shirley. *The Turquoise Trail.* Philadelphia: Lippincott, 1950.

Seton, Anya. *The Turquoise.* Boston: Houghton Mifflin, 1946.

Simmons, Marc. *The Old Trail to Santa Fe: Collected Essays.* Albuquerque : University of New Mexico Press, 1996.

———. "Women on the Santa Fe Trail: Diaries, Journals, Memoirs. An Annotated Bibliography." *New Mexico Historical Review* 61 (July 1986): 233–43.

Slotkin, Richard. *The Fatal Environment: The Myth of the Frontier in the Age of Industrialization, 1800–1890.* New York: Atheneum, 1985.

Smith, Sherry L. "Officers' Wives, Indians, and Indian Wars." *Order of the Indian Wars Journal* 1(Winter 1980): 35–46.

———. *The View from Officers' Row: Army Perceptions of Western Indians.* Tucson: University of Arizona Press, 1990.

———. "A Window on Themselves: Perceptions of Indians by Military Officers and Their Wives." *New Mexico Historical Review* 64 (October 1989): 447–61.

Smith-Baranzini, Marlene. "Out of the Shadows: Louise Clappe's Life and Early California Writing." *California History* 78 (1999–2000): 238–61, 299–303.

Stallard, Patricia Y. *Glittering Misery: Dependents of the Indian Fighting Army.* Fort Collins, CO: Old Army Press, 1978.

Starr, Kevin, and Richard J. Orsi, eds. *Rooted in Barbarous Soil: People, Culture, and Community in Gold Rush California.* Berkeley: University of California Press, 2000.

Stauffer, Helen, and Susan J. Rosowski, eds. *Women and Western American Literature.* Troy, NY: Whitston, 1982.

Stern, Madeline B. "A Feminist Association." *Manuscripts* 35 (1983): 113–17.

———. "Two Letters from the Sophisticates of Santa Cruz." *The Book Club of California Quarterly Newsletter* 33 (Summer 1968): 51–62.

Stillman, Jacob D. B. *Around the Horn to California in 1849.* 1877. Rpt. Palo Alto, CA: Lewis Osborne, 1967.

Stout, Janis P. *The Journey Narrative in American Literature: Patterns and Departures.* Westport, CT: Greenwood Press, 1983.

Taniguchi, Nancy T. "Weaving a Different World: Women and the California Gold Rush." *California History* 79 (2000): 141–68.

Timmons, Wilbert H. *James Wiley Magoffin: Don Santiago — El Paso Pioneer.* El Paso: Texas Western Press, 1999.

Tuan, Yi-Fu. *Space and Place: The Perspective of Experience.* Minneapolis: University of Minnesota Press, 1977.

Turner, Frederick Jackson. *The Frontier in American History.* Tucson: University of Arizona Press, 1992.

Unruh, John D. *The Plains Across: The Overland Emigrants and the Trans-Mississippi West, 1840–1860.* Urbana: University of Illinois Press, 1979.

Vestal, Stanley. *The Old Santa Fe Trail.* Lincoln: University of Nebraska Press, 1996.

Victor, Frances Fuller. *Women of the Gold Rush: "The New Penelope" and Other Stories.* Ed. Ida Rae Egli. Berkeley, CA: Heyday Books, 1998.

Viele, Teresa Griffin. *"Following the Drum": A Glimpse of Frontier Life.* 1858. Rpt. with an introduction by Sandra L. Myres. Lincoln: University of Nebraska Press, 1984.

Webb, James Josiah. *Adventures in the Santa Fe Trade, 1844–1847.* Ed. Ralph P. Bieber. Lincoln: University of Nebraska Press, 1995.

Welter, Barbara. "The Cult of True Womanhood: 1820–1860." *American Quarterly* 18 (Summer 1966): 158–59.

Werner, Emmy E. *Pioneer Children on the Journey West.* Boulder: Westview Press, 1995.

Wesley, Marilyn. *Secret Journeys: The Trope of Women's Travel in American Literature.* Albany: State University of New York Press, 1998.

West, Elliott. *Growing Up with the Country: Childhood on the Far Western Frontier.* Albuquerque: University of New Mexico Press, 1989.

Wilson, Luzena Stanley. *Luzena Stanley Wilson, '49er: Memories Recalled for Her Daughter, Correnah Wilson Wright.* Mills College, CA: Eucalyptus Press, 1937.

Wink, Amy. *She Left Nothing in Particular: The Autobiographical Legacy of Nineteenth-Century Women's Diaries.* Knoxville: University of Tennessee Press, 2001.

Wyatt, David. *Five Fires: Race, Catastrophe, and the Shaping of California.* Reading, MA: Addison-Wesley Publishing, 1997.

Young, Iris Marion. *Throwing Like a Girl and Other Essays in Feminist Philosophy and Social Theory.* Bloomington: Indiana University Press, 1990.

San Francisco, California, 55–58, 87–88, 100–01; Montgomery House, 31, 56; publishing houses of, 61–62
Sanders, Scott Russell, 21
Santa Fe, New Mexico, 25–26
Santa Fe Trail, 9–10. *See also* landscape
Scharff, Virginia, 2, 12
Schlissel, Lillian, 2, 4, 19, 42
Seifert, Shirley, 12
Sharp, Joanne P., 2
Simmons, Marc, 12
Slotkin, Richard, 129
spiritual autobiography, 36, 51
Summerhayes, Martha, 120

Taylor, Zachary, 31
Tompkins, Jane, 51
travel narratives, 92–93, 131
Tuan, Yi-Fu, 54
Turner, Frederick Jackson, 48, 110

Unruh, John, 43, 46

Viele, Teresa Griffin, 107
vigilante committee, 57, 75–76. *See also* mining camps, vigilante justice
voyeurism, 41, 75–76; cross-cultural, 24, 40–41, 75–76, 121–22

Weaverville, California, 52–55
White, Barbara, 98
women: and childbirth, 22; friendships, 31–32, 73, 96; perceptions of Indians, 17, 22–23, 27–28, 46, 70–71, 119–22; perceptions of Mexicans, 22, 24–25, 27, 75–76, 122; and duties in California, 53–54, 74

Young, Iris Marion, 11

Zwinger, Ann, 90